DISCUSSION COURSE ON

CHOICES FOR SUSTAINABLE LIVING

ecochallenge
dot org

By

ecochallenge
dot org

Ecochallenge.org
107 SE Washington Street
Portland, OR 97214
(503) 227-2807

contact@ecochallenge.org

ecochallenge.org

Layout and Typography: Margaret Parker
Cover Design: Lee Benson
Curriculum Development and Editing: Lacy Cagle

This publication was printed using 100 percent post-consumer waste,
FSC certified recycled paper, and UV inks (voc-free), and is 100% process-chlorine free.
This publication was produced using windmill-powered energy through Premier Press.

TABLE OF CONTENTS

All of us. One better shared future.

Our Vision. We believe in a better shared future, one with fresh air to breathe, clean water to drink, and a stable climate to live in.

Our Model for Change. And we believe that our individual behaviors are pivotal in creating this world, one that is realized by the collective impact of everyday people raising voices and taking action.

Our Approach. We believe in solutions. Through our Ecochallenge Platform and Discussion Courses, we connect you with research-backed actions and with fellow humans who want to take these actions with you. We show you how our collective behavior — and your personal transformation — connect with something big, shared, and better.

Our Commitment to Justice & Equity. Our solutions-focused work encompasses upholding and revitalizing just and equitable systems. We know a better shared future can only exist when we hold in earnest all inhabitants on this dot we call *home*.

Together. We are connecting the dots between our actions, our impact, and our will to create significant global change. Each time our dots are connected, we take another step forward, toward our better shared future. So here we are. Let's begin.

Together, we're connecting the dots.

ABOUT THIS CURRICULUM

Lacy Cagle (Editor) is the Director of Learning at Ecochallenge.org, where she oversees the development of discussion courses and other educational programs, and chairs Ecochallenge.org's Diversity, Equity and Inclusion Committee. She holds a MS in Educational Leadership and Policy with a focus on Leadership in Sustainability Education from Portland State University. Lacy's expertise is in sustainability pedagogy, transformative learning, and behavior change. When not working on sustainability-related projects, she sustains herself by exploring new and old places, cooking, playing trivia, and hanging out with her amazing rescue pup, Huey, in St. Louis, Missouri.

CURRICULUM COMMITTEE

This discussion course would not exist without the expertise and time volunteered by the people on our curriculum committee. Ecochallenge.org would like to offer sincere and deep appreciation for the many hours of time they collectively invested in this project.

Emily Mauro (Curriculum and Research Intern) is responsible for helping with curriculum development with Ecochallenge.org, particularly with developing and publicizing a new program on sustainability leadership for change. Her trip to Ecuador in 2015 shed some light on the Rights of Nature, Ecuador's addition to its constitution in 2008. This led her to probe the ethics of biocentrism–ultimately altering her perception of the complex natural world that we are all a part of. She is interested in further exploring the intersections between social equity and environmental sustainability, along with environmental stewardship and its relation to human health. She spends her free time planting trees in urban settings, and volunteering on local farms.

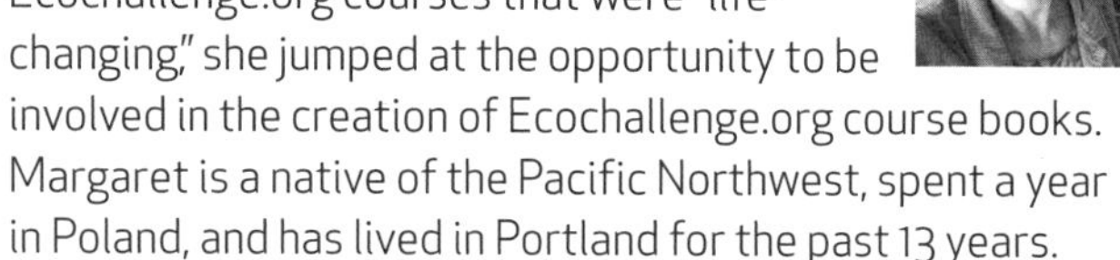

Margaret Parker (Layout Editor) is a freelance graphic artist in Portland, Oregon. She says that after taking several Ecochallenge.org courses that were "life-changing," she jumped at the opportunity to be involved in the creation of Ecochallenge.org course books. Margaret is a native of the Pacific Northwest, spent a year in Poland, and has lived in Portland for the past 13 years.

Lee Benson (Cover Designer) is a freelance graphic designer living in Portland, Oregon. After obtaining a Bachelor's degree in Film & Digital Media, he moved to Portland to study design, earning an AAS at Portland Community College. Since graduating, he has been sole proprietor of City Limit Design. He enjoys working with local nonprofits that work to improve quality of life. In his spare time, he enjoys crafting cocktails, riding his bike and watching classic movies.

Miguel Arellano enjoys taking advantage of the all the great adventures Oregon has to offer with his partner and daughters. Miguel is currently the Coordinator of the Multicultural Center at Portland Community College, where he provides transformative learning opportunities for students through leadership, social change, and civic engagement opportunities where students can engage in shaping a better self and a better world. Miguel's passion lies in the power of education and stories, both in and outside the classroom.

Rick D. Barnes is Professor of Psychology and Environmental Studies at Randolph College in Lynchburg, Virginia, where he teaches courses in social psychology, history of psychology, and environmental studies. He received his BA in psychology from Vanderbilt University and his Ph.D. in social and environmental psychology from the University of Wisconsin—Madison. He was a member of the City of Lynchburg Planning Commission for nine years and has been active in promoting sustainable development at the local level. Dr. Barnes has given workshops and presentations on sustainable campus and city planning at national and international conferences, and has taught courses in sustainable lifestyles and sustainable communities with the Semester at Sea program.

Lisa L. Cagle conducts Public Policy Research through her role at Bi-State Development Research Institute in St. Louis, Missouri. She holds a Master of Arts in Philosophy from the University of Missouri – St. Louis (UMSL), and studied sustainable development at the University of Oslo in Norway on a Fulbright Fellowship. Lisa's current research examines transportation policy from a social and racial justice perspective. Lisa stays busy outside of her work at Bi-State as a leader and active participant in numerous community action groups. She is also a member of the St. Louis Earth Day board of directors.

Jenn DeRose is Program Manager of the Green Dining Alliance (GDA), a program of St. Louis Earth Day. The Green Dining Alliance is a certification program for St. Louis-area restaurants to assess and improve their sustainable practices, which include reducing their waste, water, and carbon footprint, while encouraging the sourcing of local, responsibly raised foods. The GDA also works to educate the public about waste reduction, energy and water consumption, and the importance of fostering a healthy, resilient food system. Jenn is a freelance writer for the Riverfront Times, student of Sustainability at Washington University, and a LEED GA. She enjoys camping, foraging, birdwatching, vegan brownies, and cycling.

Felipe Ferreira (pronouns: he/him/his, they/them/theirs) is a dreamer and budding sustainability educator hailing from Brasilia, Brazil. He has recently graduated from Portland State University with a master's degree in Educational Leadership and Policy with emphases in Leadership for Sustainability Education and Gender, Race, and Nations. As a critical sustainability scholar, his research interests include productions of nature, popular culture and sustainability, and critical consciousness development.

Viniece Jennings, Ph.D., is a research scientist based in Athens, Georgia, who explores the role of urban green spaces on various aspects of health and well-being. Through the years, she has also been involved in initiatives to enhance environmental and sustainability education. Viniece is also a Senior Fellow with the Environmental Leadership Program.

Betty Shelley has been an Ecochallenge.org volunteer since 1994. Betty often tells people "Ecochallenge.org has changed my life." She is a Master Recycler and a former Recycling Information Specialist for Metro Regional Government in Portland, Oregon. In addition, she and her husband have produced just one 35-gallon can of garbage per year since 2006. She offers "Less is More" classes on reducing resource waste in the Portland area. In 2013, she was honored with the NW Earth Institute Founders Award, recognizing her vast contributions to both Ecochallenge.org and sustainability education and practice more broadly.

Liz Zavodsky is the Director of Membership and Engagement at Ecochallenge.org . Liz oversees program engagement with businesses nationwide, sponsorship and corporate partnerships, in addition to managing donor relationships and records. Before joining Ecochallenge.org , Liz worked in Higher Education and Residence Life. She received her BA from University of Northern Colorado, and her MA in Human Development from University of Denver. Previously, she and her husband worked for Semester at Sea, and spent time living in Edinburgh, Scotland.

INTRODUCTION

At this point, the idea of sustainability has infiltrated most of our societies. "Sustainable" products, "sustainable" lifestyles, "sustainable" food, "sustainable" development — the term is used often and widely, and even contradictorily. Regularly, "sustainable" really means "less unsustainable," which can be misleading, at best. The definitions and visions of sustainability differ with each culture in which it is envisioned, and with the agenda of each person or organization promoting it. Sustainability is a complex and contested concept, but at its essence represents the hope for a healthy, just and bright future for us all. We offer this 25th anniversary edition of *Choices for Sustainable Living* as an opportunity to move beyond the hype to explore sustainability more deeply. The course focuses less on defining sustainability than envisioning sustainability — what would a sustainable world look like? And how can we create it together?

We also want to explore with you the idea of "choices" for sustainable living. Some of us have more choice or agency than others, and as individuals, our choices are often constricted or manipulated by complicated and power-laden systems (for example, recent reports suggest just 100 corporations are responsible for the majority of our greenhouse gas emissions). This course book focuses on the choices you do have, in your individual daily life, to contribute to a healthier, more just and more sustainable world. It also focuses on the choices you have to exercise bigger positive impact, by being a leader or agent of change in your communities and in larger systems.

In order to explore the idea of choice, we have to look at power and privilege as well. Those who have power and privilege have bigger voices in our public conversations and often have bigger impact in the world. The perspectives of people with power often become the dominant ones, and some of them can be or have been quite harmful. But just because a perspective is the dominant one, it does not mean it is the most accurate one. Not all opinions are equally valid. We can, however, come to better understandings of sustainability that are grounded in evidence, context, and equity. With that in mind, we have exercised intention in selecting articles that represent distinct views of sustainability, but we have not represented them all. We have elevated less dominant perspectives to encourage conversation about what is both equitable and achievable. We have prioritized content that helps you to connect with your peers, create a community of support, contrast differing views, reflect on your own values and assumptions, and move to action.

Throughout this course, you will examine and envision sustainability from individual, societal and global perspectives. The readings are intended to invoke meaningful discussion. Each week as you meet with your group, we invite you to bring your own experience and critical thinking to the process. Whether you agree or disagree, you will have an opportunity to clarify your views and values. Ultimately, we hope this process inspires you and others to make choices to live with more intention on Earth.

Choices for Sustainable Living is comprised of eight sessions designed for weekly discussion. Each session includes readings, videos, Suggested Discussion Questions, one or more Suggested Group Activities, and a Reflection prompt. We suggest coming up with a group goal or project during the optional "Call to Action" session. This last session is encouraged as a way for your group to celebrate the completion of the course, share goals and progress and consider ways the group might continue to work together.

INTEGRATING WITH ECOCHALLENGE

For the first time ever, *Choices for Sustainable Living* is using our Ecochallenge platform to enhance your learning experience. Ecochallenge challenges you to choose actions to reduce your impact and stick with each one for one week. You design your Challenge and set a goal that stretches your comfort zone and makes a difference for you, your community and the planet.

Use Ecochallenge for the best possible experience of this course — it will allow your group to better connect, reflect, and act together by opening up new opportunities previously unavailable. Not only does Ecochallenge help your group stay connected in between session meetings, it connects you to others, expanding your network to everyone around the world who is participating in *Choices for Sustainable Living*. It extends your learning, by better connecting you to additional resources and opportunities for action. It allows new opportunities for reflection with your peers by allowing you to share your thoughts as they arise and get feedback from your group. And Ecochallenge is proven to better incentivize your action by providing more ideas for action, more accountability to your commitments, and more support for your attempts. You will see the impact of your individual and Team actions, as well as the collective impact of everyone participating in the Choices Ecochallenge.

Here is how to use the Ecochallenge platform with this course:

1. **Organize your discussion group as an Ecochallenge Team.** Before your first session meeting, sign up for the Ecochallenge using your unique Team URL, which your Team Captain will send to you. Through the Ecochallenge platform, your Team will be able to connect with each other outside of meetings and with other discussion group Teams around the world.
2. **Respond to Reflection prompts offered on the first page of each Session.** Reflection prompts ask participants to post their thoughts and feelings about the session topic in their Ecochallenge Feed each week. Teammates can then respond to each other's posts to offer insight, support and encouragement.
3. **Choose an Action goal to complete on the Ecochallenge platform.** Follow the prompts in the "Putting It Into Practice" boxes at the end of the session readings. These Actions are related to the content for each session and help participants learn more, apply their learning locally, and take action toward a more sustainable way of living. Participants are encouraged to set a goal that stretches their comfort zone and makes a difference for themselves, their community, and the planet. A variety of Actions are available for each session, including Actions that allow participants to measure their individual impact and see the collective impact of everyone doing the Ecochallenge.

The Facilitator for the week should remind participants at the end of the session meeting to log into **choices.ecochallenge.org** to post a Reflection and commit to an Action. It is helpful to allow a few minutes at the end of each session meeting to allow the group to discuss their progress, successes, and difficulties in taking their selected Actions. Remind people that they can stay connected with each other between sessions by posting at **choices.ecochallenge.org**.

You can still use the Reflection and Action prompts even if you choose not to use the Ecochallenge platform, but the best use and experience of *Choices for Sustainable Living* will be with the Ecochallenge helping you to connect with others, reflect on your learning, and act toward a more sustainable world.

Thank you for participating in this discussion course process. For resources on getting your discussion group started, visit **ecochallenge.org/take-action/discussion-courses** to find organizing guides and tips for facilitation. You may also contact our office at (503) 227-2807 or **contact@ecochallenge.org**.

Much of our funding comes from individual donors. Donate to Ecochallenge.org and help us share our programs with others at **ecochallenge.org/donate** or by completing the form on page 155.

GUIDELINES

FOR THE FACILITATOR, OPENER AND NOTETAKER

This Ecochallenge.org Discussion Course is designed to be much more than a reader; it is designed to be a guide for community building, transformative learning and life-changing action.

When you break big issues into bite-sized pieces and talk through them with others, you discover insights and inspiration that are hard to find on your own. You learn, together. You build a personal network of shared stories and support that makes it easy to take action. In short, you become part of a community for change.

Below you will find guidelines for three of the roles participants can play in this course: the Facilitator, the Opener and the Notetaker. For each session of this course, one participant brings an "Opening," a second participant facilitates the discussion, and a third participant takes notes on the Group Activity (if you choose to do it) and Actions group members commit to. The roles are designed to rotate each week with a different group member doing the opening, facilitating and notetaking, so that each participant has a chance to share leadership in the group. This process is at the core of Ecochallenge.org culture — it assumes we gain our greatest insights through self-discovery, promoting discussion among equals, with each person learning with and from each other. Learn more about organizing an Ecochallenge.org discussion course at **ecochallenge.org/take-action/discussion-courses**.

FOR THE SESSION FACILITATOR

As Facilitator, your role is to stimulate and moderate the discussion. You do not need to be an expert or the most knowledgeable person about the topic. Your role is to:

- Remind the Opener ahead of time to bring their opening, and remind all participants to read the session before you meet.
- Begin and end on time.
- Ask the questions included in each session, or your own. The Circle Question is designed to get everyone's voice in the room — be sure to start the discussion with it and that everyone answers it briefly without interruption or comment from other participants.
- Remind your group members to log their Actions and Reflections on the Choices Ecochallenge site (**choices.ecochallenge.org**).
- Keep the discussion focused on the session's topic. A delicate balance is best — don't force the group to answer the questions, but don't allow the discussion to drift too far.
- Manage the group process, using the guidelines below.

A primary goal is for everyone to participate and to learn from themselves and each other. Draw out quiet participants by creating an opportunity for each person to contribute. Don't let one or two people dominate the discussion. Thank them for their opinions and then ask others to share.

Be an active listener. You need to hear and understand what people say if you are to guide the discussion effectively. Model this for others.

The focus should be on personal reactions to the readings — on personal values, feelings, and experiences. The course is not for judging others' responses. You do not have to come to a consensus on what everyone should say or do.

Each week, course participants will choose an Action goal to complete on the Choices Ecochallenge platform. Participants are encouraged to set a goal that stretches their comfort zone and makes a difference for themselves, their community and the planet. Reflection prompts are also offered in each session for participants to respond to in their Ecochallenge Feed. The Facilitator should remind participants at the end of the session meeting to log into **choices.ecochallenge.org** to commit to an Action and post a Reflection. It is helpful to allow a few minutes at the end of each session meeting to allow the group to discuss their progress, successes, and difficulties in taking their selected Actions. Remind people that they can stay connected with each other between sessions by posting at **choices.ecochallenge.org**.

FOR THE SESSION OPENER

The purpose of the Opening is twofold. First, it provides a transition from other activities of the day into the group discussion. Second, since the Opening is personal, it allows the group to get better acquainted with you. This aspect of the course can be very rewarding.

Bring a short opening, not more than a couple of minutes. It should be something meaningful to you, or that expresses your personal appreciation for the natural world. Examples: a short personal story, an object or photograph that has special meaning, a poem, a visualization, etc. We encourage you to have fun and be creative.

FOR THE NOTETAKER

If your group chooses to use the Group Activity in each session, you will need a Notetaker. It is your responsibility as Notetaker to record the group discussion, any resources shared, and commitments to action, as outlined by the particular Group Activity in the session. Send the notes you took on the Group Activity to each person in your group at the end of your group meeting.

COURSE SCHEDULE FOR *CHOICES FOR SUSTAINABLE LIVING*

This course schedule may be useful to keep track of meeting dates and of who is serving in which role for the next meeting.

Course Coordinator :____________________ Contact Info:____________

Location For Future Meetings :____________________

SESSION	DATE	OPENING	FACILITATOR	NOTETAKER
A Call to Sustainability				
Ecological Principles				
Food				
Water				
Community				
Transportation				
Consumption & Economy				
Visions of Sustainability				
			PLANNERS	
Celebration and Call to Action*				

*After the last regular session, your group may choose to have a final meeting and celebration. This meeting celebrates the completion of the course, and may include a potluck lunch or dinner and is an opportunity for evaluation and consideration of next steps.

EVALUATION

You can choose to print out this evaluation or complete it online at ecochallenge.org/discussion-course-evaluations

PART 1: Please fill out from your weekly notes.

Rate each session.

1. **A CALL TO SUSTAINABILITY** — NOT AT ALL / VERY MUCH

How informative was this session? (Did you learn anything new?) 1 2 3 4 5

How much did this session help you in changing your behavior or committing to action? 1 2 3 4 5

Did you complete the activity for this session? YES NO

Additional thoughts or comments:

2. **ECOLOGICAL PRINCIPLES** — NOT AT ALL / VERY MUCH

How informative was this session? (Did you learn anything new?) 1 2 3 4 5

How much did this session help you in changing your behavior or committing to action? 1 2 3 4 5

Did you complete the activity for this session? YES NO

Additional thoughts or comments:

3. **FOOD** — NOT AT ALL / VERY MUCH

How informative was this session? (Did you learn anything new?) 1 2 3 4 5

How much did this session help you in changing your behavior or committing to action? 1 2 3 4 5

Did you complete the activity for this session? YES NO

Additional thoughts or comments:

4. **WATER** — NOT AT ALL / VERY MUCH

How informative was this session? (Did you learn anything new?) 1 2 3 4 5

How much did this session help you in changing your behavior or committing to action? 1 2 3 4 5

Did you complete the activity for this session? YES NO

Additional thoughts or comments:

5. **COMMUNITY** — NOT AT ALL / VERY MUCH

How informative was this session? (Did you learn anything new?) 1 2 3 4 5

How much did this session help you in changing your behavior or committing to action? 1 2 3 4 5

Did you complete the activity for this session? YES NO

Additional thoughts or comments:

6. **TRANSPORTATION**

	NOT AT ALL	VERY MUCH
How informative was this session? (Did you learn anything new?)	1 2 3	4 5
How much did this session help you in changing your behavior or committing to action?	1 2 3	4 5
Did you complete the activity for this session?	YES	NO

Additional thoughts or comments: ______

7. **CONSUMPTION & ECONOMY**

	NOT AT ALL	VERY MUCH
How informative was this session? (Did you learn anything new?)	1 2 3	4 5
How much did this session help you in changing your behavior or committing to action?	1 2 3	4 5
Did you complete the activity for this session?	YES	NO

Additional thoughts or comments: ______

8. **VISIONS OF SUSTAINABILITY**

	NOT AT ALL	VERY MUCH
How informative was this session? (Did you learn anything new?)	1 2 3	4 5
How much did this session help you in changing your behavior or committing to action?	1 2 3	4 5
Did you complete the activity for this session?	YES	NO

Additional thoughts or comments: ______

PART 2: PLEASE COMPLETE AT THE END OF THE COURSE.

Has this course made a difference in your life (i.e. your attitudes, beliefs, perspectives, goals, habits)? If so, how?

Please describe what actions you are taking or you plan to take in response to this course.

What has been the most valuable aspect of this course?

Are there other resources you would like to see included in this course?

Do you have any additional thoughts or comments to share?

Complete your evaluation online at **ecochallenge.org/discussion-course-evaluations**, or send your completed evaluation via email to **contact@ecochallenge.org** or via snail mail to Ecochallenge.org, 107 SE Washington St., Portland, OR 97214. Thank you for your participation!

Donate to Ecochallenge.org today at **ecochallenge.org/donate**

Follow us at:

SESSION 1

A CALL TO SUSTAINABILITY

"On my first Boy Scout trip, in the mid-1950s, I learned the basic environmental principle that we should leave the campsite as we found it. We were told that the next group of hikers deserved no less, and that in fact we should clean the site up if those before us had been careless. I did not as a child understand that the campsite would be global or that the next hikers would include unborn generations."

— John Sitter

LEARNING OBJECTIVES

- **Identify some ways in which modern human societies have become unsustainable.**
- **Critically examine ways of defining and measuring sustainability, and what each definition assumes and values. Articulate the meanings and measures that align with your values and goals.**
- **Reflect on the roles individuals have in creating and changing practices in society.**
- **Begin to understand and apply systems thinking in your daily life.**

SESSION DESCRIPTION

While sustainability is a term and concept widely referenced around the world, it remains elusive and contested. The definitions and visions of sustainability differ with each culture in which it is envisioned, and the term "sustainable" can be used to promote divergent views. For example, sustainable development places the emphasis on human activity and well-being, while sustainable ecosystems require paying attention to all of the organisms and their relationships within an ecosystem. In this session, we consider ways of grasping the meaning and vision of sustainability, and our roles in creating a sustainable world. The idea and practice of systems thinking as a way toward more sustainable solutions is also introduced.

REFLECTION

What do you hope to gain from this course? Name at least one goal each for something you want to learn, a behavior you want to change to be more sustainable, and something you can contribute to your group. Post your Reflection to your Dashboard on **choices.ecochallenge.org**. If you are not using the Ecochallenge site, write your thoughts in a journal and then reflect with your group.

Where do you find your deepest connection to the world?

Reminder to the facilitator: The circle question should move quickly. Elicit an answer from each participant without questions or comments from others. The facilitator's guidelines are on page 10.

SUGGESTED DISCUSSION QUESTIONS

1. Did your conception or definition of sustainability change after reading the articles in Session 1? If so, how is it different?
2. Paul Hawken uses many business metaphors in "You Are Brilliant and the Earth Is Hiring." What non-business metaphors might be used to describe the idea that the Earth needs you?
3. LaDuke believes that " indigenous ways of living are the only sustainable ways of living. Most indigenous ceremonies, if you look to their essence, are about the restoration of balance — they are a reaffirmation of our relationship to creation. That is our intent: to restore, and then to retain balance and honor our part in creation." What do you agree or disagree with in this statement? Why is balance important to sustainability?
4. Identify one value, belief, or assumption from your culture that you believe contributes to the development of a more sustainable world. What is it about this particular value, belief, or assumption that aligns it with sustainability?
5. Name and discuss one or more aspects of your culture that you think hinder sustainable practices.
6. How does systems thinking shift your perception of the world? Please provide one concrete example.
7. What surprised you the most about the effects of the wolves being reintroduced into Yellowstone? After watching the video about the wolves' effects on the Yellowstone ecosystem, what suggestions do you have to improve your local ecosystem?
8. How sustainable was your life 5 years ago? How sustainable would you say your life is today?

SUGGESTED GROUP ACTIVITY

If you would like to do an activity with your group, we recommend these.

- As a group, use the individual definitions of sustainability you wrote this week to create a group definition of sustainability. Is it possible to include all elements?
- Use the Iceberg Model in this session to examine a local issue that your group cares about.
- If you have some extra time, allow yourselves 30+ minutes for the opening this week. The Opener starts by modelling a short (3 minutes or less) story about an experience, place or person that was significant to them in developing their ecological identity. Feel free to bring pictures or items that signify important aspects of your story. The Opener then invites each participant to tell a short story about a significant factor in the development of their own ecological identity.

FURTHER RESOURCES

Interested in finding out more on the topics presented in this session?
Visit our website for further readings and resources: **ecochallenge.org/discussion-course-resources.**
Follow our Facebook page to continue the discussion online:
facebook.com/Ecochallengeorg/

OUR VIEW OF SUSTAINABILITY

By Felipe Ferreira for Ecochallenge.org

Environment, climate change, renewable energy, pollution, recycling, just economies, appropriate technologies... If we were to co-create a word cloud for the term "sustainability," it is very likely that these and/or similar terms would occupy the largest space in it. You can probably brainstorm several more sustainability-related terms right now. But what exactly does sustainability mean?

In its most general sense, sustainability refers to the capacity to maintain a process over time. For example, a business is considered financially sustainable when it can continue to make enough money to pay its employees and produce its products or services. In ecology, a sustainable system is one whose most fundamental functions and features — its carrying capacities — are preserved over time. In practical terms, ecosystems tend to increase in biodiversity, complexity, and overall ecological output until they eventually reach a climactic state where they are able to maintain themselves unless their integrity and balance are compromised.

Sustainability's origins in Western culture can be traced back to the writings of philosophers and pioneering environmentalists like John Locke, Aldo Leopold, and Rachel Carson. Sustainability as an aspirational idea was first discussed during 1) the Limits to Growth debates in the 1960s and 70s, when a number of people suggested that economic and population growth were the direct cause of environmental degradation and were therefore unsustainable and should be limited; and 2) the 1972 United Nations (UN) Stockholm Conference, the UN's first major conference on international environmental issues. Since then, it has been used by many to describe a vision, to inspire aspirations, to outline a set of values, and even as a marketing buzzword. Despite conflicting opinions over what the terms 'sustainability' and its variant 'sustainable development' actually mean, they have gained a lot of traction in the last two decades. They have been explored and applied across different environmental, social, economic, and geographical contexts. Perhaps the most commonly quoted definition of sustainable development is that of the *World Commission on Environment and Development* (WCED), who in 1987 stated that "sustainable development is development that meets the needs of the present without compromising the ability of future generations to meet their own needs."

In part because the concept of sustainability was developed in response to growing environmental degradation, sustainability as a Western concept has focused on reactions to or cures to our immediate crises instead of offering alternative paradigms that can actually generate lasting, ecologically sound transformations. Perhaps due to the Western assumption that the future is one of endless economic growth and steadily evolving technology, sustainability has relied primarily on technological and economic fixes that treat the symptoms rather than the underlying causes of the pressures we face: the values, beliefs, and mental models that we hold about each other and the planet we inhabit. And as Albert Einstein once put it, "No problem can be solved from the same consciousness that created it." Only by delving into the origins of our current 'ethos of unsustainability' can we really come up with new paradigms that are

DEFINITIONS

Capitalism: An economic system in which investment in and ownership of the means of production, distribution, and exchange of wealth is made and maintained chiefly by private individuals or corporations,especially as contrasted to cooperatively or state-owned means of wealth.

Commodification: The transformation of goods, services, ideas and people into commodities, or objects of trade.

Consumer culture: A form of capitalism in which the economy and culture are focused on the buying and selling of consumer goods and the spending of consumer money. Most economists agree that the United States is a consumer culture.

Culture: The way of life or social norms of a particular people, especially as shown in their everyday behavior and habits, their attitudes toward each other, their values, and their moral and religious beliefs.

Ecological identity: A person's view of their relationship to, their responsibility to, and how they interact with natural and social ecosystems.

Feedback loop: A structure or function of a system that causes output from one part of the system to "feed back" into the system, eventually influencing input to that same part of the system.

Resilience: The ability to recover from or adjust easily to difficulties or change.

Systems thinking: A way of conceptualizing and understanding the world that focuses on how various elements within a system — which could be an ecosystem, an organization, or something more dispersed such as a supply chain — are related to and influence one another.

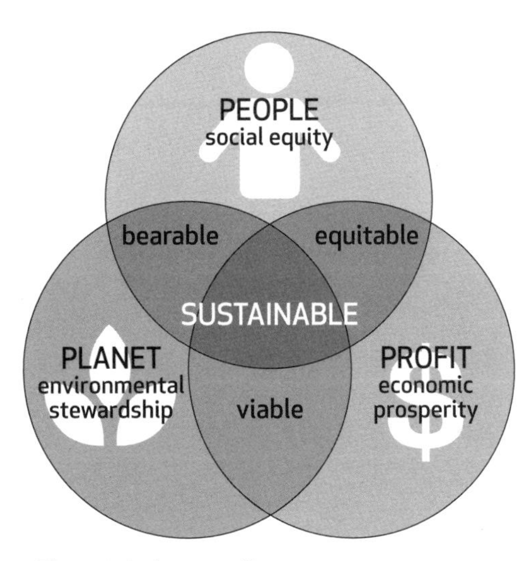

Figure 1. The triple bottom line system.

capable of encouraging the significant shifts in individual and collective consciousness required to advance sustainability. By unearthing the roots of the crises that sustainability attempts to address, it becomes clearer that the dominant culture — the culture that is the most powerful, widespread, or influential within a society — is at the core of the environmental crisis. If we challenge and rethink our mental models and values, we can lay down the groundwork for the social and cultural innovations necessary to heal our alienation from each other and the wider ecological community.

In addition to questioning the cultural norms and worldviews that guide the 'ethos of unsustainability,' if sustainability is to prove useful and beneficial, it needs to be future-oriented and emphasize the power of transformational envisioning and 'futures thinking.'

FUTURES THINKING

In a nutshell, futures thinking is the process of imagining the potential consequences of past and current human activities by critically analyzing them today. Futures thinking involves forecasting probable futures, possible futures, and unexpected futures. Applying futures thinking can help us move away from a way of thinking that relies solely on critique and doomsday scenarios to one that is about personal and collective transformation and hope. We can use futures thinking to build new, more just and sustainable futures. By understanding sustainability as a constant, dynamic envisioning exercise, we can unshackle our imaginations from the limits of what is possible or impossible in our current context and expand the landscape of possibilities for the future. A critical approach to futures thinking can transcend both the crisis of imagination and the crisis of power that often prevent the development of sustainable realities. As lifelong activist Dorothy Day once said, "Just because something is impossible doesn't mean you shouldn't do it." By freeing our minds from the limits of today's current systems, we can develop an empowering sense of agency and responsibility for our choices and actions — and their complex consequences — in ways that spark both personal and collective transformation.

NESTED SYSTEMS AND SUSTAINABILITY

Unlike the more common models informed by the WCED and their focus on the triple bottom line system (Figure 1), which fail to recognize the ecological constraints that human cultures and economies must operate within, we advocate for the framing of a deeper, more critical and visionary sustainability that highlights the nested quality of ecological systems (Figure 2): each individual system is an integrated whole while also being a part of larger systems; changes within one system can impact the health of the systems that are nested within it as well as the larger systems in which it lives. This model recognizes that economies are subsets of human cultures — they only exist within the context of our societies — and similarly, that human societies and economic activities are completely constrained by the ecosystems of the planet. This lens is not only more ecologically literate, but it also challenges the Western notion that humans are separate from nature and that ecological and socio-economic issues are not interconnected. It holds that an actual sustainable society is one where wider matters of social and economic needs

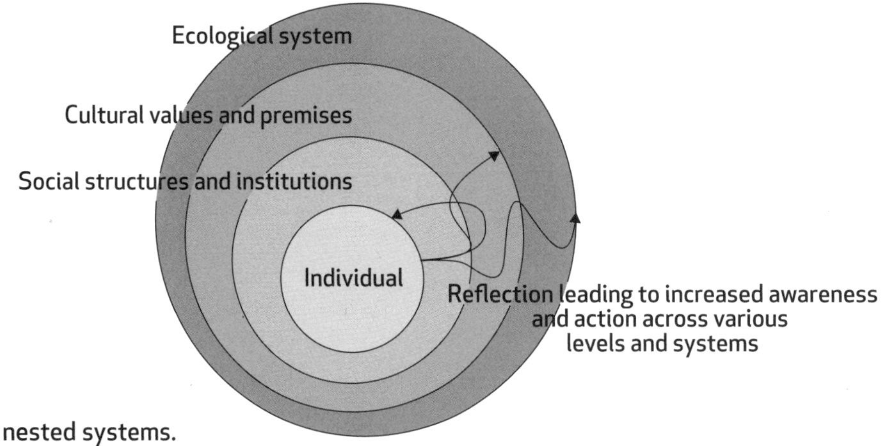

Figure 2. Sustainability and nested systems.

are intrinsically connected to the dynamic limits set by supporting ecosystems.

The concept of nested sustainability is rooted in systems thinking — the capacity to collectively examine complex systems across different domains (society, environment, and economy) and across different scales (local to global). Because of this, nested sustainability argues for localized visions of sustainability that are situated within and, therefore, in conversation with, the larger, global context.

Local contexts often provide the most immediate and effective space for real change. Solutions that are conceived and implemented on the local level offer more flexibility and are generally more tangible than global ones. They are often the most participatory and effective since they can address issues that are specific to a particular community or region and be tailored to local ecosystems. However, in an economically globalized world, these local solutions ought to be envisioned through a "glocal" prism, one that is characterized by both local and global considerations. This understanding of the interconnections between the various dimensions and scales of sustainability is key to the development of context-oriented solutions to the complex issues we face currently and into the future.

SUSTAINABILITY, POSITIONALITY, AND EQUITY

Sustainability has the potential to provide a holistic framework that can bridge the gap that is often found between socio-economic justice and environmental considerations. After all, recent studies indicate that the issue of environmental quality is inevitably linked to that of human equity, and thus they need to be thought about together. When we talk about equity, it is necessary to consider how our different socio-cultural and ecological identities shape our perspectives, assumptions, and values. Here we refer to the need to envision sustainability by looking at the issues at stake through a position-based lens, or "positionality" — how we perceive the world from different lived experiences, identities and perspectives. By examining how our cultural and ecological locations mold our mental models and patterns of thinking, we can frame sustainability as an ongoing dialogue between various viewpoints that complement each other in an effort to generate diverse and localized solutions to complex global problems.

Just because a perspective is the dominant one, it does not mean it is the most accurate one. With that in mind, the authors of this course book have exercised intention in selecting articles that represent distinct views of sustainability, but we have not represented them all. We have elevated less dominant perspectives to encourage conversation about what is both equitable and achievable. We have prioritized content that helps you to connect with your peers, create a community of support, contrast differing views, reflect on your own values and assumptions, and move to action.

A CALL FOR INDIVIDUAL AND SYSTEMIC CHANGE

Starting to work toward sustainability almost always starts with individual actions. Changing your own lifestyle — reducing your waste, using active transportation, or eating less meat, for example — is the easiest, most accessible way to start to understand and interact with larger systems.

This session is a call to sustainability for you as an individual. We need you to act. We need everyone to do what they can to create the shift to a more sustainable world. But, while behavior change toward sustainability starts at the individual level, for broad and more lasting change to occur, it cannot stop there. Individual actions collectively have a big impact, but we also need to change policies, structures, laws, and, ultimately, our cultural premises and values in order to create a sustainable world. As we mentioned above, focusing on the local level while keeping a global perspective can often be the most effective lever for creating lasting change. At the same time, people studying and practicing sustainability need to be able to both deconstruct current systems through analysis and critique, as well as envision and enact alternatives to our current destructive systems.

The continuum of systemic change (Figure 3) helps us think about the different ways to be involved in systemic change. It is very natural to move from one place to another over time depending on our positions and the work we want to or can do. Different parts of involvement are placed on particular parts of the continuum to reflect the places where they typically arise. Yet, it is important to recognize that they can shift and might be placed on different parts of the continuum depending on how we engage in them.

We hope that this course book will empower and inspire you to help improve the communities in which you live. We believe that we, both individually and collectively, should be able to make those decisions that affect our lives, and that engaged participation in systemic change is essential to that. It starts with individual people and arises from many sources, from changes in technology to shifts in economic systems and to larger, paradigmatic transformations.

We conclude this introduction with a few words of wisdom by cultural anthropologist Margaret Mead: "Never doubt that a small group of thoughtful, committed citizens can change the world. Indeed, it is the only thing that ever has."

QUESTIONS FOR REFLECTION

- How would you define sustainability using your own words? Has your definition changed after reading this article? If so, describe how it has changed.
- How does this framing of sustainability contrast/compare to the more common definition of sustainability?

CONTINUUM OF SOCIAL CHANGE

This continuum helps us think about the different ways to be involved in social change. Over time it is natural to move from one place to another along the continuum. Sometimes it is necessary to shift your position to be able to do the work you want to do. Different types of involvement are placed on particular parts of the continuum to reflect the places where they typically arise. However, it is important to keep in mind how they can shift and might be placed on different parts of the continuum depending on how we engage in them.

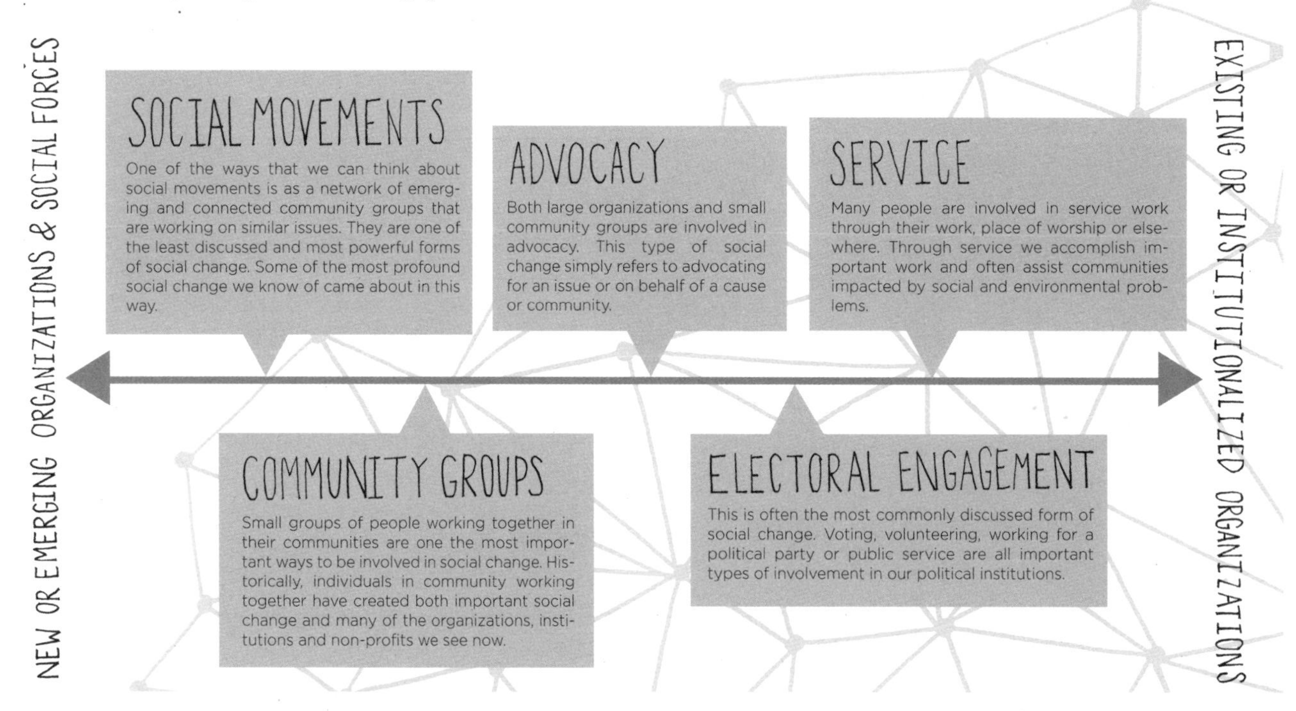

Figure 3. Continuum of systemic change. Appeared in *Resource Guide for Continuing Engagement*. Created by David Osborn, Portland State University, 2014. Used with permission.

- Identify one value, belief, or assumption from your culture that you believe contributes to the development of a more sustainable world. What is it about this particular value, belief, or assumption that makes it more in line with sustainability? Now try to do this same exercise but with an aspect of your culture that you think hinders sustainable practices.
- What do you believe the term 'ethos of sustainability' mean? Why is it important (if at all)?
- Sustainability is typically perceived, at least in the Western world, as relating primarily, if not exclusively, to environmental concerns. How does this article challenge that premise?
- What does your vision of a sustainable community look like? What would need to be changed in order for such vision to become reality?

Felipe Ferreira is a dreamer and budding sustainability educator hailing from Brasilia, Brazil. As a critical sustainability scholar, his research interests include productions of nature, popular culture and sustainability, and critical consciousness development.

CULTURE TREE

By Zaretta Hammond

It can be helpful to think of sustainability as a cultural framework for viewing and interacting in the world, otherwise known as a "worldview." But what is culture?

Culture, it turns out, is the way that every brain makes sense of the world. That is why everyone, regardless of race or ethnicity, has a culture. Think of culture as software for the brain's hardware. The brain uses cultural information to turn everyday happenings into meaningful events.

LEVELS OF CULTURE

Culture operates on a surface level, an intermediate or shallow level, and a deep level.

Surface culture

This level is made up of observable and concrete elements of culture such as food, dress, music, and holidays. This level of culture has a low emotional charge so that changes don't create great anxiety in a person or group.

Shallow culture

This level is made up of unspoken rules around everyday social interactions and norms, such as courtesy, attitudes toward elders, nature of friendship, concepts of time, personal space between people, nonverbal communication, rules about eye contact, or appropriate touching. It's at this level of culture that we put into action our deep cultural values.

This level has a strong emotional charge. At the same time, at this level we interpret certain behaviors as disrespectful, offensive, or hostile. Social violation of norms at this level can cause mistrust, distress, or social friction.

Deep culture

This level is made up of tacit knowledge and unconscious assumptions that govern our worldview. It also contains the cosmology (view of good or bad) that guides ethics, spirituality, health, and theories of group harmony (i.e., competition or cooperation). Deep culture also governs how we learn new information. Elements at this level have an intense emotional charge. Mental models at this level help the brain interpret threats or rewards in the environment.

The culture tree

Compare culture to a tree. A tree is part of a bigger ecosystem that shapes and impacts its growth and development. Shallow culture is represented in the trunk and branches of the tree while we can think of surface culture as the observable fruit that the tree bears. Surface and shallow culture are not static; they change and shift over time as social groups move around and ethnic groups intermarry, resulting in a cultural mosaic just as branches and fruit on a tree change in response to the seasons and its environment. Deep culture is like the root system of a tree. It is what grounds the individual and nourishes his mental health. It is the bedrock of self-concept, group identity, approaches to problem solving, and decision making.

Zaretta Hammond is a teacher educator and the author of *Culturally Responsive Teaching and The Brain: Promoting Authentic Engagement and Rigor Among Culturally and Linguistically Diverse Students*, from which this article is excerpted.

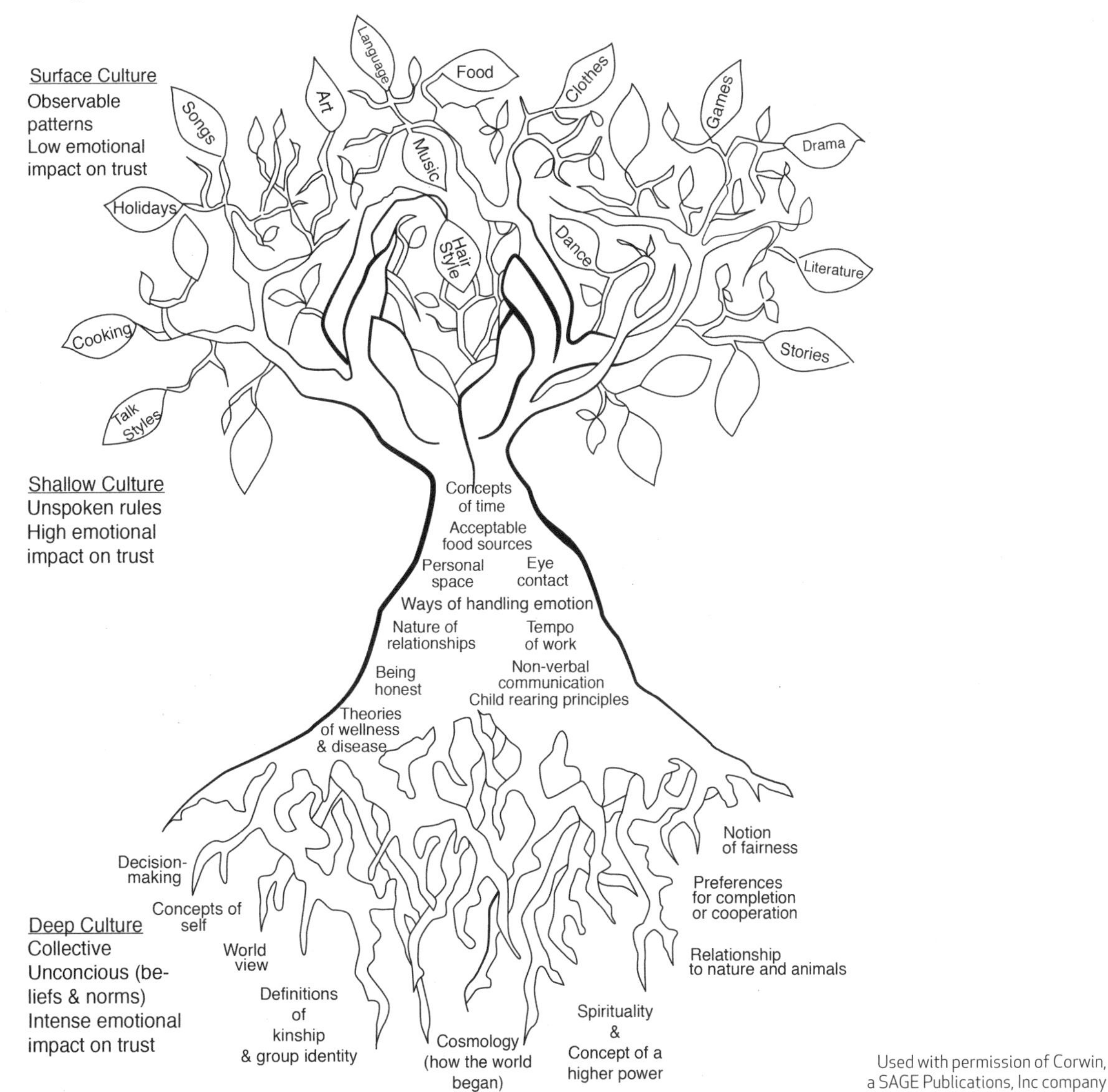

UNITED NATIONS SUSTAINABLE DEVELOPMENT GOALS

On September 25th, 2015, world leaders in the United Nations adopted a set of seventeen goals to end poverty, protect the planet, and ensure prosperity for all as part of a new sustainable development agenda. The goals cover global challenges that are crucial for the survival of humanity. Over the next fifteen years, with these new Goals that universally apply to all, countries will mobilize efforts to end all forms of poverty, fight inequalities and tackle climate change, while ensuring that no one is left behind. For the goals to be reached, everyone needs to do their part: governments, the private sector, civil society and people like you. Find a list of suggestions for taking action at **un.org/sustainabledevelopment/takeaction/**

SUSTAINABLE DEVELOPMENT GOALS

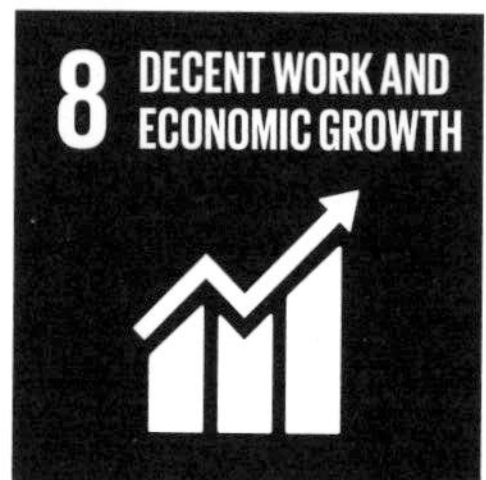

YOU ARE BRILLIANT, AND THE EARTH IS HIRING

By Paul Hawken

When I was invited to give this speech, I was asked if I could give a simple short talk that was "direct, naked, taut, honest, passionate, lean, shivering, startling, and graceful." No pressure there.

Let's begin with the startling part. You are going to have to figure out what it means to be a human being on earth at a time when every living system is declining, and the rate of decline is accelerating. Kind of a mind-boggling situation... but not one peer-reviewed paper published in the last thirty years can refute that statement. Basically, civilization needs a new operating system, you are the programmers, and we need it within a few decades.

This planet came with a set of instructions, but we seem to have misplaced them. Important rules like don't poison the water, soil, or air, don't let the earth get overcrowded, and don't touch the thermostat have been broken. Buckminster Fuller said that spaceship earth was so ingeniously designed that no one has a clue that we are on one, flying through the universe at a million miles per hour, with no need for seat belts, lots of room in coach, and really good food — but all that is changing.

There is invisible writing on the back of the diploma you will receive, and in case you didn't bring lemon juice to decode it, I can tell you what it says: You are Brilliant, and the Earth is Hiring. The earth couldn't afford to send recruiters or limos to your school. It sent you rain, sunsets, ripe cherries, night blooming jasmine, and that unbelievably cute person you are dating. Take the hint. And here's the deal: Forget that this task of planet-saving is not possible in the time required. Don't be put off by people who know what is not possible. Do what needs to be done, and check to see if it was impossible only after you are done.

When asked if I am pessimistic or optimistic about the future, my answer is always the same: If you look at the science about what is happening on earth and aren't pessimistic, you don't understand the data. But if you meet the people who are working to restore this earth and the lives of the poor, and you aren't optimistic, you haven't got a pulse. What I see everywhere in the world are ordinary people willing to confront despair, power, and incalculable odds in order to restore some semblance of grace, justice, and beauty to this world. The poet Adrienne Rich wrote, "So much has been destroyed I have cast my lot with those who, age after age, perversely, with no extraordinary power, reconstitute the world." There could be no better description. Humanity is coalescing. It is reconstituting the world, and the action is taking place in schoolrooms, farms, jungles, villages, campuses, companies, refugee camps, deserts, fisheries, and slums.

You join a multitude of caring people. No one knows how many groups and organizations are working on the most salient issues of our day: climate change, poverty, deforestation, peace, water, hunger, conservation, human rights, and more. This is the largest movement the world has ever seen. Rather than control, it seeks connection. Rather than dominance, it strives to disperse concentrations of power. Like Mercy Corps, it works behind the scenes and gets the job done. Large as it is, no one knows the true size of this movement. It provides hope, support, and meaning to billions of people in the world. Its clout resides in idea, not in force. It is made up of teachers, children, peasants, businesspeople, rappers, organic farmers, nuns, artists, government workers, fisherfolk, engineers, students, incorrigible writers, weeping Muslims, concerned mothers, poets, doctors without borders, grieving Christians, street musicians, the President of the United States of America, and as the writer David James Duncan would say, the Creator, the One who loves us all in such a huge way.

There is a rabbinical teaching that says if the world is ending and the Messiah arrives, first plant a tree, and then see if the story is true. Inspiration is not garnered from the litanies of what may befall us; it resides in humanity's willingness to restore, redress, reform, rebuild, recover, reimagine, and reconsider. "One day you finally knew what you had to do, and began, though the voices around you kept shouting their bad advice," is Mary Oliver's description of moving away from the profane toward a deep sense of connectedness to the living world.

Millions of people are working on behalf of strangers, even if the evening news is usually about the death of strangers. This kindness of strangers has religious, even mythic origins, and very specific eighteenth-century roots.

Abolitionists were the first people to create a national and global movement to defend the rights of those they did not know. Until that time, no group had filed a grievance except on behalf of itself. The founders of this movement were largely unknown — Granville Clark, Thomas Clarkson, Josiah Wedgwood — and their goal was ridiculous on the face of it: at that time three out of four people in the world were enslaved. Enslaving each other was what human beings had done for ages. And the abolitionist movement was greeted with incredulity. Conservative spokesmen ridiculed the abolitionists as liberals, progressives, do-gooders, meddlers, and activists. They were told they would ruin the economy and drive England into poverty. But for the first time in history a group of people organized themselves to help people they would never know, from whom they would never receive direct or indirect benefit. And today tens of millions of people do this every day. It is called the world of non-profits, civil society, schools, social entrepreneurship, non-governmental organizations, and companies who place social and environmental justice at the top of their strategic goals. The scope and scale of this effort is unparalleled in history.

The living world is not "out there" somewhere, but in your heart. What do we know about life? In the words of biologist Janine Benyus, life creates the conditions that are conducive to life. I can think of no better motto for a future economy. We have tens of thousands of abandoned homes without people and tens of thousands of abandoned people without homes. We have failed bankers advising failed regulators on how to save failed assets. We are the only species on the planet without full employment. Brilliant. We have an economy that tells us that it is cheaper to destroy earth in real time rather than renew, restore, and sustain it. You can print money to bail out a bank but you can't print life to bail out a planet. At present we are stealing the future, selling it in the present, and calling it gross domestic product. We can just as easily have an economy that is based on healing the future instead of stealing it. We can either create assets for the future or take the assets of the future. One is called restoration and the other exploitation. And whenever we exploit the earth we exploit people and cause untold suffering. Working for the earth is not a way to get rich, it is a way to be rich.

The first living cell came into being nearly 40 million centuries ago, and its direct descendants are in all of our bloodstreams. Literally you are breathing molecules this very second that were inhaled by Moses, Mother Teresa, and Bono. We are vastly interconnected. Our fates are inseparable. We are here because the dream of every cell is to become two cells. And dreams come true. In each of you are one quadrillion cells, 90 percent of which are not human cells. Your body is a community, and without those other microorganisms you would perish in hours. Each human cell has 400 billion molecules conducting millions of processes between trillions of atoms. The total cellular activity in one human body is staggering: one septillion actions at any one moment, a one with twenty-four zeros after it. In a millisecond, our body has undergone ten times more processes than there are stars in the universe, which is exactly what Charles Darwin foretold when he said science would discover that each living creature was a "little universe, formed of a host of self-propagating organisms, inconceivably minute and as numerous as the stars of heaven."

So I have two questions for you all: First, can you feel your body? Stop for a moment. Feel your body. One septillion activities going on simultaneously, and your body does this so well you are free to ignore it, and wonder instead when this speech will end. You can feel it. It is called life. This is who you are. Second question: who is in charge of your body? Who is managing those molecules? Hopefully not a political party. Life is creating the conditions that are conducive to life inside you, just as in all of nature. Our innate nature is to create the conditions that are conducive to life. What I want you to imagine is that collectively humanity is evincing a deep innate wisdom in coming together to heal the wounds and insults of the past.

Ralph Waldo Emerson once asked what we would do if the stars only came out once every thousand years. No one would sleep that night, of course. The world would create new religions overnight. We would be ecstatic, delirious, made rapturous by the glory of God. Instead, the stars come out every night and we watch television.

This extraordinary time when we are globally aware of each other and the multiple dangers that threaten civilization has never happened, not in a thousand years, not in ten thousand years. Each of us is as complex and beautiful as all the stars in the universe. We have done great things and we have gone way off course in terms of honoring creation. You are graduating to the most amazing, stupefying challenge ever bequested to any generation. The generations before you failed. They didn't stay up all night. They got distracted and lost sight of the fact that life is a miracle every moment of your existence. Nature beckons you to be on her side. You couldn't ask for a better boss. The most unrealistic person in the world is the cynic, not the dreamer. Hope only makes sense when it doesn't make sense to be hopeful. This is your century. Take it and run as if your life depends on it.

Paul Hawken is a renowned entrepreneur, visionary environmental activist, and author of many books, including *Blessed Unrest: How the Largest Movement in the World Came into Being and Why No One Saw It Coming* (2007). He was presented with an honorary doctorate of humane letters by University president Father Bill Beauchamp, C.S.C., in May 2009, when he delivered this speech at the University of Portland. www.paulhawken.com

OUR HOME ON EARTH

By Winona LaDuke

Giiwedinong means "going home" in the Anishinaabeg language — it also means North, which is the place from which we come. This is a key problem that modern industrial society faces today. We cannot restore our relationship with the Earth until we find our place in the world. This is our challenge today: where is home?

I returned to the White Earth Reservation in Minnesota about twenty-five years ago after being raised off-reservation, which is a common circumstance for our people. White Earth is my place in the Universe. It's where the headwaters of the Mississippi and Red Rivers are.

PEOPLE OF THE LAND

Anishinaabeg is our name for ourselves in our own language, it means "people." We are called Ojibwe, referring to "ojibige" (meaning "to write") on our birch bark scrolls. Our aboriginal territory, and where we live today, is in the northern part of five U.S. states and the southern part of four Canadian Provinces. We are people of lakes, rivers, deep woods and lush prairies.

Now, if you look at the United States, about 4 percent of the land is held by Indian people. But if you go to Canada, about 85% of the population north of the fiftieth parallel is native. If you look at the whole of North America, you'll find that the majority of the population is native in about a third of the continent. Within this larger area indigenous people maintain their own ways of living and their cultural practices.

There are a number of countries in the Western Hemisphere in which native peoples are the majority of the population: in Guatemala, Ecuador, Peru, and Bolivia. In some South American countries we control as much as 22 to 40 percent of the land. Overall, the Western Hemisphere is not predominantly white. Indigenous people continue their ways of living based on generations and generations of knowledge and practice on the land.

On a worldwide scale there are about five thousand indigenous nations. Nations are groups of indigenous peoples who share common language, culture, history, territory and government institutions. It is said that there are currently about five hundred million of us in the world today, depending on how you define the term indigenous. I define it as peoples who have continued their way of living for thousands of years.

Indigenous peoples believe fundamentally in a state of balance. We believe that all societies and cultural practices must exist in accordance with the laws of nature in order to be sustainable. We also believe that cultural diversity is as essential as biological diversity in maintaining sustainable societies. Indigenous people have lived on Earth sustainably for thousands of years, and I suggest to you that indigenous ways of living are the only sustainable ways of living. Most indigenous ceremonies, if you look to their essence, are about the restoration of balance — they are a reaffirmation of our relationship to creation. That is our intent: to restore, and then to retain balance and honor our part in creation.

Therefore, when I harvest wild rice on our reservation, I always offer asemaa (tobacco) because when you take something, you must always give thanks to its spirit for giving itself to you. We are very careful when we harvest. Anthropologists call this reciprocity. This means that when you take, you always give. We also say that you must take only what you need and leave the rest. Because if you take more than you need, you have brought about imbalance, you have been selfish. To do this in our community is a very big disgrace. It is a violation of natural law, and it leaves you with no guarantee that you will be able to continue harvesting.

We have a word in our language which describes the practice of living in harmony with natural law: minocimaatisiiwin. This word describes how you behave as an individual in a relationship with other individuals and in relationship with the land and all things. We have tried to retain this way of living and this way of thinking in spite of all that has happened to us over the centuries. I believe we do retain most of these practices in our community, even if they are overshadowed at times by individualism.

THE CLASH OF INDIGENOUS AND INDUSTRIAL WORLDVIEWS

I would like to contrast indigenous thinking with what I call "industrial thinking," which is characterized by five key ideas that run counter to what we as native people believe.

1. Instead of believing that natural law is preeminent, industrial society believes that humans are entitled to full dominion over nature. It believes that man — and it is usually man of course — has some God-given right to all that is around him. Industrial society puts its faith in man's laws: that pollution regulations, allowable catches, etc. are sustainable.

2. In indigenous societies, we notice that much in nature is cyclical: the movement of moons, the tides, the seasons, and our bodies. Time itself is cyclical. Instead of modeling itself on the cyclical structure of nature, industrial society is patterned on linear thinking. Industrial society strives to continually move in one direction defined by things like technology and economic growth.

3. Industrial society holds a different attitude toward what is wild as opposed to what is cultivated or "tame." In our language we have the word indinawayuuganitoog (all our relations). That is what we believe — that our relatives

may have wings, fins, roots or hooves. Industrial society believes wilderness must be tamed. This is also the idea behind colonialism: that some people have the right to civilize other people.

4. Industrial society speaks in a language of inanimate nouns. Things of all kinds are not spoken of as being alive and having spirit; they are described as mere objects, commodities. When things are inanimate, "man" can take them, buy and sell them, or destroy them. Some scholars refer to this as the "commodification of the sacred."

5. The last aspect of industrial thinking is the idea of capitalism itself (which is always unpopular to question in America). The capitalist goal is to use the least labor, capital, and resources to make the most profit. The intent of capitalism is accumulation. So the capitalist's method is always to take more than is needed. With accumulation as its core, industrial society practices conspicuous consumption. Indigenous societies, on the other hand, practice what I would call "conspicuous distribution." We focus on the potlatch — the act of giving away. In fact, the more you give away, the greater your honor.

Modern industrial societies must begin to see the interlocking interests between their own ability to survive and the survival of indigenous peoples' culture. Indigenous peoples have lived sustainably on the land for thousands of years. I am absolutely sure that our societies could live without yours, but I'm not so sure that your society can continue to live without ours.

SUSTAINABILITY IN ACTION

All across the continent there are small groups of native peoples who are trying to regain control of and restore their communities.

I'll use my own people as an example. The White Earth Reservation is thirty-six by thirty-six miles square, which is about 837,000 acres. A treaty reserved it for our people in 1867 in return for relinquishing a much larger area of northern Minnesota. Out of all our territory we chose this land for its richness and diversity. There are forty-seven lakes on the reservation. There's maple sugar, there are hardwoods, and there are all the different medicine plants my people use. We have wild rice, we have deer, we have beaver, we have fish — we have every food we need. On the eastern part of the reservation there are stands of white pine; to the west is prairieland where the buffalo once roamed. Our word for prairie is mashkode (place of burned medicine) referring to native practices of burning as a form of nurturing the soil and plants.

Our traditional forms of land use and ownership are similar to those found in community land trusts being established today. The land is owned collectively, and each family has traditional areas where it fishes and hunts. We call our concept of land ownership Anishinaabeg akiing: "the land of the people," which doesn't imply that we own our land, but that we belong on it. Unfortunately, our definition doesn't stand up well in court because this country's legal system upholds the concept of private property.

We have maintained our land by means of careful management. For example, we traditionally have "hunting bosses" and "rice chiefs," who make sure that resources are used sustainably in each region. Hunting bosses oversee rotation of trap lines, a system by which people trap in an area for two years and then move to a different area to let the land rest. Rice chiefs coordinate wild rice harvesting. The rice on each lake has its own unique taste and ripens at its own time. Traditionally, we have a "tallyman," who makes sure there are enough animals for each family in a given area. If a family can't sustain itself, the tallyman moves them to a new place where animals are more plentiful. These practices are essential to sustainability, and to maintaining what some now call the commons.

THE LOSS OF WHITE EARTH, AND HOW WE PLAN TO GET IT BACK

Our reservation was reserved by treaty in 1867. In 1887 the Nelson Act and subsequently the General Allotment Act was passed to teach Indians the concept of private property, but also to facilitate the removal of more land from Indian Nations. The federal government divided our reservation into eighty-acre parcels of land and allotted each parcel to an individual Indian, hoping that this would somehow force us to become farmers and adopt the notion of progress — in short, to be civilized.

The allotment system was alien to our traditional concepts of land. In our society a person harvested rice in one place, trapped in another place, gathered medicines in a third place, and picked berries in a fourth. These locations depended on the ecosystem; they were not necessarily contiguous. But the government said to each Indian, "Here are your eighty acres; this is where you'll live." Then, after each Indian had received an allotment, the rest of the land was declared "surplus" and given to white people to homestead or "develop". What happened to my reservation happened to reservations all across the country.

The state of Minnesota took our pine forests away and sold them to timber companies, and then taxed us for the land that was left. When the Indians couldn't pay the taxes, the state confiscated the land. But how could these people pay taxes? In 1910, they could not even read or write English.

I'll tell you a story about how my great-grandma was cheated by a loan shark. She lived on Many-Point Lake, where she was allotted land. She had run up a bill at the local store because she was waiting until fall when she could get some money from wild rice harvesting and a payment coming from a treaty annuity. So she went to a land speculator named Lucky Waller, and she said, "I need to pay this bill." She asked to borrow fifty bucks from him until the fall, and he said: "Okay, you can do that. Just sign here and I'll loan you that fifty bucks." So she signed with the thumbprint and went back to her house on Many-Point Lake. About three months later she was ready to repay him the fifty bucks, and the loan shark said: "No, you keep that money. I bought your land from you." He had purchased her eighty acres on Many-Point Lake for fifty bucks. Today that location is a Boy Scout camp.

The White Earth Reservation lost two hundred and fifty thousand acres to the state of Minnesota because of unpaid taxes. By 1920, 99 percent of the original White Earth Reservation land was in non-Indian hands. This was done to native peoples across the country.

We have exhausted all legal recourse for getting back our land. The Federal Circuit Court ruled that to regain their land Indian people had to have filed a lawsuit within seven years of the original time of taking. Still, we believe that we must get our land back. We really do not have any other place to go. That's why we started the White Earth Land Recovery Project. Our project is like several other projects in Indian communities. We are not trying to displace people who have settled there. A third of our land is held by federal, state and country governments. That land should just be returned to us. It certainly would not displace anyone. Some of the privately held land on our reservation is held by absentee landholders — many of whom have never seen that land; they do not even know where it is. It is a commodity to them, not home. We hope to persuade them to return it to us.

Our project also works to reacquire our land. We bought some land as a site for a roundhouse, a building that holds one of our ceremonial drums. We bought back our burial grounds, which were on private land, because we believe that we should hold the land where our ancestors rest. We purchased a former elementary school, which is now the home of our new radio station and a wind turbine. In 2009, which is the 20th anniversary of our project, we had acquired 1400 acres. We use some of this land to grow and gather sustainable products that we sell: wild rice, maple syrup and candy, berry jams, and Birch bark crafts.

SUSTAINABLE COMMUNITIES, NOT SUSTAINABLE DEVELOPMENT

In conclusion, I want to say there is no such thing as sustainable development. Community is the only thing in my experience that is sustainable. We all need to be involved in building communities- not solely focused on developing things. We can each do that in our own way, whether it is European-American communities or indigenous communities, by restoring a way of life that is based on the land.

The only way you can manage a commons is if you share enough cultural experiences and values so that what you take out of nature doesn't upset the natural balance — minobimaatisiiwin, as we call it. The reason native cultures have remained sustainable for all these centuries is that

we are cohesive communities. A common set of values is needed to live together on the land.

Finally, I believe industrial societies continue to consume too much of the world's resources. When you need that many resources, it means constant intervention in other peoples' land and other peoples' countries. It is meaningless to talk about human rights unless you talk about consumption. In order for native communities to live and teach the world about sustainability, the dominant society must change. If modern society continues in the direction it is going, indigenous people's way of life will continue to bear the consequences.

Winona LaDuke lives on the White Earth Reservation in Minnesota, where she founded the White Earth Land Recovery Project to regain the Anishinaabeg people's original lands. Recipient of the International Reebok Human Rights Award, LaDuke serves as co-chair of the "Indigenous Women's Network": http://nativeharvest.com/winona_laduke

THOUGHTS ON SUSTAINABILITY

As we mentioned earlier this session, humans have a variety of ways of thinking about and framing sustainability. Sustainability means different things to different people. Consider these strong, widely-accepted, and substantiated thoughts as a starting point for developing your own sustainability framework.

"*Sustainable development is meeting the needs of the present without compromising the ability of future generations to meet their own needs.*

— Our Common Future, *UN World Commission on Environment and Development*

"*We stand at a critical moment in Earth's history, a time when humanity must choose its future. As the world becomes increasingly interdependent and fragile, the future at once holds great peril and great promise. To move forward we must recognize that in the midst of a magnificent diversity of cultures and life forms we are one human family and one Earth community with a common destiny. We must join together to bring forth a sustainable global society founded on respect for nature, universal human rights, economic justice, and a culture of peace. Towards this end, it is imperative that we, the peoples of Earth, declare our responsibility to one another, to the greater community of life, and to future generations.*

— The Preamble to *The Earth Charter*

"*[I define sustainability] with great difficulty, because I'm a fluent speaker of my language, and if I try to translate that, or even interpret that into my language, it's not a very good word. It's a very inadequate word... Sustainability on one level means to be able to maintain and sustain the fullness of health that needs to be there for us to thrive, and for everything else to thrive... But the way in my language that it translates is sustaining the human abuse to a certain level, and keeping it at a level that it doesn't quite destroy everything. So that's not an adequate definition... What does it mean to 'sustain'?. .. If we look at the truth of what that might mean, that means that there should be no animal, or bird, or fish, or no plant that is on the endangered list, or that is on the species at-risk list. There should be no peoples who are in danger, or at risk or disappearing, or at the bottom of the economic curve, or the social curve... You're remaining ignorant and you're remaining uncivilized, if you cannot achieve one hundred percent sustainability of everything that you're using."*

— Jeannette Armstrong, Okanagan author and indigenous rights activist, "Native Perspectives on Sustainability: Jeannette Armstrong (Syilx)" [Interview transcript].

"*Sustainability is equity over time. As a value, it refers to giving equal weight in your decisions to the future as well as the present. You might think of it as extending the Golden Rule through time, so that you do unto future generations (as well as to your present fellow beings) as you would have them do unto you.*

— Robert Gilman, Director, Context Institute

"*The time has come for a global effort to build a new economic system no longer based on the dangerous illusions that irresponsible growth is possible on our finite planet and that endless material gain promotes well-being. Instead it will be a system that promotes harmony and respect for nature and for each other, that respects our ancient wisdom traditions and protects our most vulnerable people as our own family, and that gives us time to live and enjoy our lives and to appreciate rather than destroy our world. Sustainability is the essential basis and precondition of such a sane economic system."*

— Lyonchhen Jigmi Y. Thinley, former Prime Minister of Bhutan, in "Sustainability and Happiness: A development philosophy for Bhutan and the world"

"*Sustainability means living within Earth's limits... Now is the time for fundamental change so that future generations can enjoy resources we take for granted — like clean air and water — and do not pay the price because we squandered this wealth.*

— David Suzuki, Co-Founder of the David Suzuki Foundation

SYSTEMS THINKING: A NECESSARY PERSPECTIVE IN OUR CHANGING WORLD

By the Worldwatch Institute

The word "system" is the most radical word spoken in any language. It is radical in the true sense because it points to our inescapable rootedness in the fabric of life, from microbes that inhabit our bodies to the air we breathe. The word symbolizes our implicatedness in the world and our dependence on things beyond ourselves. The modern celebration of individualism stands at the other extreme as an assertion of autonomy and independence from the friends, families, communities, societies, and ecologies on which we depend. Systems thinkers, in contrast, see the world as networks of interdependence, not merely as a stage for individual performance.[1]

One result of a systems perspective ought to be gratitude for the things that have been given to us that owe nothing to our individual efforts. In large measure, we are the result of our genes, upbringing, local conditions, teachers, cultures, and the particular places that nurture every moment of our lives, inside and out. We live, in other words, within a web of obligations and relationships that transcend the conventional boundaries by which we organize academic disciplines and bureaucracies.

Thinking of the world as a network of systems begins in natural history, ecology, and the study of biophysical conditions, both within and without. It likely begins early in life, in a child's curiosity about what is connected to what. It is grounded in the physical sciences, but it extends through every discipline in the curriculum. The tools of systems thinking range from complicated computer modeling to intuition and the vague hunch that something is missing.

Systems thinking leads to the recognition of the counterintuitive results of human action, to an awareness of the unpredictability of events, and, in turn, to the necessary precaution that leaves wide margins for error, malfeasance, and acts of God. But the scope, scale, and technological velocity of change now threaten the future of civilization. This gives us every reason to avoid making irrevocable and irreversible system changes without due diligence and a great deal of careful thought. Applied to policy and law, systems thinking would cause us to act with greater precaution and foresight.

The idea of systems is fundamentally political, because it underscores our interrelatedness and mutual dependence. The political community and the ecological community are one and indivisible, but they are not equal. The human community, in all of its manifestations, is a subset of the larger web of life. But the essential questions of politics — who gets what, when, and how — pertain throughout the entire system. The millions of human decisions that have appropriated the majority of the planet's net primary productivity for human use are political choices that cross species lines. The preservation of half of the Earth as a sanctuary for biodiversity, as proposed by biologist Edward O. Wilson, would be a political choice as well.[2]

This is familiar ground to most of the readers of Worldwatch's annual State of the World reports. But it is not well known or comprehended by the great majority of people in the United States, Europe, or elsewhere — a failure of education that has large consequences. The elections of 2016 in Western democracies, for example, showed the fault lines emerging in our civic culture. They are not, first and foremost, the standard disagreements between liberals and conservatives about the size and role of governments and markets. Rather, they are a dispute between advocates of competing paradigms about the possible and desirable scale of human domination of the ecosphere and who benefits and who loses.

The upshot is that recent political events in the United States and Europe reveal large disparities in scientific knowledge and in the command of factual evidence about Earth systems, ecology, oceans, and so forth. We might expect that, under growing ecological stress, there also would be a rise in demonization of "others," hatred, fear, demagoguery, and violence. In such circumstances, public ecological literacy will become increasingly important to inform and moderate political discourse and to improve governance under conditions of what political theorist William Ophuls once described broadly as "ecological scarcity."[3]

This essay is an excerpt from *EarthEd: Rethinking Education on a Changing Planet* by the Worldwatch Institute. For 40 years, Worldwatch Institute has been a leader in big-picture sustainability insight and multidisciplinary research..

WATCH THIS VIDEO!

For an example of how systems thinking acknowledges the interrelationships in networks, watch this video to see what happened when wolves were reintroduced back into Yellowstone National Park in 1995: tinyurl.com/systemswolves

A SYSTEMS THINKING MODEL: THE ICEBERG

Systems thinking is a way of conceptualizing and understanding the world that focuses on how various elements within a system — which could be an ecosystem, an organization, or something more dispersed such as a supply chain — are related to and influence one another.

Systems thinking helps us approach problem more effectively. Rather than reacting to individual problems that arise, a systems thinker will ask about relationships to other activities within the system, look for patterns over time, and seek root causes.

"...we are not seeing a new world, but rather our old world through new eyes."

One systems thinking model that is helpful for understanding global issues is the Iceberg Model. We know that an iceberg has only 10 percent of its total mass above the water while 90 percent is underwater. But that 90 percent is what the ocean currents act on, and what creates the iceberg's behavior at its tip. Global issues can be viewed in this same way.

LEVELS OF THINKING

1. THE EVENT LEVEL

   The Event Level is the level at which we typically perceive the world: for instance, waking up one morning

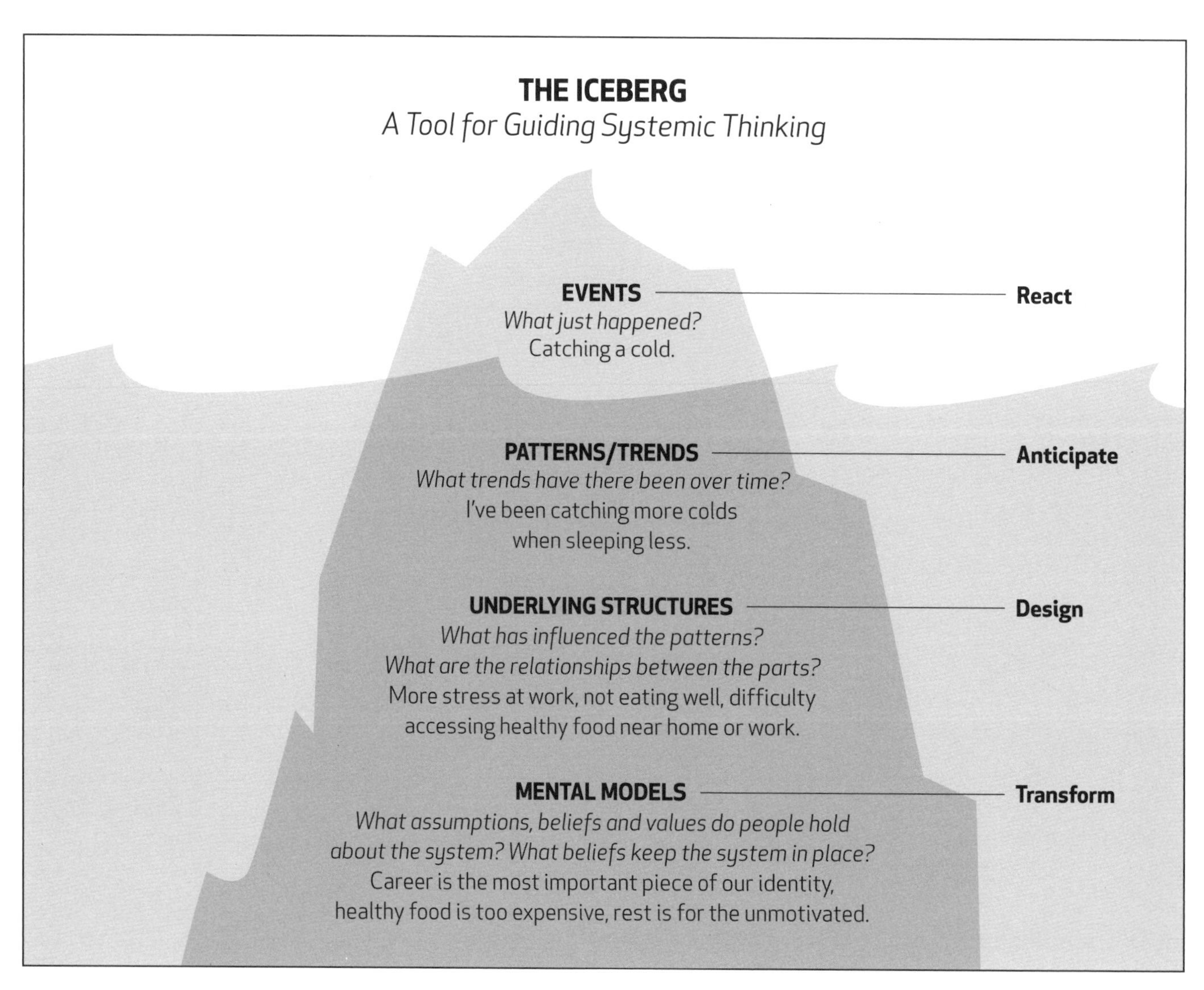

to find we have caught a cold. While problems observed at the Event Level can often be addressed with a simple readjustment, the Iceberg Model pushes us not to assume that every issue can be solved by simply treating the symptom or adjusting at the Event Level.

2. **THE PATTERN LEVEL**

   If we look just below the Event Level, we often notice patterns. Similar events have been taking place over time — we may have been catching more colds when we haven't been resting enough. Observing patterns allows us to forecast and forestall events.

3. **THE STRUCTURE LEVEL**

   Below the Pattern Level lies the Structure Level. When we ask, "What is causing the pattern we are observing?" the answer is usually some kind of structure. Increased stress at work due to the new promotion policy, the habit of eating poorly when under stress, or the inconvenient location of healthy food sources could all be structures at play in our catching a cold. According to Professor John Gerber, structures can include the following:

   1. Physical things — like vending machines, roads, traffic lights or terrain.
   2. Organizations — like corporations, governments, and schools.
   3. Policies — like laws, regulations, and tax structures.
   4. Ritual — habitual behaviors so ingrained, they are not conscious.

4. **THE MENTAL MODEL LEVEL**

   Mental models are the attitudes, beliefs, morals, expectations, and values that allow structures to continue functioning as they are. These are the beliefs that we often learn subconsciously from our society or family and are likely unaware of. Mental models that could be involved in us catching a cold could include: a belief that career is deeply important to our identity, that healthy food is too expensive, or that rest is for the unmotivated.

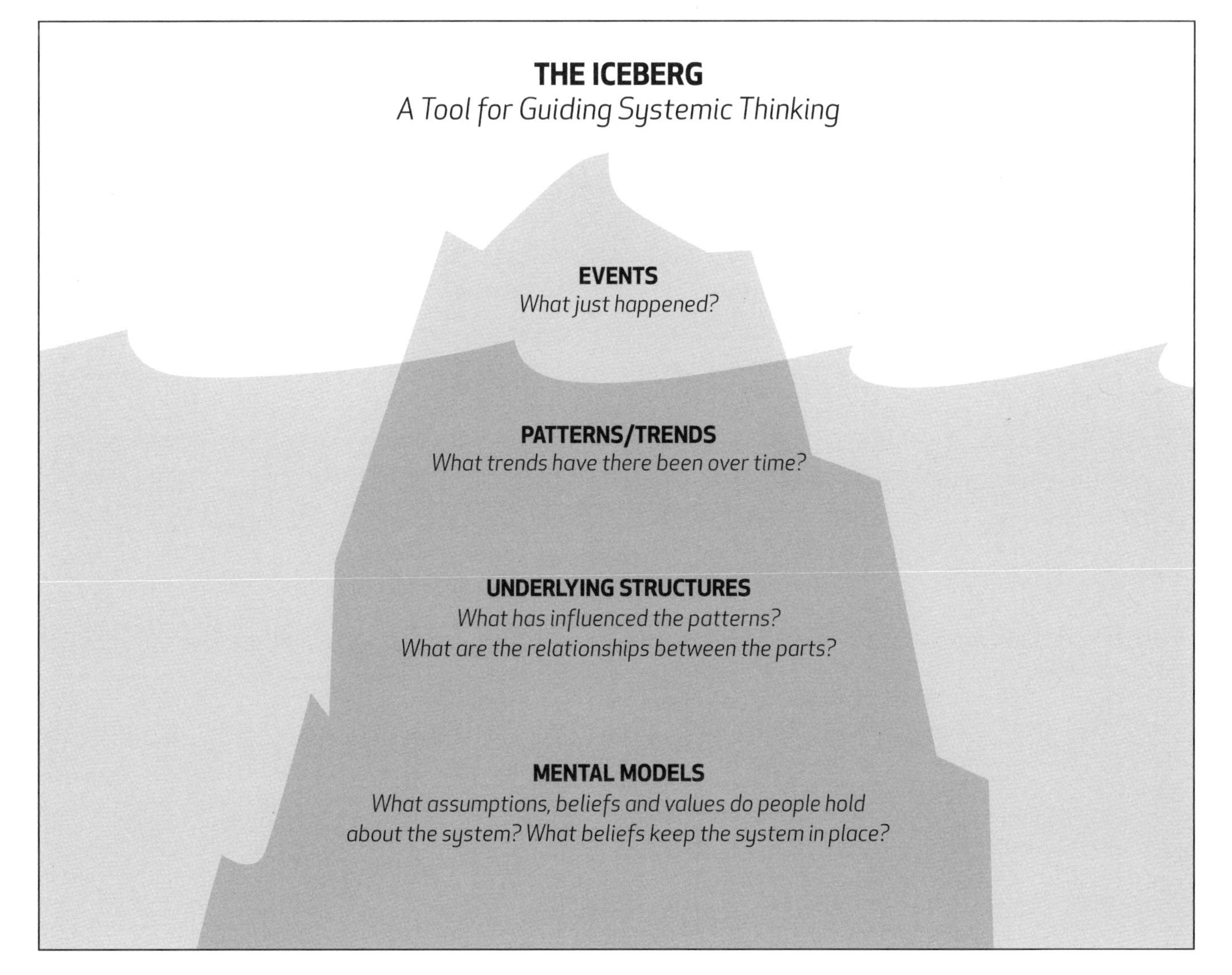

PUTTING THE LEVELS TOGETHER

Take a look at the diagram on the previous page to see the Iceberg Model applied to an instance of catching a cold.

GIVE IT A TRY!

As you go through the course, select a sustainability-related event that strikes you as urgent, important, or interesting. Write the event (what is observable about the event) at the top of the blank Iceberg below and work your way down through the patterns, underlying systems and mental models, adding as many as you can think of. It can also be useful to move up and down between levels as you think more about the event. Events to start with could include: the inclusion of a favorite animal on the Endangered Species list, the lack of access to healthy food in your neighborhood, a problem you encountered while taking public transit recently, the pollution of your local water source, or any other events you find significant.

QUESTIONS TO CONSIDER AFTER TRYING OUT THE ICEBERG MODEL

1. Does the Iceberg Model help broaden your perspective? If so, how might this new perspective be helpful?
2. Consider the concept of entry, or "leverage" points. These are points where one can intervene in a system in order to completely transform the system. Does the exercise show you any new entry points at which you are inspired to intervene?
3. What issues that have frustrated you might be interesting to analyze with the Iceberg Model?

Find this exercise online at **ecochallenge.org/iceberg-model**

ECOCHALLENGE: PUTTING IT INTO PRACTICE

Here are some ideas for putting what you learned this week into action. Find more ideas and commit to one Ecochallenge this week at **choices.ecochallenge.org**

- Think Local. Find out what local sustainability issues are most urgent in your region, including both social and environmental justice concerns.
- Practice political engagement. Sign a petition in support of an environmental or social initiative in your state.
- Get to know your local ecosystems. Explore at least one new hiking trail or nature walk in your area.
- Spread the word. Tell others why sustainability is important to you and what your vision for a sustainable world is.

"The sustainability revolution will be organic. It will arise from the visions, insights, experiments and actions of billions of people. The burden of making it happen is not on the shoulders of any one person or group. No one will get the credit, but everyone can contribute."

— Donella L. Meadows

SESSION 2

ECOLOGICAL PRINCIPLES

"Humankind has not woven the web of life. We are but one thread within it. Whatever we do to the web, we do to ourselves. All things are bound together. All things connect."

— Chief Seattle

LEARNING OBJECTIVES

- Explore ecological principles as a foundation of sustainability.
- Identify some of the complex global issues we currently face. Use systems thinking to analyze their causes, impacts, and how they are connected.
- Consider how to further align your behavior with ecological principles.

SESSION DESCRIPTION

"Everything is connected" might sound like a tired platitude, but it is an accurate description of the systems that enable all of the inhabitants of planet Earth to remain alive. As humans, we can use the principles of living systems to make decisions and develop strategies for building — or rebuilding — our human systems, including our communities and social institutions, to be sustainable and just for all. In this session, we will explore ecological principles and how to apply them to address some of the big, complex issues we currently face.

REFLECTION

How can you apply ecological principles to your life to make your ecological footprint smaller? Post your Reflection to your Dashboard on **choices.ecochallenge.org**. If you are not using the Ecochallenge site, write your thoughts in a journal and then reflect with your group.

Circle Question

Think of a principle (ethical, ecological, etc.) or value that helps guide you in making decisions. What is the principle or value? How is it helpful?

Reminder to the facilitator: The circle question should move quickly. Elicit an answer from each participant without questions or comments from others. The facilitator's guidelines are on page 10.

SUGGESTED DISCUSSION QUESTIONS

1. What concerns you the most about how we are affecting the planet? Consider both local and global actions.
2. What does Richard Heinberg mean by "You can't just do one thing..."? How does systems thinking apply to efforts to encourage more sustainable lifestyles?
3. How could you further align your behavior with ecological principles? What are some practices you can implement to support a sustainable society?
4. How does the I=PAT equation help us think about different strategies for achieving a sustainable society?
5. Discuss how environmental conditions have contributed to the Syrian refugee crisis.
6. How do you think food and water scarcity, along with climate change, are likely to affect future migrations of population?
7. What areas of the world are most likely to experience population disruption because of environmental issues (e.g. drought, flooding, famine, pollution)? What areas of your own region are most vulnerable?
8. What did you think about the results for your ecological footprint? How could you realistically change some aspects of your lifestyle to reduce your environmental footprint?

SUGGESTED GROUP ACTIVITY

Share and discuss your Ecological Footprint results with each other. Where can you make the most change individually? As a group?

DEFINITIONS

Anthropocene: A proposed epoch dating from the commencement of significant human impact on Earth's geology and ecosystems, including, but not limited to, anthropogenic climate change.

Ecological Footprint: A measure of the human demand on Earth's ecosystems. Ecological footprint analysis compares human demands on nature with the biosphere's ability to regenerate resources and provide services.

Resilience: The ability to recover from or adjust easily to difficulties or change.

System conditions of a sustainable society: The basic conditions that must be met if we want to maintain the essential natural resources, structures and functions that sustain human society.

Systems thinking: A way of conceptualizing and understanding the world that focuses on how various elements within a system — which could be an ecosystem, an organization, or something more dispersed such as a supply chain — are related to and influence one another.

FURTHER RESOURCES

Interested in finding out more on the topics presented in this session?
Visit our website for further readings and resources: **ecochallenge.org/discussion-course-resources.**
Follow our blog at **ecochallenge.org/blog/**; we post links to new resources and inspiring stories regularly.

YOU CAN'T DO JUST ONE THING: A CONVERSATION WITH RICHARD HEINBERG

By Michael K. Stone

Michael Stone: When you think about the systems view of life, what comes to mind?

Richard Heinberg: A lot of things. One is the phrase, "You can't do just one thing." The world is filled with relationships, and anything we do is going to impact parts of the system that we may never have even thought of.

The whole systems view stems from ecology, the study of the relationships between organisms and their environment — which is a discipline that got its start way back in the 1860s. Until ecology came along, we were studying organisms in isolation. Once we look at the ecology of, say, hummingbirds, we're also looking at both their external environment and the way they relate to other organisms; we even have to consider their internal microbial environment.

This way of thinking is fundamentally different from other aspects of Western science, and has altered the way many of us see the world. For example, in my work, which mostly has to do with energy, I've found that in taking a systems view, energy becomes a window through which to see and better understanding both natural ecosystems and human social systems.

When we look at human societies through the energy lens, we find ourselves seeing food as energy, technologies as ways of leveraging energy, and social complexity as a by-product of high rates of energy usage. Of course, we also become more keenly aware of the environmental impacts of energy production and consumption. As we become more energy literate we also pay more attention to how much energy we get back from our efforts at producing energy — whether growing food crops or drilling oil wells — and energy-returned-on-energy-invested (or EROEI) becomes a useful tool for evaluating potential energy sources.

There are many important questions that don't arise if we look at energy from a linear, one-thing-at-a-time point of view, which, unfortunately, is still largely dominant in our society. When you take a systems view, it's like seeing in 3-D and in color.

MS: Is there a reason why people have difficulty doing this?

RH: I think it mostly has to do with the history of Western thought and our tendency to divide reality into subject areas. It also has to do with our focus on naming things. Some languages are big on verbs, and some are big on nouns. We inheritors of the Indo-European language group have concentrated more on nouns and a little less on verbs than people in some other societies, such as the Native Americans. When we see life as a process rather than as a thing, we tend to take more of a systems view. Is that a crow — a static object — or is it life "crowing"?

MS: Is there something in our cultural history or our evolutionary history that slants us towards one way of thinking?

RH: The linearity of Western thought has a lot to do with forms of logic pioneered by the Greco-Roman philosophers. But in a larger sense, civilization itself fosters a "divide and conquer" attitude, and this is true no matter whether we're talking about Chinese, Aztec, or European civilization. City-centered living requires a constant harvesting of wealth from local ecosystems and also from peripheral peoples. It's no accident that civilizations gave rise to money, trade, and sophisticated weaponry.

MS: What are the ways that help people become aware of an alternative way of thinking?

RH: I don't think there's anything that helps more than spending time in nature, especially if we have someone along who can describe to us what we are seeing so that see a little more deeply. A lot of us are simply tone deaf to nature. Even if we go outside and look around, we don't understand what we're seeing. It helps to have a guide who can interpret the ecological tapestry. Once we learn the code, we can begin to understand those relationships for ourselves; it's like learning to read: once you have that skill, whole worlds open up. I'm still mostly a novice in this department, but I'm fortunate to have spent some time with a few fluent nature interpreters, and even that little bit of guidance has been an enormous help.

MS: Where would this view of life make the most difference in the issues facing people today?

RH: It would make the most difference at higher policy levels. We have applied the divide-and-conquer attitude across the board to energy, natural resources, finance, you name it, and the results are uniformly dire. What we've gotten as a result is a brief spurt of economic growth, with worsening environmental problems and an increasing rate of depletion of resources. Civilizations often seem to do this: they trade resilience and sustainability for short-term wealth.

As I argue in my latest book, we've probably hit the limits to economic growth already or are in the process of doing so. So it's extremely important that we learn to adapt to natural limits in a way that doesn't jeopardize future generations — and that's going to require systems thinking.

MS: Are people more open to that view than they used to be?

RH: I think more people are now than was the case a few years ago, but we are seeing a substantial backlash from some folks who feel threatened by ecological thinking. They want to eat their cake and have it too. They feel that they're entitled to returns on their investments, and if the environment isn't cooperating and providing them with those, then it must be somebody's fault. The solution therefore is to find out whose fault it is and deal with them — whether it's the EPA, the perpetrators of the climate change "fraud," or whoever. If your solution to life's problems is to find villains, there are always plenty of candidates around.

MS: Do people sometimes turn this around and say, "We're the villains, and we have to change"?

RH: Yes, and in fact I think that's the inevitable conclusion when taking a systems view. In some ways, we're victims of our own success. Our strategy of dividing and conquering nature has given us enormous wealth and power, but also put us in profound peril because of changing climate, species extinctions, depleting topsoil, depleting energy resources, and more.

We can't solve those problems one by one, in isolation. We can't address topsoil depletion without addressing our entire agricultural paradigm. And that leads us to reconsider the extractive, industrial paradigm.

MS: Are there things that make you hopeful that there is an audience for this message?

RH: I don't think one can be around young people without having a sense of hope. I was just at a conference put on by students at Harvard around the idea of creating a new economic paradigm, much along the lines of systems thinking, and it was exciting to meet and talk with these very bright young people, who are obviously concerned about the future.

There are several hundred Transition Initiatives around the world and over a hundred here in the US; these are grassroots efforts to move communities away from oil dependency and build resilience…

MS: Any other thoughts about the systems view?

RH: Eric Sevareid once said, "The main cause of problems is solutions." He was saying that the way we currently go about solving problems simply creates more problems. When we look at our problems in isolation, we address them in ways that just dig us into a deeper and deeper hole. But when we become systems thinkers, we find there are sometimes universally beneficial ways of addressing problems. We mimic nature's ways of doing things. If we're coming up with a solution that works for a whole array of problems, it's probably a good way to go, and it's most likely either coming from a systems approach or leading towards one.

Michael K. Stone is senior editor at the Center for Ecoliteracy and the primary author of the Center's book, *Smart by Nature: Schooling for Sustainability and Ecological Literacy: Educating Our Children for a Sustainable World*. Richard Heinberg is the author of thirteen books including *Our Renewable Future: Laying the Path for One Hundred Percent Clean Energy* (co-authored with David Fridley). He is Senior Fellow of the Post Carbon Institute and is regarded as one of the world's foremost advocates for a shift away from our current reliance on fossil fuels.

ECOLOGICAL PRINCIPLES

By Michael K. Stone

In order to create sustainable communities that are compatible with nature's processes we need basic ecological knowledge. Center for Ecoliteracy cofounder Fritjof Capra lists these as some of the fundamental facts of life:

- Matter cycles continually through the web of life.
- Most of the energy driving the ecological cycles flows from the sun.
- Diversity assures resilience.
- One species' waste is another species' food.
- Life did not take over the planet by combat but by networking.

Understanding these facts requires first understanding the patterns and processes by which nature sustains life, including networks, nested systems, cycles, flows, development, and dynamic balance.

NETWORKS. All living things in an ecosystem are interconnected through networks of relationship. They depend on this web of life to survive. For example: In a garden, a network of pollinators promotes genetic diversity; plants, in turn, provide nectar and pollen to the pollinators.

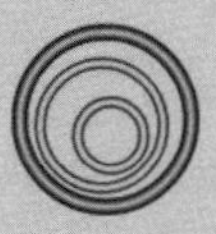

NESTED SYSTEMS. Nature is made up of systems that are nested within systems. Each individual system is an integrated whole and — at the same time — part of larger systems. Changes within a system can affect the sustainability of the systems that are nested within it as well as the larger systems in which it exists. For example: Cells are nested within organs within organisms within ecosystems.

CYCLES. Members of an ecological community depend on the exchange of resources in continual cycles. Cycles within an ecosystem intersect with larger regional and global cycles. For example: Water cycles through a garden and is also part of the global water cycle.

FLOWS. Each organism needs a continual flow of energy to stay alive. The constant flow of energy from the sun to Earth sustains life and drives most ecological cycles. For example: Energy flows through a food web when a plant converts the sun's energy through photosynthesis, a mouse eats the plant, a snake eats the mouse, and a hawk eats the snake. In each transfer, some energy is lost as heat, requiring an ongoing energy flow into the system.

DEVELOPMENT. All life — from individual organisms to species to ecosystems — changes over time. Individuals develop and learn, species adapt and evolve, and organisms in ecosystems coevolve. For example: Hummingbirds and honeysuckle flowers have developed in ways that benefit each other; the hummingbird's color vision and slender bill coincide with the colors and shapes of the flowers.

DYNAMIC BALANCE. Ecological communities act as feedback loops, so that the community maintains a relatively steady state that also has continual fluctuations. This dynamic balance provides resiliency in the face of ecosystem change. For example: Ladybugs in a garden eat aphids. When the aphid population falls, some ladybugs die off, which permits the aphid population to rise again, which supports more ladybugs. The populations of the individual species rise and fall, but balance within the system allows them to thrive together.

 For more information, visit www.ecoliteracy.org Michael K. Stone is senior editor at the Center for Ecoliteracy and the primary author of the Center's book, *Smart by Nature: Schooling for Sustainability and Ecological Literacy: Educating Our Children for a Sustainable World.*

THE ANTHROPOCENE EPOCH: SCIENTISTS DECLARE DAWN OF HUMAN-INFLUENCED AGE

By Damian Carrington

Humanity's impact on the Earth is now so profound that a new geological epoch — the Anthropocene — needs to be declared, according to an official expert group who presented the recommendation to the International Geological Congress in Cape Town [in August 2016].

The new epoch should begin about 1950, the experts said, and was likely to be defined by the radioactive elements dispersed across the planet by nuclear bomb tests, although an array of other signals, including plastic pollution, soot from power stations, concrete, and even the bones left by the global proliferation of the domestic chicken were now under consideration.

The current epoch, the Holocene, is the 12,000 years of stable climate since the last ice age during which all human civilisation developed. But the striking acceleration since the mid-20th century of carbon dioxide emissions and sea level rise, the global mass extinction of species, and the transformation of land by deforestation and development mark the end of that slice of geological time, the experts argue. The Earth is so profoundly changed that the Holocene must give way to the Anthropocene.

"The significance of the Anthropocene is that it sets a different trajectory for the Earth system, of which we of course are part," said Prof Jan Zalasiewicz, a geologist at the University of Leicester and chair of the Working Group on the Anthropocene (WGA), which started work in 2009.

"If our recommendation is accepted, the Anthropocene will have started just a little before I was born," he said. "We have lived most of our lives in something called the Anthropocene and are just realising the scale and permanence of the change."

Prof Colin Waters, principal geologist at the British Geological Survey and WGA secretary, said: "Being able to pinpoint an interval of time is saying something about how we have had an incredible impact on the environment of our planet. The concept of the Anthropocene manages to pull all these ideas of environmental change together."

Prof Chris Rapley, a climate scientist at University College London and former director of the Science Museum in London said: "The Anthropocene marks a new period in which our collective activities dominate the planetary machinery.

"Since the planet is our life support system — we are essentially the crew of a largish spaceship — interference with its functioning at this level and on this scale is highly significant. If you or I were crew on a smaller spacecraft, it would be unthinkable to interfere with the systems that provide us with air, water, fodder and climate control. But the shift into the Anthropocene tells us that we are playing with fire, a potentially reckless mode of behaviour which we are likely to come to regret unless we get a grip on the situation." Rapley is not part of the WGA.

Martin Rees, the astronomer royal and former president of the Royal Society, said that the dawn of the Anthropocene was a significant moment. "The darkest prognosis for the next millennium is that bio, cyber or environmental catastrophes could foreclose humanity's immense potential, leaving a depleted biosphere," he said.

But Lord Rees added that there is also cause for optimism. "Human societies could navigate these threats, achieve a sustainable future, and inaugurate eras of post-human evolution even more marvellous than what's led to us. The dawn of the Anthropocene epoch would then mark a one-off transformation from a natural world to one where humans jumpstart the transition to electronic (and potentially immortal) entities, that transcend our limitations and eventually spread their influence far beyond the Earth."

The evidence of humanity's impact on the planet is overwhelming, but the changes are very recent in geological terms, where an epoch usually spans tens of millions of years. "One criticism of the Anthropocene as geology is that it is very short," said Zalasiewicz. "Our response is that many of the changes are irreversible."

To define a new geological epoch, a signal must be found that occurs globally and will be incorporated into deposits in the future geological record. For example, the extinction of the dinosaurs 66m years ago at the end of the Cretaceous epoch is defined by a "golden spike" in sediments around the world of the metal iridium, which was dispersed from the meteorite that collided with Earth to end the dinosaur age.

For the Anthropocene, the best candidate for such a golden spike are radioactive elements from nuclear bomb tests, which were blown into the stratosphere before settling down to Earth. "The radionuclides are probably the sharpest — they really come on with a bang," said Zalasiewicz. "But we are spoiled for choice. There are so many signals."

Other spikes being considered as evidence of the onset of the Anthropocene include the tough, unburned carbon spheres emitted by power stations. "The Earth has been smoked, with signals very clearly around the world in the mid-20th century," said Zalasiewicz.

Other candidates include plastic pollution, aluminium and concrete particles, and high levels of nitrogen and phosphate in soils, derived from artificial fertilisers. Although the world is currently seeing only the sixth mass extinction of species in the 700m-year history of complex life on Earth, this is unlikely to provide a useful golden spike as the animals are by definition very rare and rarely dispersed worldwide.

In contrast, some species have with human help spread rapidly across the world. The domestic chicken is a serious contender to be a fossil that defines the Anthropocene for future geologists. "Since the mid-20th century, it has become the world's most common bird. It has been fossilised in thousands of landfill sites and on street corners around the world," said Zalasiewicz. "It is is also a much bigger bird with a different skeleton than its pre-war ancestor."

The 35 scientists on the WGA — who voted 30 to three in favour of formally designating the Anthropocene, with two abstentions — will now spend the next two to three years determining which signals are the strongest and sharpest. Crucially, they must also decide a location which will define the start of the Anthropocene. Geological divisions are not defined by dates but by a specific boundary between layers of rock or, in the case of the Holocene, a boundary between two ice layers in a core taken from Greenland and now stored in Denmark.

The scientists are focusing on sites where annual layers are formed and are investigating mud sediments off the coast of Santa Barbara in California and the Ernesto cave in northern Italy, where stalactites and stalagmites accrete annual rings. Lake sediments, ice cores from Antarctica, corals, tree rings and even layers of rubbish in landfill sites are also being considered.

Once the data has been assembled, it will be formally submitted to the stratigraphic authorities and the Anthropocene could be officially adopted within a few years. "If we were very lucky and someone came forward with, say, a core from a classic example of laminated sediments in a deep marine environment, I think three years is possibly viable," said Zalasiewicz.

EVIDENCE OF THE ANTHROPOCENE

Human activity has:

- Pushed extinction rates of animals and plants far above the long-term average. The Earth is on course to see 75% of species become extinct in the next few centuries if current trends continue.
- Increased levels of climate-warming CO2 in the atmosphere at the fastest rate for 66m years, with fossil-fuel burning pushing levels from 280 parts per million before the industrial revolution to 400ppm and rising today.
- Put so much plastic in our waterways and oceans that microplastic particles are now virtually ubiquitous, and plastics will likely leave identifiable fossil records for future generations to discover.
- Doubled the nitrogen and phosphorous in our soils in the past century with fertiliser use. This is likely to be the largest impact on the nitrogen cycle in 2.5bn years.
- Left a permanent layer of airborne particulates in sediment and glacial ice such as black carbon from fossil fuel burning.

This would be lightning speed for such a geological decision, which in the past would have taken decades and even centuries to make. The term Anthropocene was coined only in 2000, by the Nobel prize-winning scientist Paul Crutzen, who believes the name change is overdue. He said in 2011: "This name change stresses the enormity of humanity's responsibility as stewards of the Earth." Crutzen also identified in 2007 what he called the "great acceleration" of human impacts on the planet from the mid-20th century.

Despite the WGA's expert recommendation, the declaration of the Anthropocene is not yet a foregone conclusion. "Our stratigraphic colleagues are very protective of the geological time scale. They see it very rightly as the backbone of geology and they do not amend it lightly," said Zalasiewicz. "But I think we can prepare a pretty good case."

Rapley also said there was a strong case: "It is highly appropriate that geologists should pay formal attention to a change in the signal within sedimentary rock layers that will be clearly apparent to future generations of geologists for as long as they exist. The 'great acceleration' constitutes a strong, detectable and incontrovertible signal."

Damian Carrington is head of environment at the Guardian. He has been a journalist for 15 years and previously worked for the *Financial Times*, *New Scientist* and *BBC News Online*.

PLASTIC
BY THE NUMBERS

Tons of petroleum-based plastics humans have created since 1950:

9.1 billion

Percent of that plastic that has been produced in the past 13 years:

50

Tons that have already become waste:

6.9 billion

Percent of plastic waste that has been recycled:

9

If current production and waste management trends continue, the amount of plastic waste that will be in landfills or in the natural environment by 2050:

13.2 billion

Source: Geyer, R., Jambeck, J. R., & Law, K. L. (2017). Production, use, and fate of all plastics ever made. *Science Advances*, 3(7). doi:10.1126/sciadv.1700782

THE FOUR SYSTEM CONDITIONS OF A SUSTAINABLE SOCIETY

Originating in Sweden in 1989, the Natural Step is a global network of nonprofit organizations that share the same brand, core identity and purpose and that has been at the forefront of sustainable development internationally for more than twenty-five years. Their mission is to accelerate the transition to a sustainable society. Part of their Framework for Strategic Sustainable Development are the four system conditions of a sustainable society, outlined here:

Left to its own devices, the earth is a sustainable system. As we continue to learn, however, the accumulated impacts of human activity over the past two centuries are now threatening our continued well-being. An international network of scientists have unanimously and publically concluded that human society is damaging nature and altering life-supporting natural structures and functions in three fundamental ways. Consequently, they were able to define three basic conditions that must be met if we want to maintain the essential natural resources, structures and functions that sustain human society. Further, acknowledging that human action is the primary cause of the rapid change we see in nature today, they included a fourth system condition that focuses on the social and economic considerations that drive those actions and the capacity of human beings to meet their basic needs.

While written to be clear scientifically, the specific wording of the four system conditions can be confusing to non-scientists who try to put them to work. Fortunately, the system conditions can be reworded as basic sustainability principles that provide explicit guidance for any individual or any organization interested in moving towards sustainability. The table below contains the four system conditions on the left and the reworded the basic sustainability principles on the right. In most instances, we refer to the basic sustainability principles.

At first reading, the system conditions and basic principles might seem to imply that we must rid society of all materials extracted from the earth and all substances produced by society and that, further, we must never disturb a natural landscape. But that's not what they mean. The problem is not that we mine and use heavy metals, or use chemicals and compounds produced by society, or disrupt natural processes, or even temporarily interfere with people's capacity to meet their basic needs. It is, rather, that our industrial system has developed so that substances extracted from the earth and produced by society will continue to build up indefinitely in natural systems. That means a systematically increasing concentration of pollutants and substances that not only harm us directly but damage natural processes that have taken billions of years to develop.

The Four System Conditions...	**. . . Reworded as The Four Sustainability Principles**
In a sustainable society, nature is not subject to systematically increasing:	To become a sustainable society we must eliminate our contributions to...
1. concentrations of substances extracted from the earth's crust	1. the *systematic increase* of concentrations of substances extracted from the Earth's crust (for example, heavy metals and fossil fuels)
2. concentrations of substances produced by society	2. the *systematic increase* of concentrations of substances produced by society (for example, plastics, dioxins, PCBs and DDT)
3. degradation by physical means	3. the *systematic* physical degradation of nature and natural processes (for example, over harvesting forests, destroying habitat and overfishing); and...
4. and, in that society, people are not subject to conditions that systemically undermine their capacity to meet their needs	4. conditions that *systematically* undermine people's capacity to meet their basic human needs (for example, unsafe working conditions and not enough pay to live on).

THE REFUGEE CRISIS IS A SIGN OF A PLANET IN TROUBLE

By David Korten

The plight of immigrant families in the United States facing threat of deportation has provoked a massive compassionate response, with cities, churches, and colleges offering sanctuary and legal assistance to those under threat. It is an inspiring expression of our human response to others in need that evokes hope for the human future. At the same time, we need to take a deeper look at the source of the growing refugee crisis.

There is nothing new or exceptional about human migration. The earliest humans ventured out from Africa to populate the Earth. Jews migrated out of Egypt to escape oppression. The Irish migrated to the United States to escape the potato famine. Migrants in our time range from university graduates looking for career advancement in wealthy global corporations to those fleeing for their lives from armed conflicts in the Middle East or drug wars in Mexico and Central America. It is a complex and confusing picture.

There is one piece that stands out: A growing number of desperate people are fleeing violence and starvation.

I recall an apocryphal story of a man standing beside a river. Suddenly he notices a baby struggling in the downstream current. He immediately jumps into the river to rescue it. No sooner has he deposited the baby on the shore, than he sees another. The babies come faster and faster. He is so busy rescuing them that he fails to look upstream to see who is throwing them in.

According to a 2015 UN Refugee Agency (UNHCR) report, 65.3 million people were forcibly displaced by conflict or persecution in 2015, the most since the aftermath of World War II. It is the highest percentage of the total world population since UNHCR began collecting data on displaced persons in 1951.

Of those currently displaced outside their countries of origin, Syrians make up the largest number, at 4.9 million. According to observers, this results from a combination of war funded by foreign governments and drought brought on by human-induced climate change. The relative importance of conflict and drought is unknown, because there is no official international category for environmental refugees.

Without a category for environmental refugees, we have no official estimate of their numbers, but leading scientists tell us the numbers are large and expected to grow rapidly in coming years. Senior military officers warn that food and water scarcity and extreme weather are accelerating instability in the Middle East and Africa and "could lead to a humanitarian crisis of epic proportions." Major General Munir Muniruzzaman, former military advisor to the president of Bangladesh and now chair of the Global Military Advisory Council on Climate Change, notes that a one-meter sea level rise would flood 20 percent of his country and displace more than 30 million people.

Already, the warming of coastal waters due to accelerating climate change is driving a massive die-off of the world's coral reefs, a major source of the world's food supply. The World Wildlife Federation estimates the die-off threatens the livelihoods of a billion people who depend on fish for food and income. These same reefs protect coastal areas from storms and flooding. Their loss will add to the devastation of sea level rise.

All of these trends point to the tragic reality that the world community will be facing an ever-increasing stream of refugees that we must look upstream to resolve.

This all relates back to another ominous statistic. As a species, humans consume at a rate of 1.6 Earths. Yet we have only one Earth. As we poison our water supplies and render our lands infertile, ever larger areas of Earth's surface become uninhabitable. And as people compete for the remaining resources, the social fabric disintegrates, and people turn against one another in violence.

The basic rules of nature present us with an epic species choice. We can learn to heal our Earth and shift the structures of society to assure that Earth remains healthy and everyone has access to a decent livelihood. Or we can watch the intensifying competition for Earth's shrinking habitable spaces play out in a paroxysm of violence and suffering.

David Korten wrote this opinion piece for *YES! Magazine* as part of his series of biweekly columns on "A Living Earth Economy." Dr. David C. Korten is the co-founder and board chair of *YES! Magazine*, founder and president of the Living Economies Forum, an associate fellow of the Institute for Policy Studies, and a full member of the Club of Rome. He is best known for his seminal books framing a new economy for the Ecological Civilization to which humanity must now transition.

THE EARTH IS FULL

By Paul Gilding

Let me begin with four words that provide the context for this week. Four words that will come to define this century. Here they are — The Earth Is Full.

Full of us. Full of our stuff. Full of our waste. Full of our demands. Yes, we are a brilliant and creative species. But we have created a little too much stuff.

So much in fact, that our economy is now bigger than its host, our planet. This is not a philosophical statement. It's just science — based in physics, chemistry and biology.

There are many science-based analyses of this. They all point to the same conclusion — we're living beyond our means. The eminent scientists of the Global Footprint Network for example, calculate we need about 1.6 earths to sustain this economy — so to keep operating at our current level, we would need [more than] 50% more earth than we've got. In financial terms, this would be like always spending 50% more than your income, going further into debt every year. But you can't borrow natural resources, so we're burning through our capital — or stealing from the future.

So when I say full, I mean really full — well past any margin for error, well past any dispute about methodology.

What this means is our economy is not sustainable. I'm not saying it's not nice, or pleasant. Or that it's bad for polar bears or forests, though it certainly is. I'm saying our approach simply can't be sustained. This is those pesky rules of physics. When things aren't sustainable, they stop.

So our economy will stop growing. Stop because of the end of cheap resources and because of the economic impacts of having so degraded the planet, especially our oceans, fresh water, climate and soil.

But that's not possible you might think. We can't stop economic growth — society will fall apart!

Economic growth is an idea so central to our society that it is rarely questioned. While growth has certainly delivered many benefits, we sustain a belief that is crazy — that we can have infinite growth on a finite planet. A belief that somehow, markets can overcome the laws of physics.

Well, I'm here to tell you, the emperor has no clothes, the crazy idea is just that — crazy. And now, with the earth full, it's game over.

Mother nature doesn't negotiate — she just sets rules and explains consequences. And these are not esoteric limits — this is about food, water, soil and climate — the practical and economic foundations of our lives.

So the idea, that we can smoothly transition to a highly efficient, solar powered, knowledge based economy, transformed by science and technology so that 9 billion people in 2050 can lead lives of abundance and digital downloads is a delusion. The many billions of poor people in China, India and Africa don't want an iTunes store, they want cars, chickens, milk, houses and TVs. They want stuff that is made with other stuff.

It's not that it's not possible to feed, clothe and house us all, and have us live decent lives. We certainly could. But the idea that we will smoothly grow our way there from here, with a few minor hiccups, is just wrong. And it is dangerously wrong because it means we're not getting ready for what's really going to happen.

See, what happens when you push a system past it's limits, past the margin for error and then keep on going, at an ever accelerating rate, is that the system stops working and breaks down. That's what will happen to us.

Many of you will be thinking, but we can still stop this. If it's really that bad, we'll react. Let's look at that idea. We've had 50 years of warnings, thorough science proving the urgency of change, economic analysis that shows not only can we afford it, but it's much cheaper to act early. Yet, the reality is we've done pretty much nothing to change course.

We're not even slowing down. On climate change for example, last year we had the highest global emissions ever. The story on food, on water, on fisheries is all much the same.

So when does this breakdown begin? In my view it is well underway.

I understand that most people don't see it. Although the world is an integrated system, we rarely see it that way. We see individual issues — the Occupy protests, various debt crises and growing inequality; resource constraint, financial system overload and spiking food prices. Recessions, money's influence in politics or accelerating climate chaos. But we mistakenly see them in isolation, as individual problems to be solved.

In fact it's the system in the painful process of breaking down. Our system — of debt fuelled economic growth, of ineffective democracy, of overloading planet earth — is eating itself alive.

I could give you countless statistics and studies that show this. I'm not going to, because, if you choose to see it, that evidence is all around you.

I want to talk to you about fear. I want to do so because the biggest threat to civilisation is not collapsing ice shelves or wars over resources. We can survive and move past those, but only if our minds are ready. This is the biggest issue we now face. The crisis is no longer preventable; the question is how will we respond?

Of course we can't know what will happen, but just take a moment now and imagine how this might unfold based on what the best science is telling us.

Imagine our economy, when the carbon bubble bursts — when the financial markets realise that if we are to stop the climate spiraling out of control, the oil and coal industries are finished.

Imagine war between China, India and Pakistan as climate impacts spark conflict over food and refugees.

Imagine the Middle East without oil income, and collapsing governments. Imagine our just in time, low margin food industry, and our highly stressed agricultural system, failing and supermarket shelves being empty.

Imagine 30% unemployment in America and a real debt default as the global economy is gripped by fear and uncertainty.

Imagine what you will tell your children. When they ask you: "So, what was it like? When you'd just had the hottest decade on record, for the third decade in a row, when every scientific body in the world told you we had a major problem, when the oceans were acidifying, when food and oil prices were hitting record highs, when people were rioting in the streets of London and Occupying Wall St. When the system was so clearly breaking down, mum and dad — What did you think? What did you do?"

So how do you feel when you imagine the lights going out on the global economy, when your assumptions about your future fade away.

Take a moment and breathe, and ask yourself. What do you feel right now? Perhaps anger? Denial? Or fear?

We can't know the future, and we have to live with uncertainty. But when we think about such possibilities, and denial ends, fear tends to be the dominant response, and for good reason. We are in danger, all of us — and we've evolved to respond to danger with fear — to motivate a powerful reaction, to help us bravely face a threat.

But this time it's not a tiger at the cave mouth. You can't see the danger at your door, but if you look, you can see it at the door of your civilisation.

That's why we need to feel our response now, while the lights are still on. If we wait, until the crisis takes hold, we may panic and hide. If we feel it now and think it through, we will realise we have nothing to fear, but fear itself.

Yes, things are going to get ugly. It will happen soon, certainly in our lifetime. But there's every reason to believe we can get through all of what's coming.

You see, those people who have faith that humans can solve any problem; that technology is limitless; that markets can be a force for good, are in fact right. The only thing they're missing is that it takes a good crisis to get us moving. When we feel fear, and we fear loss, we can achieve extraordinary things.

Consider our response in war. When Pearl Harbour was bombed, in took just 4 days for the Government to ban the production of civilian cars and redirect the auto industry. From there to rationing of food and energy. Consider how a company responds when faced with bankruptcy and how change that seemed impossible just gets done. Consider how a person diagnosed with a life threatening illness, can suddenly make lifestyle changes that were previously too difficult.

Scientists like James Hansen tell us, we may need to eliminate net CO_2 emissions from the economy, in just a few decades. I wanted to know what that would take. So I worked with Professor Jorgen Randers from Norway to develop a plan — we called it the One Degree War Plan, indicating the scale of focus and mobilisation required. To my surprise achieving zero net CO_2 emissions in two decades is actually pretty easy and pretty cheap. Not very cheap but certainly less than the cost of a collapsing civilisation.

You can read the details, but in summary, we can transform our society and our economy; we can do it with proven technology, at an affordable cost with existing political structures. The only thing we have to change is how we think and how we feel.

This is where you come in.

When we think about the future I paint, we should all feel a bit of fear. But fear can be paralyzing or motivating. We need to accept the fear, then we need to act.

We need to act like the future depends on it. We need to act like we only have one planet. We can do this. I know the free market fundamentalists tell you, that more growth, more stuff and 9 billion people going shopping, is the best we can do. They're wrong. We can be more. Much more.

We have achieved remarkable things since working out how to grow food some 10,000 years ago. We have a powerful foundation of science, technology and knowledge — more than enough to build a society where 9 billion people can lead decent, meaningful and satisfying lives. The earth can support that. If we choose the right path.

We can choose this moment of crisis to ask, and answer, the big questions of society's evolution.

What do we want to be when we grow up? When we move past this bumbling adolescence, where we think there are no limits and suffer delusions of immortality. Well, it's now time to grow up. To be wiser, and calmer and more considered.

Like generations before us, we'll be growing up in war. Not a war between civilizations, but a war for civilization. For the extraordinary opportunity to build a stronger, happier society. One that plans on staying around into middle age.

We can choose life over fear. We can do what we need to do. But it will take every entrepreneur, every artist, every scientist and every communicator. Every mother, every father and every child. Every one of us.

This could be our finest hour.

Paul Gilding delivered this speech at TED 2012 Long Beach California on February 28, 2012. Former global CEO of Greenpeace, Paul is an independent writer, advisor and advocate for action on climate change and sustainability.

TOO MANY PEOPLE, TOO MUCH CONSUMPTION

By Paul Ehrlich and Anne H. Ehrlich

Over some 60 million years, Homo sapiens has evolved into the dominant animal on the planet, acquiring binocular vision, upright posture, large brains, and — most importantly — language with syntax and that complex store of non-genetic information we call culture. However, in the last several centuries we've increasingly been using our relatively newly acquired power, especially our culturally evolved technologies, to deplete the natural capital of Earth — in particular its deep, rich agricultural soils, its groundwater stored during ice ages, and its biodiversity — as if there were no tomorrow.

The point, all too often ignored, is that this trend is being driven in large part by a combination of population growth and increasing per capita consumption, and it cannot be long continued without risking a collapse of our now-global civilization. Too many people — and especially too many politicians and business executives — are under the delusion that such a disastrous end to the modern human enterprise can be avoided by technological fixes that will allow the population and the economy to grow forever. But if we fail to bring population growth and overconsumption under control — the number of people on Earth is expected to grow from 6.5 billion today to 9 billion by the second half of the 21st century — then we will inhabit a planet where life becomes increasingly untenable because of two looming crises: global heating, and the degradation of the natural systems on which we all depend.

Our species' negative impact on our own life-support systems can be approximated by the equation I=PAT. In that equation, the size of the population (P) is multiplied by the average affluence or consumption per individual (A), and that in turn is multiplied by some measure of the technology (T) that services and drives the consumption. Thus commuting in automobiles powered by subsidized fossil fuels on proliferating freeways creates a much greater T factor than commuting on bikes using simple paths or working at home on a computer network. The product of P, A, and T is Impact (I), a rough estimate of how much humanity is degrading the ecosystem services it depends upon.

The equation is not rocket science. Two billion people, all else being equal, put more greenhouse gases into the atmosphere than one billion people. Two billion rich people disrupt the climate more than two billion poor people. Three hundred million Americans consume more petroleum than 1.3 billion Chinese. And driving an SUV is using a far more environmentally malign transportation technology than riding mass transit.

The technological dimensions of our predicament —

such as the need for alternatives to fossil fuel energy — are frequently discussed if too little acted upon. Judging from media reports and the statements of politicians, environmental problems, to the degree they are recognized, can be solved by minor changes in technologies and recycling (T). Switching to ultra-light, fuel-efficient cars will obviously give some short-term advantage, but as population and consumption grow, they will pour still more carbon dioxide (and vaporized rubber) into the atmosphere and require more natural areas to be buried under concrete. More recycling will help, but many of our society's potentially most dangerous effluents (such as hormone-mimicking chemicals) cannot practically be recycled. There is no technological change we can make that will permit growth in either human numbers or material affluence to continue to expand. In the face of this, the neglect of the intertwined issues of population and consumption is stunning.

Many past human societies have collapsed under the weight of overpopulation and environmental neglect, but today the civilization in peril is global. The population factor in what appears to be a looming catastrophe is even greater than most people suppose. Each person added today to the population on average causes more damage to humanity's critical life-support systems than did the previous addition — everything else being equal. The reason is simple: Homo sapiens became the dominant animal by being smart. Farmers didn't settle first on poor soils where water was scarce, but rather in rich river valleys. That's where most cities developed, where rich soils are now being paved over for roads and suburbs, and where water supplies are being polluted or overexploited.

As a result, to support additional people it is necessary to move to ever poorer lands, drill wells deeper, or tap increasingly remote sources to obtain water — and then spend more energy to transport that water ever greater distances to farm fields, homes, and factories. Our distant ancestors could pick up nearly pure copper on Earth's surface when they started to use metals; now people must use vast amounts of energy to mine and smelt gigantic amounts of copper ore of ever poorer quality, some in concentrations of less than one percent. The same can be said for other important metals. And petroleum can no longer be found easily on or near the surface, but must be gleaned from wells drilled a mile or more deep, often in inaccessible localities, such as under continental shelves beneath the sea. All of the paving, drilling, fertilizer manufacturing, pumping, smelting, and transporting needed to provide for the consumption of burgeoning numbers of people produces greenhouse gases and thus tightens the connection between population and climate disruption.

So why is the topic of overpopulation so generally ignored? There are some obvious reasons. Attempts by governments to limit their nation's population growth are anathema to those on the right who believe the only role for governments in the bedroom is to force women to take unwanted babies to term. Those on the left fear, with some legitimacy, that population control could turn racist or discriminatory in other ways — for example, attempting to reduce the numbers of minorities or the poor. Many fear the specter of more of "them" compared to "us," and all of us fear loss of liberty and economic decline (since population growth is often claimed necessary for economic health). And there are religious leaders who still try to promote over-reproduction by their flocks, though in much of the world their efforts are largely futile (Catholic countries in Europe tend to be low-birthrate leaders, for example).

But much of the responsibility must go to ignorance, which leads mainstream media, even newspapers like *The New York Times*, to maintain a pro-natalist stance. For example, the Times had an article on June 29 about a "baby bust" in industrialized countries in which the United States (still growing) was noted as a "sparkling exception." Beyond the media, great foundations have turned their "population programs" away from encouraging low fertility rates and toward topics like "changing sexual mores" — avoiding discussion of the contribution demographics is making to a possible collapse of civilization.

Silence on the overconsumption (Affluence) factor in the I=PAT equation is more readily explained. Consumption is still viewed as an unalloyed good by many economists, along with business leaders and politicians, who tend to see jacking up consumption as a cure-all for economic ills. Too much unemployment? Encourage people to buy an SUV or a new refrigerator. Perpetual growth is the creed of the cancer cell, but third-rate economists can't think of anything else. Some leading economists are starting to tackle the issue of overconsumption, but the problem and its cures are tough to analyze. Scientists have yet to develop consumption condoms or morning-after-shopping-spree pills.

And, of course, there are the vexing problems of consumption of people in poor countries. On one hand, a billion or more people have problems of underconsumption. Unless their basic needs are met, they are unlikely to be able to make important contributions to attaining sustainability. On the other hand, there is also the issue of the "new consumers" in developing economies such as China and India, where the wealth of a sizable minority is permitting them to acquire the consumption habits (e.g., eating a lot of meat and driving automobiles) of the rich nations. Consumption regulation is a lot more complex than population regulation, and it is much more difficult to find humane and equitable solutions to the problem.

The dominant animal is wasting its brilliance and its wonderful achievements; civilization's fate is being determined by decision makers who determinedly look the other way in favor of immediate comfort and profit. Thousands of scientists recently participated in a Millennium Ecosystem Assessment that outlined our current environmental dilemma, but the report's dire message made very little impact. Absent attention to that message, the fates of Easter Island, the Classic Maya civilization, and Nineveh — all of which collapsed following environmental degradation — await us all.

We believe it is possible to avoid that global denouement. Such mobilization means developing some consensus on goals — perhaps through a global dialogue in which people discuss the human predicament and decide whether they would like to see a maximum number of people living at a minimum standard of living, or perhaps a much lower population size that gives individuals a broad choice of lifestyles. We have suggested a forum for such a dialogue, modeled partly on the Intergovernmental Panel on Climate Change, but with more "bottom up" participation. It is clear that only widespread changes in norms can give humanity a chance of attaining a sustainable and reasonably conflict-free society.

How to achieve such change — involving everything from demographic policies and transformation of planet-wide energy, industrial, and agricultural systems, to North-South and interfaith relationships and military postures — is a gigantic challenge to everyone. Politicians, industrialists, ecologists, social scientists, everyday citizens, and the media must join this debate. Whether it is possible remains to be seen; societies have managed to make major transitions in the recent past, as the civil rights revolution in the United States and the collapse of communism in the Soviet Union clearly demonstrate.

We'll continue to hope and work for a cultural transformation in how we treat each other and the natural systems we depend upon. We can create a peaceful and sustainable global civilization, but it will require realistic thinking about the problems we face and a new mobilization of political will.

Paul and Anne Ehrlich are in the Department of Biology and the Center for Conservation Biology at Stanford University, where he is Bing Professor of Population Studies and Professor of Biological Sciences and she is the policy coordinator at the Center for Conservation Biology.

ECOCHALLENGE: PUTTING IT INTO PRACTICE

Calculating your ecological footprint

Taking action

Use your ecological footprint (see below) results to target specific ways to reduce your negative impact and increase your positive impact on Earth. Here are some ideas for putting what you learned this week into action. Find more ideas and commit to one Ecochallenge this week at **choices.ecochallenge.org**

- Challenge your city leaders to support sustainability policies.
- Walk, bike, carpool or take public transportation more often. What are the options that work for your neighborhood and lifestyle?
- Reduce your food waste by planning your meals before you go shopping and creatively using leftovers.
- Find out if your local utilities offer an option for supporting renewable energy investment.
- Research what options are available for the sharing economy in your community. Are there tool libraries, toy libraries, time banks, or repair cafes that already exist? Can you start one? Or see if you can share tools like shop vacs, lawn mowers, or power drills with your friends and neighbors.

As a goal, sustainability is hard to visualize. The ecological footprint is a metaphor that helps bring the concept of sustainability to life. It provides a way to measure our individual impact on the earth, both locally and globally. An awareness of the impact of our community's actions on finite world resources is the first step toward shrinking that footprint. Learn more about ecological footprints in the short video below.

Before you meet with your group to discuss this session, please take the time to calculate your ecological footprint using the Global Footprint Network's Footprint Calculator: **footprintcalculator.org/**

SESSION 3

FOOD

"Eat food. Not too much. Mostly plants."

— Michael Pollan

LEARNING OBJECTIVES

- **Explore the relationship between our eating decisions and greenhouse gas emissions, pollution, waste, and social justice.**
- **Identify some of the resources required to produce the food we eat.**
- **Commit to personal change toward food choices that support a more sustainable world.**

SESSION DESCRIPTION

Eating is an essential natural process for all living organisms, yet many of us have limited awareness of how our eating habits impact ourselves, let alone the rest of the world. With industrialized agricultural practices and increased processing, marketing, and bioengineering, many people in industrialized nations are far removed from the sources of our food. In this session, we look at some of the complex issues we currently face in our food systems, as well as various practical steps to take toward producing and eating food sustainably.

REFLECTION

Keep a food journal for a week. What surprised you about your food habits? What would you like to change? Post your Reflection to your Dashboard on **choices.ecochallenge.org**. If you are not using the Ecochallenge site, write your thoughts in a journal and then reflect with your group.

Circle Question

In what ways can our discussion of food systems help us to act toward an equitable, healthy and sustainable world?

Reminder to the facilitator: The circle question should move quickly. Elicit an answer from each participant without questions or comments from others. The facilitator's guidelines are on page 10.

SUGGESTED DISCUSSION QUESTIONS

1. Consider all the ways in which fossil fuels might have been used to produce or transport the foods you ate today.
2. Were you raised with the "botanically outrageous" idea of "having everything always?" Name some foods you eat regularly whose seasonality and origins you haven't considered.
3. What opportunities exist for you to eat more locally and/or seasonally? What are the barriers?
4. What contributes to people in the U.S. and Canada eating more meat than any other countries, and what does this say about U.S./Canadian values, ways of living, and ideology? How do we start shifting a meat-focused food culture?
5. In "Beyond Free or Fair Trade," Mike Wold highlights some of the effects of NAFTA trade policies. Who or what is at the winning and losing ends as a result of these policies? What are the consequences for each?
6. It is often said that "you can't feed the world with just organic food." What is your response to that statement after reading this session?
7. What efforts would help food insecure regions have access to local, seasonal foods?
8. Were you inspired this week to change any of your food habits? What will you do as a result of what you learned and discussed in this session?

SUGGESTED GROUP ACTIVITY

Choose a food everyone in your group eats and look into how it is grown, harvested, transported, processed, etc. Create a "food web" to capture these connections and impacts. Note the differences between conventionally grown produce and organically grown produce, CAFO-raised animal products and humane-certified or pasture-raised animal products, and similar distinctions. This activity can help you see not only the environmental and justice impacts of the production of certain foods, but also how much certain companies are willing to share about their operations and employee treatment. Find the full instructions for the activity at **ecochallenge.org/discussion-course-resources**.

FURTHER RESOURCES

Interested in finding out more on the topics presented in this session?
Visit our website for further readings and resources: **ecochallenge.org/discussion-course-resources.**
Follow our Facebook page to continue the discussion online:
facebook.com/Ecochallengeorg/

DEFINITIONS

Agribusiness: In the agriculture industry, agribusiness is a broad term for various businesses involved in food production. When used by critics of industrialized agriculture, agribusiness is synonymous with large-scale, industrialized, corporate farming.

CAFO: Standing for Concentrated Animal Feeding Operation, the United States Department of Agriculture defines a CAFO as a farm in which animals are raised in confinement and has over 1000 "animal units" confined for over 45 days a year. An animal unit is "an animal equivalent of 1000 pounds live weight and equates to 1000 head of beef cattle, 700 dairy cows, 2500 swine weighing more than 55 lbs, 125 thousand broiler chickens, or 82 thousand laying hens or pullets." A CAFO is also an animal feeding operation of any size that discharges its waste into a waterway. As of July 2017, there were more than 50,000 facilities in the US classified as CAFOs.

Fair Trade: According to FINE, an informal association of the four main fair trade networks, fair trade is "a trading partnership, based on dialogue, transparency and respect, that seeks greater equity in international trade. It contributes to sustainable development by offering better trading conditions to, and securing the rights of, marginalized producers and workers — especially in the global South. Fair trade organizations, backed by consumers, are engaged actively in supporting producers, awareness raising and in campaigning for changes in the rules and practice of conventional international trade."

Food Desert: The Food Empowerment Project defines food deserts as "geographic areas where residents' access to affordable, healthy food options (especially fresh fruits and vegetables) is restricted or nonexistent due to the absence of grocery stores within convenient travelling distance." Food deserts are most commonly found in communities of color and low-income areas, where residents may not have access to cars.

Food Insecurity: The USDA defines food insecurity as "the limited or uncertain availability of nutritionally adequate and safe foods or limited or uncertain ability to acquire acceptable foods in socially acceptable ways."

Food Justice: According to Just Food, food justice is "communities exercising their right to grow, sell, and eat healthy food. Healthy food is fresh, nutritious, affordable, culturally-appropriate, and grown locally with care for the well-being of the land, workers, and animals. People practicing food justice leads to a strong local food system, self-reliant communities, and a healthy environment."

Free Trade: A trade system that allows and encourages traders to trade across national boundaries without government interference, such as taxes or other trade barriers. Most countries of the world are members of the World Trade Organization (WTO), which limits tariffs and trade barriers in international trade. Many argue against the practices of free trade and the WTO, claiming that free trade exploits workers and increases economic and social inequality between the rich and the poor.

Monoculture: The agricultural practice of producing a single crop on a wide area of land. It is a very commonly used practice in industrial agriculture and is designed to allow large yields by standardizing the planting, maintenance and harvesting of a crop. However, monocultures are much more vulnerable to disease than polycultures and can quickly deplete soil of important nutrients.

Organic: The term organic can refer to a form of agriculture, the food produced using those organic farming methods, or the accreditation that organic producers receive. Organic foods are produced without synthetic pesticides and chemical fertilizers, are not genetically modified, and are not processed using irradiation, industrial solvents or chemical food additives. The organic farming movement was birthed in the 1940s as a response to the industrialization of agriculture.

Social Justice: The fair and equitable distribution of wealth, resources, opportunities, and privileges within a society.

"Agricultural sustainability doesn't depend on agritechnology. To believe it does is to put the emphasis on the wrong bit of 'agriculture.' What sustainability depends on isn't agri — so much as culture."

— Raj Patel

WHAT'S EATING AMERICA

By Michael Pollan

Descendants of the Maya living in Mexico still sometimes refer to themselves as "the corn people." The phrase is not intended as metaphor. Rather, it's meant to acknowledge their abiding dependence on this miraculous grass, the staple of their diet for almost 9,000 years.

For an American like me, growing up linked to a very different food chain, yet one that is also rooted in corn, not to think of himself as a corn person suggests either a failure of imagination or a triumph of capitalism.

Or perhaps a little of both. For the great edifice of variety and choice that is an American supermarket rests on a remarkably narrow biological foundation: corn. It's not merely the feed that the steers and the chickens and the pigs and the turkeys ate; it's not just the source of the flour and the oil and the leavenings, the glycerides and coloring in the processed foods; it's not just sweetening the soft drinks or lending a shine to the magazine cover over by the checkout. The supermarket itself — the wallboard and joint compound, the linoleum and fiberglass and adhesives out of which the building itself has been built — is in no small measure a manifestation of corn.

There are some 45,000 items in the average American supermarket, and more than a quarter of them contain corn. At the same time, the food industry has done a good job of persuading us that the 45,000 different items or SKUs (stock keeping units) represent genuine variety rather than the clever rearrangements of molecules extracted from the same plant.

How this peculiar grass, native to Central America and unknown to the Old World before 1492, came to colonize so much of our land and bodies is one of the plant world's greatest success stories. I say the plant world's success story because it is no longer clear that corn's triumph is such a boon to the rest of the world.

At its most basic, the story of life on earth is the competition among species to capture and store as much energy as possible — either directly from the sun, in the case of plants, or, in the case of animals, by eating plants and plant eaters. The energy is stored in the form of carbon molecules and measured in calories: the calories we eat, whether in an ear of corn or a steak, represent packets of energy once captured by a plant. Few plants can manufacture quite as much organic matter (and calories) from the same quantities of sunlight and water and basic elements as corn.

The great turning point in the modern history of corn, which in turn marks a key turning point in the industrialization of our food, can be dated with some precision to the day in 1947 when the huge munitions plant at Muscle Shoals, Alabama, switched over from making explosives to making chemical fertilizer. After World War II, the government had found itself with a tremendous surplus of ammonium nitrate, the principal ingredient in the making of explosives. Ammonium nitrate also happens to be an excellent source of nitrogen for plants. Serious thought was given to spraying America's forests with the surplus chemical, to help the timber industry. But agronomists in the Department of Agriculture had a better idea: spread the ammonium nitrate on farmland as fertilizer. The chemical fertilizer industry (along with that of pesticides, which are based on the poison gases developed for war) is the product of the government's effort to convert its war machine to peacetime purposes. As the Indian farmer activist Vandana Shiva says in her speeches, "We're still eating the leftovers of World War II."

F1 hybrid corn is the greediest of plants, consuming more fertilizer than any other crop. Though F1 hybrids were introduced in the 1930s, it wasn't until they made the acquaintance of chemical fertilizers in the 1950s that corn yields exploded. The discovery of synthetic nitrogen changed everything — not just for the corn plant and the farm, not just for the food system, but also for the way life on earth is conducted.

All life depends on nitrogen; it is the building block from which nature assembles amino acids, proteins and nucleic acid; the genetic information that orders and perpetuates life is written in nitrogen ink. But the supply of usable nitrogen on earth is limited. Although earth's atmosphere is about 80 percent nitrogen, all those atoms are tightly paired, nonreactive and therefore useless; the 19th-century chemist Justus von Liebig spoke of atmospheric nitrogen's "indifference to all other substances." To be of any value to plants and animals, these self-involved nitrogen atoms must be split and then joined to atoms of hydrogen.

Chemists call this process of taking atoms from the atmosphere and combining them into molecules useful to living things "fixing" that element. Until a German Jewish chemist named Fritz Haber figured out how to turn this trick in 1909, all the usable nitrogen on earth had at one time been fixed by soil bacteria living on the roots of leguminous plants (such as peas or alfalfa or locust trees) or, less commonly, by the shock of electrical lightning, which can break nitrogen bonds in the air, releasing a light rain of fertility.

In his book Enriching the Earth: Fritz Haber, Carl Bosch and the Transformation of World Food Production, Vaclav Smil pointed out that "there is no way to grow crops and human bodies without nitrogen." Before Haber's invention, the sheer amount of life earth could support — the size of crops and therefore the number of human bodies — was limited by the amount of nitrogen that bacteria and lightning could fix. By 1900, European scientists had recognized that unless a way was found to augment this naturally occurring nitrogen, the growth of the human population would soon grind to a very painful halt. The same recognition by Chinese scientists a few decades later is probably what compelled China's opening to the West: after Nixon's 1972 trip, the first major order the Chinese government placed was for 13 massive fertilizer factories. Without them, China would have starved.

This is why it may not be hyperbole to claim, as Smil does, that the Haber-Bosch process for fixing nitrogen (Bosch gets the credit for commercializing Haber's idea) is the most important invention of the 20th century. He estimates that two of every five humans on earth today would not be alive if not for Fritz Haber's invention. We can easily imagine a world without computers or electricity, Smil points out, but without synthetic fertilizer billions of people would never have been born. Though, as these numbers suggest, humans may have struck a Faustian bargain with nature when Fritz Haber gave us the power to fix nitrogen.

Fritz Haber? No, I'd never heard of him either, even though he was awarded the Nobel Prize in 1918 for "improving the standards of agriculture and the well-being of mankind." But the reason for his obscurity has less to do with the importance of his work than an ugly twist of his biography, which recalls the dubious links between modern warfare and industrial agriculture: during World War I, Haber threw himself into the German war effort, and his chemistry kept alive Germany's hopes for victory, by allowing it to make bombs from synthetic nitrate. Later, Haber put his genius for chemistry to work developing poison gases — ammonia, then chlorine. (He subsequently developed Zyklon B, the gas used in Hitler's concentration camps.) His wife, a chemist sickened by her husband's contribution to the war effort, used his army pistol to kill herself; Haber died, broken and in flight from Nazi Germany, in a Basel hotel room in 1934.

His story has been all but written out of the 20th century. But it embodies the paradoxes of science, the double edge to our manipulations of nature, the good and evil that can flow not only from the same man but from the same knowledge. Even Haber's agricultural benefaction has proved to be a decidedly mixed blessing.

When humankind acquired the power to fix nitrogen, the basis of soil fertility shifted from a total reliance on the energy of the sun to a new reliance on fossil fuel. That's because the Haber-Bosch process works by combining nitrogen and hydrogen gases under immense heat and pressure in the presence of a catalyst. The heat and pressure are supplied by prodigious amounts of electricity, and the hydrogen is supplied by oil, coal or, most commonly today, natural gas. True, these fossil fuels were created by the sun, billions of years ago, but they are not renewable in the same way that the fertility created by a legume nourished by sunlight is. (That nitrogen is fixed by a bacterium living on the roots of the legume, which trades a tiny drip of sugar for the nitrogen the plant needs.)

Liberated from the old biological constraints, the farm could now be managed on industrial principles, as a factory transforming inputs of raw material — chemical fertilizer — into outputs of corn. And corn adapted brilliantly to the new industrial regime, consuming prodigious quantities of fossil fuel energy and turning out ever more prodigious quantities of food energy. Growing corn, which from a biological perspective had always been a process of capturing sunlight to turn it into food, has in no small measure become a process of converting fossil fuels into food. More than half of all the synthetic nitrogen made today is applied to corn.

From the standpoint of industrial efficiency, it's too bad we can't simply drink petroleum directly, because there's a lot less energy in a bushel of corn (measured in calories) than there is in the half-gallon of oil required to produce it. Ecologically, this is a fabulously expensive way to produce food — but "ecologically" is no longer the operative standard. In the factory, time is money, and yield is everything.

One problem with factories, as opposed to biological systems, is that they tend to pollute. Hungry for fossil fuel as hybrid corn is, farmers still feed it far more than it can possibly eat, wasting most of the fertilizer they buy. And what happens to that synthetic nitrogen the plants don't take up? Some of it evaporates into the air, where it acidifies the rain and contributes to global warming. Some seeps down to the water table, whence it may come out of the tap. The nitrates in water bind to hemoglobin, compromising the blood's ability to carry oxygen to the brain. (I guess I was wrong to suggest we don't sip fossil fuels directly; sometimes we do.)

It has been a century since Fritz Haber's invention, yet already it has changed earth's ecology. More than half of the world's supply of usable nitrogen is now man-made. (Unless you grew up on organic food, most of the kilo or so of nitrogen in your body was fixed by the Haber-Bosch process.) "We have perturbed the global nitrogen cycle," Smil wrote, "more than any other, even carbon." The effects may be harder to predict than the effects of the global warming caused by our disturbance of the carbon cycle, but they are no less momentous.

The flood of synthetic nitrogen has fertilized not just the farm fields but the forests and oceans, too, to the benefit of some species (corn and algae being two of the biggest beneficiaries) and to the detriment of countless others. The ultimate fate of the nitrates spread in Iowa or Indiana is to flow down the Mississippi into the Gulf of Mexico, where their deadly fertility poisons the marine ecosystem. The nitrogen tide stimulates the wild growth of algae, and the algae smother the fish, creating a "hypoxic," or dead, zone as big as New Jersey — and still growing. By fertilizing the world, we alter the planet's composition of species and shrink its biodiversity.

And yet, as organic farmers (who don't use synthetic fertilizer) prove every day, the sun still shines, plants and their bacterial associates still fix nitrogen, and farm animals still produce vast quantities of nitrogen in their "waste," so-called. It may take more work, but it's entirely possible to nourish the soil, and ourselves, without dumping so much nitrogen into the environment. The key to reducing our dependence on synthetic nitrogen is to build a more diversified agriculture — rotating crops and using animals to recycle nutrients on farms — and give up our vast, nitrogen-guzzling monocultures of corn. Especially as the price of fossil fuels climbs, even the world's most industrialized farmers will need to take a second look at how nature, and those who imitate her, go about creating fertility without diminishing our world.

This article appeared in the June 15, 2006 issue of *Smithsonian*. Michael Pollan is an award-winning author of numerous books and articles on the interactions between humans and nature. His work includes *The Omnivore's Dilemma: A Natural History of Four Meals* and *The Botany of Desire: A Plant's-Eye View of the World*.

EWG'S 2017 SHOPPER'S GUIDE TO PESTICIDES IN PRODUCE™

Eating organic produce is one way — but not the only way — to eat a healthier diet for you and the planet. This handy guide by the Environmental Working Group can help you prioritize which produce to buy organic.

DIRTY DOZEN

We found the produce on this list to contain the highest levels of pesticide residues. Buy these organic or from pesticide-free local farms when you can.

1 Strawberries
2 Spinach
3 Nectarines
4 Apples
5 Peaches
6 Pears
7 Cherries
8 Grapes
9 Celery
10 Tomatoes
11 Sweet bell peppers
12 Potatoes
+ Hot Peppers +

CLEAN FIFTEEN

The produce on this list is least likely to contain pesticide residues.

1* Sweet Corn*
2 Avocados
3 Pineapples
4 Cabbage
5 Onions
6 Sweet peas frozen
7* Papayas*
8 Asparagus
9 Mangos
10 Eggplant
11 Honeydew Melon
12 Kiwi
13 Cantaloupe
14 Cauliflower
15 Grapefruit

* A small amount of sweet corn, papaya and summer squash sold in the US is produced from genetically modified seeds. Buy organic varieties of these crops if you want to avoid genetically modified produce.

CUTTING MEAT CONSUMPTION CAN MAKE A HUGE DENT IN CLIMATE CHANGE

By Fiona Harvey

Growing food for the world's burgeoning population is likely to send greenhouse gas emissions over the threshold of safety, unless more is done to cut meat consumption, a recent report has found. The study, entitled "Analysis and Valuation of the Health and Climate Change Co-Benefits of Dietary Change, was published in the Proceedings of the National Academy of Sciences in March 2016. A widespread switch to vegetarianism would cut emissions by nearly two-thirds, it said.

In three decades, emissions related to agriculture and food production are likely to account for about half of the world's available "carbon budget" — the limited amount of carbon dioxide and its equivalents that can be poured into the atmosphere if we are to hold global warming to no more than 2C (3.6F).

While energy generation, transport and buildings have long been a target for governments, businesses and campaigners looking to reduce emissions, the impact from food production has often been left out. But with intensive agriculture increasingly geared towards livestock rearing, food production is becoming a major concern.

The research, led by scientists at the Oxford Martin School, found that shifting to a mostly vegetarian diet, or even simply cutting down meat consumption to within accepted health guidelines, would make a large dent in greenhouse gases. Adhering to health guidelines on meat consumption could cut global food-related emissions by nearly a third by 2050, the study found, while widespread adoption of a vegetarian diet would bring down emissions by 63%. The additional benefit of going further, with the widespread adoption of veganism, brought a smaller incremental benefit, with emissions falling by about 70% in the projections.

Such steps would also save lives, argued Dr Marco Springmann, lead author of the study. "Imbalanced diets, such as diets low in fruits and vegetables and high in red and processed meat, are responsible for the greatest health burden globally and in most regions," he said. "At the same time, the food system is responsible [currently] for more than a quarter of all greenhouse gas emissions, and therefore a major driver of climate change."

More than 5 million premature deaths could be avoided globally by 2050 if health guidelines on meat consumption were followed, rising to more than 7m with a vegetarian diet and 8 million on veganism. These steps, if widely followed, could also reduce global healthcare costs by $1 billion a year by mid-century.

Intensive livestock-rearing is a major cause of greenhouse gases, in part because of the methane produced by the animals and the massive slurry pits that accompany large farms. It also diverts water and grains to animal-rearing, which is less efficient than directing the grains towards direct human consumption. Non-intensive rearing of livestock, such as raising animals on marginal land, could be "an interesting proposal" that would allow meat-eating at lower levels with less environmental harm, said Springmann. "That is one of the discussions that could spring up as a result of our research."

Individuals were often confused by health messaging, food labelling and the availability of foodstuffs, he added, meaning that many people do not realise the harm that over-consumption of meat may be doing them. As populations around the world have grown more prosperous, with the rise of middle class societies in areas that have emerged from poverty, people have tended to switch their diets to include more meat as they have grown richer.

Governments agreed at a landmark climate conference in Paris in December [2016] to hold global warming to no more

LIVESTOCK'S IMPACT

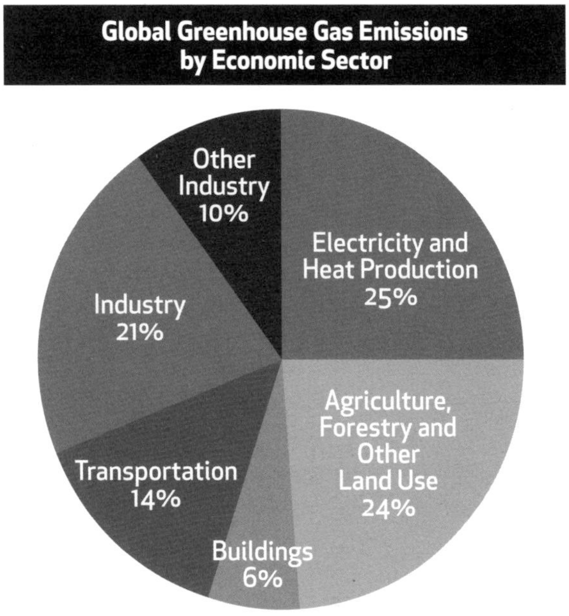

Global Greenhouse Gas Emissions by Economic Sector

Electricity and Heat Production 25%
Agriculture, Forestry and Other Land Use 24%
Buildings 6%
Transportation 14%
Industry 21%
Other Industry 10%

Total CO_2 emissions from global livestock per year: **7.1 Gigatonnes**

Percent of the livestock sector's emissions that come from cattle: **65**

Percent of the livestock sector's emissions that are attributable to milk: **20**

Percent of livestock emissions in the form of methane: **44**

Sources: https://www.epa.gov/sites/production/files/2016-05/global_emissions_sector_2015.png
http://www.fao.org/news/story/en/item/197623/icode/

than 2C above pre-industrial levels, with an aspiration of an even lower target, of 1.5C. However, the exact measures that will be required to meet the global goal, and nationally set emissions targets, have yet to be fully worked out.

Linking health and climate change in challenging our eating habits could have more effect than focusing on each of these issues alone, said Springmann. "By combining the two benefits, you have a more powerful impact. I think this will make more of an impression," he said. "We do not expect everybody to become vegan. But the climate change impacts of the food system will require more than just technological changes. Adopting healthier and more environmentally sustainable diets can be a large stop in the right direction.

"The size of the projected benefits should encourage individuals, industry and policymakers to act decisively to make sure that what we eat preserves our environment and health," he said.

Fiona Harvey is an award-winning environment journalist for the *Guardian*. She has reported on every major environmental issue, from as far afield as the Arctic and the Amazon, and her wide range of interviewees include Ban Ki-moon, Tony Blair, Al Gore and Jeff Immelt.

WHAT'S THE BEEF? DO THE MATH

The agriculture sector is responsible for about 9 percent of total U.S. greenhouse gas emissions.

Livestock accounts for almost half of that figure—**4.2 percent**—more than the emissions from the aviation sector.

This is mostly due to something called **"enteric fermentation."** Like all ruminants, beef and dairy cattle naturally emit methane, a greenhouse gas that is **25 times more heat-trapping than CO_2.**

Beef cattle alone are responsible for about a **quarter of the emissions** from U.S. agriculture.

JUDGED ON ITS CLIMATE FOOTPRINT, **MEAT FROM RUMINANTS FARES POORLY** COMPARED WITH OTHER FOODS.
Kilograms of CO_2 equivalent per kilogram of consumed food

Lamb 39.2

Beef 27.0

Cheese 13.5

Pork 12.1

Chicken 6.9

Tofu 2.0

Transitioning away from corn-finished cattle in CAFOs to grass-fed cattle has the potential to reduce emissions. Less corn cultivation (especially on marginal lands) will mean **less of the tillage** that releases carbon from the soil.

But the **gains are likely to be modest.** Improving pasture forage for cattle can limit the animals' enteric fermentation. Yet even if all U.S. pastures were converted to best practices, **it would curb emissions by less than 0.5 percent.**

Converting cropland to pasture and managing pastures better could increase soil carbon sequestration. The best estimates suggest that this sequestration would **cut another 2 percent from U.S. emissions.**

In the rosiest scenario (so far, documented only once by scientists), a transition from row crops to intensively managed pasture might offset the methane emissions from cattle. Even then, **soil carbon sequestration on rangelands would likely fall well short** of offsetting the emissions from factories, power plants, cars, and planes.

—Emily Malter and Jason Mark

SOURCES: U.S. EPA, ENVIRONMENTAL WORKING GROUP, UNION OF CONCERNED SCIENTISTS, UC DAVIS COLLEGE OF AGRICULTURAL AND ENVIRONMENTAL SCIENCES

STALKING THE VEGETANNUAL

By Barbara Kingsolver

An extraordinary feature of modern humans is that we seem to think we've broken the shackles of our food chain and walked right out of it. If we don't know beans about beans, that may be fine with us. Asparagus, potatoes, turkey drumsticks — you name it, most of us here in America don't have a clue how the world makes it. Sometimes I think I'm exaggerating the scope of the problem, and then I'll encounter an editor (at a well-known nature magazine) who's nixing the part of my story that refers to pineapples growing from the ground. She insisted they grew on trees. Or, I'll have a conversation like this one:

"What's new on the farm?" asked a friend of mine, a lifelong city dweller and gourmet cook who likes for me to keep her posted by phone. This particular conversation was in early spring, so I told her what was up in the garden: peas, potatoes, spinach.

"Wait a minute," she said. "When you say, 'the potatoes are up,' what do you mean?" She paused, reformulating her question: "What part of a potato comes up?"

"Um, the plant part," I said. "The stems and leaves."

"Wow," she said. "I never knew a potato had a plant part."

Most people of my grandparents' generation had an intuitive sense of agricultural basics: when various fruits and vegetables come into season, which ones keep through the winter, how to preserve the others. On what day autumn's frost will likely fall on their county, and when to expect the last one in spring. Which crops can be planted before the last frost, and which must wait. What animals and vegetables thrive in one's immediate region and how to live well on those, with little else thrown into the mix beyond a bag of flour, a pinch of salt, and a handful of coffee. Few people of my generation, and approximately none of our children, could answer any of those questions, let alone all of them. This knowledge has largely vanished from our culture.

If potatoes can surprise some part of their audience by growing leaves, it may not have occurred to most people that lettuce has a flower part, too. It does. They all do. Virtually all non-animal foods we eat come from flowering plants. Exceptions are mushrooms, seaweeds, and pine nuts. If other exotic edibles exist that you call food, I salute you.

Flowering plants, known botanically as angiosperms, evolved from ancestors similar to our modern-day conifers. The flower is a handy reproductive organ that came into its own during the Cretaceous era, right around the time when dinosaurs were for whatever reason getting downsized. In the millions of years since then, flowering plants have established themselves as the most conspicuously successful terrestrial lifeforms ever, having moved into every kind of habitat, in infinite variations. Flowering plants are key players in all the world's ecotypes: the deciduous forests, the rainforests, the grasslands. They are the desert cacti and the tundra scrub. They're small and they're large, they fill swamps and tolerate drought, they have settled into most every niche in every kind of place. It only stands to reason that we would eat them.

Flowering plants come in packages as different as an oak tree and a violet, but they all have a basic life history in common. They sprout and leaf out; they bloom and have sex by somehow rubbing one flower's boy stuff against another's girl parts. Since they can't engage in hot pursuit, they lure a third party, such as bees, into the sexual act — or else (depending on species) wait for the wind. From that union comes the blessed event, babies made, in the form of seeds cradled inside some form of fruit. Finally, sooner or later — because after that, what's the point anymore? — they die. Among the plants known as annuals, this life history is accomplished all in a single growing season, commonly starting with spring and ending with frost. The plant waits out the winter in the form of a seed, safely protected from weather, biding its time until conditions are right for starting over again.

Excluding the small fraction of our diet supplied by perennials — our tree fruits, berries, and nuts — we consume annuals. Our vegetal foods may be leaves, buds, fruits, grains, or other seed heads, but each comes to us from some point along this same continuum, the code all annual plants must live by. No variations are allowed. They can't set fruit, for example, before they bloom. As obvious as this may seem, it's easy enough to forget in a supermarket culture where the plant stages constantly present themselves in random order. And that's just the beginning. Biology teachers face kids in classrooms who may not even believe in the metamorphosis of bud to flower to fruit and seed, but rather, in some continuum of pansies becoming petunias becoming chrysanthemums because that's the reality they witness as landscapers come to city parks and surreptitiously yank one flower before it fades from its prime, replacing it with another.

The same disconnection from natural processes may be at the heart of our country's shift away from believing in evolution. In the past, principles of natural selection and change over time made sense to kids who'd watched it all unfold. Whether or not they knew the terminology, farm families understood the processes well enough to imitate them: culling, selecting, and improving their herds and crops. For modern kids who intuitively believe in the spontaneous generation of fruits and vegetables in the produce section, trying to get their minds around the slow speciation of the plant kingdom may be a stretch. The process by which vegetables come into season may appear, in this context, as random as the lottery.

But it isn't. Here's how it goes. First come the leaves: spinach, kale, lettuce, and chard (at my latitude, this occurs in April and May). Then more mature heads of leaves and flower heads: cabbage, romaine, broccoli, and cauliflower (May — June). Then tender young fruit-set: snow peas, baby squash, cucumbers (June), followed by green beans, green peppers, and small tomatoes (July). Then more mature, colorfully ripened fruits: beefsteak tomatoes, eggplants, red and yellow peppers (late July — August). Then the large, hard-shelled fruits with developed seeds inside: cantaloupes, honeydews, watermelons, pumpkins, winter squash (August — September). Last come the root crops, and so ends the produce parade.

To recover an intuitive sense of what will be in season throughout the year, picture an imaginary plant that bears over the course of one growing season all the different vegetable products we can harvest. We'll call it a vegetannual. Picture its life passing before your eyes like a time-lapse film: first, in the cool early spring, shoots poke up out of the ground. Small leaves appear, then bigger leaves. As the plant grows up into the sunshine and the days grow longer, flower buds will appear, followed by small green fruits. Under midsummer's warm sun, the fruits grow larger, riper, and more colorful. As days shorten into the autumn, these mature into hard-shelled fruits with appreciable seeds inside. Finally, as the days grow cool, the vegetannual may hoard the sugars its leaves have made, pulling them down into a storage unit of some kind: a tuber, bulb, or root.

Plainly, all the vegetables we consume don't come from the same plant, but each comes from a plant, that's the point — a plant predestined to begin its life in the spring and die in the fall. (A few, like onions and carrots, are attempting to be biennials but we'll ignore that for now.) What we choose to eat from each type of vegetable plant must come in its turn — leaves, buds, flowers, green fruits, ripe fruits, hard fruits — because that is the necessary order of things for an annual plant. For the life of them, they can't do it differently.

Some minor deviations and a bit of overlap are allowed, but in general, picturing an imaginary vegetannual plant is a pretty reliable guide to what will be in season, wherever you live. If you find yourself eating a watermelon in April, you can count back three months and imagine a place warm enough in January for this plant to have launched its destiny. Mexico maybe, or southern California. Chile is also a possibility. If you're inclined to think this way, consider all of the resources it took to transport a finicky fruit the size of a human toddler to your door, from that locale.

Our gardening forebears meant watermelon to be the juicy, barefoot taste of a hot summer's end, just as a pumpkin is the trademark fruit of late October. Most of us accept the latter, and limit our jack-o-lantern activities to the proper botanical season. Waiting for a watermelon is harder. It's tempting to reach for melons, red peppers, tomatoes, and other late-summer delights before the summer even arrives. But it's actually possible to wait, celebrating each season when it comes, not fretting about its being absent at all other times because something else good is at hand.

If many of us would view this style of eating as deprivation, that's only because we've grown accustomed to the botanically outrageous condition of having everything, always; this may be the closest thing we have right now to a distinctive national cuisine. Well-heeled North American epicures are likely to gather around a table where whole continents collide discreetly on a white tablecloth: New Zealand lamb with Italian porcinis, Peruvian asparagus, Mexican lettuce and tomatoes, and a hearty French Bordeaux. The date on the calendar is utterly irrelevant.

I've enjoyed my share of such meals, but I'm beginning at least to notice when I'm consuming the United Nations of edible plants and animals all in one seating (or the WTO is more like it). On a winter's day not long ago I was served a sumptuous meal like this, finished off with a dessert of raspberries. Because they only grow in temperate zones, not the tropics, these would have come from somewhere deep in the Southern Hemisphere. I was amazed that such small, eminently bruisable fruits could survive a zillion-mile trip looking so good (I myself look pretty wrecked after a mere red-eye from California), and I mumbled some reserved awe over that fact. I think my hostess was amused by my country-mouse naïveté. "This is New York," she assured me. "We can get anything we want, any day of the year."

So it is. And I don't wish to be ungracious, but we get

it at a price. Most of that is not measured in money, but in untallied debts that will be paid by our children in the currency of extinctions, economic unravelings, and global climate change. I do know it's impolite to raise such objections at the dinner table. Seven raspberries are not (I'll try to explain someday to my grandkids) the end of the world. I ate them and said "thank you." But I'm continually amazed by the manner in which we're allowed to steal from future generations, while commanding them not to do that to us, and rolling our eyes at anyone who is tediously PC enough to point this out. The conspicuous consumption of limited resources has yet to be accepted widely as a spiritual error, or even bad manners.

It's not that our culture is unacquainted with the idea of food as a spiritually loaded commodity. We're just particular about which spiritual arguments we'll accept as valid for declining certain foods. Generally unacceptable reasons: environmental destruction, energy waste, the poisoning of workers. Acceptable: it's prohibited by a holy text. Set down a platter of country ham in front of a rabbi, an imam, and a Buddhist monk, and you may have just conjured three different visions of damnation. Guests with high blood pressure may add a fourth. Is it such a stretch, then, to make moral choices about food based on the global consequences of its production and transport? In a country where 5 percent of the world's population glugs down a quarter of all the fuel, also belching out that much of the world's pollution, we've apparently made big choices about consumption. They could be up for review.

The business of importing foods across great distances is not, by its nature, a boon to Third World farmers, but it's very good business for oil companies. Transporting a single calorie of a perishable fresh fruit from California to New York takes about eighty-seven calories worth of fuel. That's as efficient as driving from Philadelphia to Annapolis and back in order to walk three miles on a treadmill in a Maryland gym. There may be people who'd do it. Pardon me while I ask someone else to draft my energy budget.

In many social circles it's ordinary for hosts to accommodate vegetarian guests, even if they're carnivores themselves. Maybe the world would likewise become more hospitable to diners who are queasy about fuel-guzzling foods... I like [the idea of "locavores"]: both scientifically and socially descriptive, with just the right hint of livin' la vida loca.

Slow Food International has done a good job of putting a smile on this eating style, rather than a pious frown, even while sticking to the quixotic agenda of fighting overcentralized agribusiness. The engaging strategy of the Slowies (their logo is a snail) is to celebrate what we have, standing up for the pleasures that seasonal eating can bring. They have their work cut out for them, as the American brain trust seems mostly blank on that subject. Consider the frustration of the man who wrote in to a syndicated food columnist with this complaint: having studied the [former] food pyramid brought to us by the U.S. Dietary Guidelines folks, he had his marching orders for "2 cups of fruit, 2- cups of vegetables a day." So he marched down to his grocery and bought (honest to Pete) eighty-three plums, pears, peaches, and apples. Outraged, he reported that virtually the entire lot was rotten, mealy, tasteless, juiceless, or hard as a rock and refusing to ripen.

Given the date of the column, this had occurred in January or February. The gentleman lived in Frostburg, Maryland, where they would still have been deeply involved in a thing called winter. I'm sure he didn't really think tasty, tree-ripened plums, peaches, and apples were hanging outside ripe for the picking in the orchards around ... um, Frost-burg. Probably he didn't think "orchard" at all — how many of us do, in the same sentence with "fruit?"Our dietary guidelines come to us without a road map.

Concentrating on local foods means thinking of fruit invariably as the product of an orchard, and a winter squash as the fruit of a late autumn farm. It's a strategy that will keep grocery money in the neighborhood, where it gets recycled into your own school system and local businesses. The green spaces surrounding your town stay green, and farmers who live nearby get to grow more food next year, for you. This also happens to be a win-win strategy for anyone with taste buds. It begins with rethinking a position that is only superficially about deprivation. Citizens of frosty worlds unite, and think about marching past the off-season fruits: you have nothing to lose but your mealy, juiceless, rock-hard and refusing to ripen.

Locally grown is a denomination whose meaning is incorruptible. Sparing the transportation fuel, packaging, and unhealthy additives is a compelling part of the story. But the plot goes beyond that. Local food is a handshake deal in a community gathering place. It involves farmers with first names, who show up at the market week after week. It involves consumers who remember that to be human is to belong to a food chain, wherever and whenever we find ourselves alive. It means remembering the truest of all truths: we are what we eat. Stepping slowly backward out of a fuel-driven industry of highly transported foods will alter more than a person's grocery list. Such small, stepwise changes in personal habits aren't trivial. Ultimately, they will add up to the story of who we were on this planet: what it took to keep us alive, what we left behind.

Barbara Kingsolver is an award-winning American author. Her books have been translated into more than two dozen languages, and have been adopted into the core literature curriculum in high schools and colleges throughout the United States. She has contributed to more than fifty literary anthologies. In 2000 she received the National Humanities Medal, the highest honor for service through the arts in the United States.

PERSPECTIVES: FOOD ACCESS

In the article below, pediatrician and childhood trauma researcher Nadine Burke and healthy food advocate Anna Lappé discuss the importance of closing the food gap and ensuring access to fresh, healthy, affordable food for all.

Q: What are some of the health challenges in vulnerable communities?

Nadine Burke: There are huge issues around environmental justice in "food deserts." Low-income neighborhoods, where people simply don't have access to nutritious, healthy food, tend to be food deserts. They tend to be targeted by the fast food industry. Obesity is a serious problem because the food that is available tends to be high-sugar, high-fat food. Low-income neighborhoods don't have as many safe places to play, so it's hard for people to get outdoors and exercise.

I did a study where we looked at the price of bread in high-income and low-income neighborhoods. We found that in low-income neighborhoods healthy foods and staple

HOW MANY PEOPLE LIVE IN FOOD-INSECURE HOUSEHOLDS IN THE US?

In 2016:

- 41.2 million people lived in food-insecure households.
- 10.8 million adults lived in households with very low food security.
- 6.5 million children lived in food-insecure households in which children, along with adults, were food insecure.
- 703,000 children (1.0 percent of the Nation's children) lived in households in which one or more child experienced very low food security.
- 31.6% of households with children headed by a single woman were food-insecure.
- 22.5% of Black, non-Hispanic households were food-insecure.
- 18.5% of Hispanic households were food-insecure.

Prevalence of food insecurity, 2016

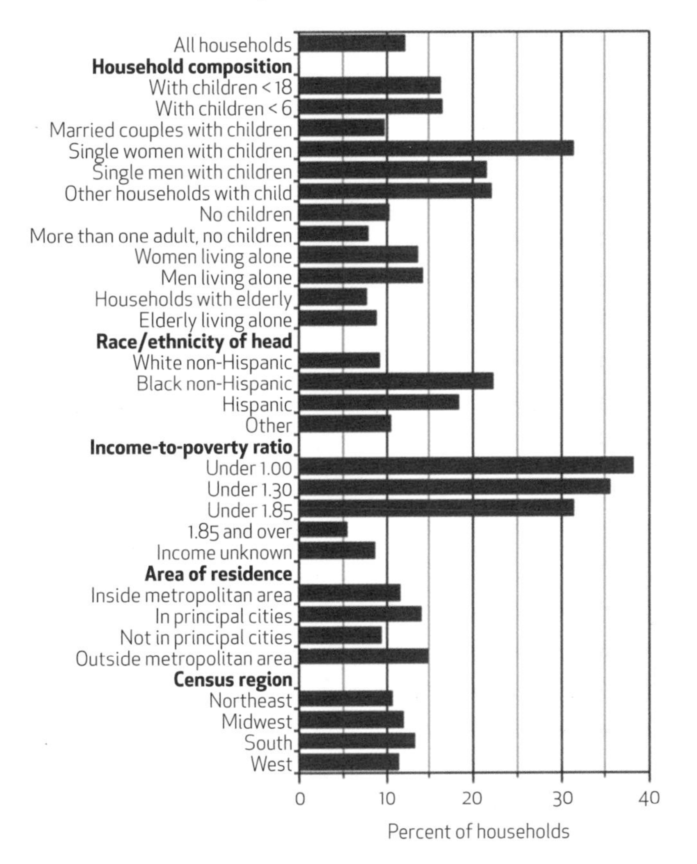

Source: USDA, Economic Research Service, using data from the December 2016 Current population Survey Food Security Supplement.

foods tend to be more expensive, and fast food is more readily available and less expensive. On top of that, we found that the high-income neighborhood had only one fast food establishment and the low-income neighborhood had six.

When we think about what our families have access to, low-income families already have a lot of challenges. Let's at least give them the ability to feed their families in a way that's healthy. I see young folks who are struggling every day because everything in their environment is stacked against them. It's time for us as a community to get together and say, "This is ridiculous. We need to change our environment. We need to do things differently."

Q: What disparities do you see in the American food system?

Anna Lappé: We have two Americas. We have one America with money, resources, and a food system that is abundant and accessible. Most people living in well-off communities have access to any food they want any time of the year. And we have another America, in which the poorest communities don't have access to any grocery store at all. If they do, it is carrying maybe some wilted lettuce, old tomatoes, and packaged food, and that's about it. It's an America where 36 million people in this country go hungry every year.

People are saying that this is not acceptable. We have the resources and the intelligence to ensure that every single one of us, no matter where we live, no matter how much money we have, has access to healthy and sustainably grown food. Within the past one or two generations, we have come to a place where very few of us are eating any fruits and vegetables anymore. In addition, of the fruits and vegetables that we are eating, almost all of the servings come from potatoes, tomatoes, and iceberg lettuce. And the potatoes are in the form of French fries, which are of dubious nutritional quality.

As a result of this incredible dietary revolution in what we're eating, some health researchers have recently said that if we don't change how kids are fed in this country, this generation may be the first generation to have a shorter life expectancy than their parents. Just as we woke up as a nation and realized that smoking was a public health crisis, we're waking up to realize that this industrial food system is a public health crisis.

FROM FOOD SECURITY TO FOOD SOVEREIGNTY

By Antonio Roman-Alcalá

It's an exciting time for the good food movement. Sometimes it can feel as though the efforts to make agriculture more sustainable are the most visible and active component of the broader environmental movement. This shouldn't be surprising. Our relationship to food is visceral, emotional, and continues daily.

If you've seen *Food, Inc.* or read any Eric Schlosser, Michael Pollan, or Rachel Carson, you know that the sustainable food movement is trying to address the social and environmental problems created by an industrial farming system in which convenience and profit trump everything else.

The responses to industrial farming have included critiques like Silent Spring, the back-to-the-land and organic farming sparks of the late 1960s, the family farm movement that resisted bankruptcy and corporate consolidation in the 1980s, and now the urban farming movement that has burgeoned in the past 10 years.

Many elements of the sustainable food movement have been organized by (or for) the two most obvious sectors of the food system: Eaters and producers. In parts of the world where populations are still largely agrarian, eaters and producers are often the same people, but here in the United States (where the farming population hovers around one percent) consumers have been the dominant focus of food policy, at least for the past 40 years.

In the global North, much of the past 20 years of activism has framed the concept of "food security" as the right of all people to have enough food to avoid hunger and malnutrition. A new effort underway to deepen food activism focuses on a more radical idea: The concept of food sovereignty. The global food sovereignty movement is making the case that reform of the food system will be insufficient if it does not democratize and make more transparent the means of food production. We'll never be able to resolve the environmental and social abuses of industrial agriculture without changing who controls the food system.

As Katherine Zavala, program manager of grassroots alliances at International Development Exchange (IDEX), a San Francisco-based organization that supports food justice in the Global South, explains it: "Food security might focus on hunger as a human rights issue, but it fails to consider many other facets of food like the ways it is produced, the social relationships it relies on, or the cultural importance it holds to communities."

Having enough to eat is important, certainly, but what

about the quality of that food? What about the way that people are treated in the process of producing that food? What about the cultural traditions of food that are left aside in a purely calorie-counting concept of "food security"? Zavala says that perhaps the biggest inadequacy of the food security concept is that it fails to address "who decides what the food system is. It doesn't address who is driving or controlling the global food system or the lack of decision-making power among people to decide what food system they want."

These deeper questions illustrate why the term "food sovereignty"–pioneered by the international peasant alliance La Via Campesina–is increasingly being adopted food movement activists across the globe. Ashoka Finley, who works for the Richmond, California urban farming organization Urban Tilth and has been closely involved in the Occupy the Farm effort at the University of California's Gill Tract, considers himself a food sovereignty activist.

He says: "Food sovereignty, like food security, is about rights. But because food sovereignty as a concept argues that food systems are determined by political and economic conditions, it's about the rights we as eaters, citizens, and communities should have to take part in effecting those conditions. It is also about how we can use food-based activism to transform the political and economic system we live in."

That "taking part" is what distinguishes food security from food sovereignty, and what makes food sovereignty such a compelling and important idea. Yes, of course, providing food for people in need is essential, but a soup kitchen a food bank or a Supplemental Nutrition Assistance Program (SNAP) card is not enough to create food sovereignty. Even planting gardens in urban areas (full disclosure: my area of employment!) doesn't amount to food sovereignty.

Direct action approaches like Occupy the Farm may not be enough, because, Zavala reminds us, "Those that are in positions of government and economic power are restricting these alternative food system models. They're not thinking about feeding people; they're mostly thinking about the bottom line. And if we all created our own food systems, how would they profit?"

The entrenched corporate opposition to food systems change has pushed food sovereignty activists beyond the direct action approach to address the institutions of power. After a long period of focusing effort outside the political system, activists are now looking to the government for change. In the mid-2000s, for example, the federal Farm Bill finally became a top priority for many sustainable agriculture advocates. Long after the law was the main target of efforts to ensure food security (through SNAP). But, it has remained close to impossible to use the Farm Bill as a tool to promote food sovereignty.

"The current political climate is an extreme difficult one, the legislative process is complex, and that process can often be quite corrupt, as we have seen numerous times," Finley says. "However, if we want food sovereignty, we can't shy away from tough political battles, because there are certain political issues that underpin or undermine food sovereignty, like land ownership or agribusiness subsidies."

Recent lobbying over the Farm Bill provides a clear example of the complexity and difficulty transitioning from a food security movement to a food sovereignty movement. Food security activists (often representing low income urban constituents) have been pitted against farm sustainability activists (more often rural-minded) over the funding that the bill controls. In an era of austerity, this can lead to Sophie's-choice like dilemmas: Either cut food stamp funding or cut programs that provide support to farmers transitioning to organic methods of production.

Luckily, there's an alternative to this false choice. That choice is to develop democratic spaces at the local and state level to craft collaborative solutions that benefit both consumers and producers. Across the country, Food Policy Councils (FPCs) are bringing together diverse constituencies to determine how local policy can be leveraged to achieve positive food system change. These local groups identify problems as a community and then seek to solve them through a process of consensus-building and pressuring local governments. Food Policy Councils have worked on things like institutional food procurement, the use of urban open space for agriculture, nutrition education and funding for food banks. More recently, FPCs are scaling up, coming together to affect policy on the state and federal levels.

The food movement's shift from security to sovereignty can be instructive for the broader movements for environmental sanity and democratic governance. By asking the simple question, "Who's in charge here?" food sovereignty elevates the importance that power has in our food systems. The concept expands our critical capacity beyond consumer choice to consider that we are all "co-producers" of the food system. "Sovereignty" is a frame that can be used to think about process in relation to natural resources, not just outcomes, and it can help encourage solidarity and cohesion amongst myriad movements and sectors within the food movement and outside of it.

Social movements focused on sovereignty can help build a more democratic and accountable political system. This, in turn, would allow for a more sustainable approach to natural resources, and a more egalitarian economic system. By talking "sovereignty" from the start, change-makers can pursue a mutual end goal from any number of individual struggles. When Paul Hawken described "the largest movement on Earth" in his book Blessed Unrest, he was clear that the millions of individual and NGO efforts to help were a movement, but just didn't act like one.

Sovereignty, whether of food or fiber or healthcare, may be the concept needed to unite these struggles into the movement they can be.

Antonio Roman-Alcalá is an educator, researcher, writer, musician, and father based in San Francisco. He holds a BA from University of California at Berkeley, and an MA from the International Institute of Social Studies (ISS). Antonio helped found and manage San Francisco's Alemany Farm, the San Francisco Urban Agriculture Alliance, and the California Food Policy Council, and his 2010 documentary film, *In Search of Good Food*, can be viewed free online.

GROWING FOOD, GROWING POWER

Will Allen has been a professional athlete and worked in corporate America. Still, he says, being a farmer is the biggest and most rewarding path he could have chosen. Will is the founder of Growing Power, an organization dedicated to teaching people in urban Milwaukee how to grow good food. "We're only six blocks away from Milwaukee's largest public housing project," he says. "When people drive by the street and they see the greenhouses on the front, they have no idea that we feed about 10,000 people just from this farm alone." Find out more about Growing Power and the power of urban agriculture by watching this short video:

tinyurl.com/growingfoodpower

BEYOND 'FREE' OR 'FAIR' TRADE: MEXICAN FARMERS GO LOCAL

By Mike Wold

Tío Joel rode his small donkey down the dirt road to his greenhouse to show us his solution to keeping small farmers on their land in southern Mexico. At about seventy years old, he could handle a machete or lift a 20-kilo sack of compost as easily as any of us, though the brace he wore around his waist was a sign of problems to come.

Taking a break from chopping green manure for compost for his popular tomatoes, he explained why a *campesino* like him could benefit from using organic methods: "In the harvest this year a lot of tomatoes were being harvested and the price went way down to five pesos per kilo, but we sell ours for seven. I go from house to house and sell it small-scale, but we sell out our tomatoes because they're well-known ... on Sunday we ran out of tomatoes, we sell so many."

Trade policy in the United States usually gets cast into two opposing camps — "free" trade and "fair" trade, a dichotomy that assumes local production in the Global South must be sold elsewhere. Indeed, we usually think of the demand for local, organic foods as coming from North America or Europe. But within countries like Mexico, there's another way to approach the issue, looking at global import and export versus local production and consumption. In the United States, it has emerged as the "locavore" movement, which to many seems an unaffordable luxury compared to the accessibility of cheap imported food. But in the state of Oaxaca, Mexico, raising and eating your own food and producing for the local market has become a strategy for cultural and economic survival in a hostile trade environment.

In southern Mexico, the cost of corn production is now higher than its world market price. By standard economic logic, Mexican *campesinos* should give up raising corn and grow another crop to sell on the world market, leave their land entirely for a job in the city, or migrate north.

Many farmers have done just that, swelling the ranks of undocumented workers in the United States and the underemployed in overpopulated cities at home. Others, however, have stayed on the land and are finding ways to survive and even prosper. I traveled with a group from the United States, organized by the nonprofits Witness for Peace, Community Alliance for Global Justice, and the Washington Fair Trade Coalition, to Oaxaca state's Mixteca region to find out how and why.

Mexico is the birthplace of corn, and corn is the mainstay of the Mexican diet. It's hard to imagine a Mexico that doesn't raise corn.

Yet when the the North American Free Trade Agreement (NAFTA) was signed [two decades] ago, one of its immediate consequences was a five-fold increase in corn imports into Mexico. U.S. corn sells at well below the cost of Mexican corn, not just because American agriculture is more "efficient" (due to heavy use of machinery and chemical-based fertilizers), but because subsidies for U.S. corn bolster the industry's economic leverage.

But in places like Oaxaca's Santo Tomás Mazaltepec, farmers — and eaters — still prefer local over the yellow corn usually grown in the United States. "The local corn produces more and better tortilla material than imported corn...and also you can tell the difference in the flavor," said one farmer we talked to. "A disadvantage is that we have really low production — we can barely produce enough for ourselves...and we have periods of the year when we have really severe drought conditions...There are the government stores that sell corn but what's sold there is the yellow corn...that may come from the United States...[there are] a lot of chemical fertilizers in it and pesticides and herbicides and they can sell it here much cheaper than we do, so we're obligated to sell ours cheaper ..."

As a result of these social and economic fluctuations, much of Mexico's countryside has been depopulated. In San Pedro Coxcaltepec, there are few young people for old-timers like Tío Joel to pass their farms on to.

According to Tío Martín, another Coxcaltepec farmer, "It used to be that there were 12 or 15 people...in each house, and now...it's two people here, two people there; there's just no people left. When we try to do *tequio* [traditional volunteer community service], it used to be...there were lots of people helping out; now it's really hard because it's just us older folks."

Eleazar García, a farmer in his thirties, added that "the important challenge is that there are [still] a number of young folks here and we want to convince them that this is dignified work and that it's a very important role in the feeding of one's family...The *campesino* always appreciates having food... to not worry about always having money in your pocket ...[as] they say around here, we're not worried — if I've got beans, I've got something to eat."

Enter the "locavore" movement — or better, the movement for food sovereignty, the principle that for a community to have control of its destiny, it must have substantive control of the production of the food it consumes. People need to be able to choose what they eat.

Subsistence farmers in southern Mexico are in a much better position to raise what they eat than most dwellers in U.S. cities. They've been doing it for a long time. In Oaxaca, there are dozens of different varieties of corn, each adapted to a particular set of climatic conditions, elevation, and soil. Even the grass that was the wild precursor of corn still grows in the Oaxaca hills.

Furthermore, over thousands of years, indigenous Mexican farmers have evolved a sophisticated means of sustainably farming on steep slopes and easily eroded soils. Unlike typical U.S. agricultural practice, Oaxacan farmers traditionally plant beans and squash in their cornfields. Beans use the cornstalks for support and add nitrogen — a nutrient that is depleted by growing corn — to the soil. Squash can grow between the corn stalks; the vines can be left in place as a green manure for adding nutrients to the field after the harvest. Farmers also allow wild greens to grow in and around the cornfield; these greens are ecologically adapted to the cornfield environment — they don't grow in such profusion away from the fields — and are an important source of vitamin A and other nutrients in the village diet.

In the 1980s, new organizations in the Oaxaca highlands, such as CEDICAM (Center for Integral Campesino Development of the Mixteca), started working with *campesinos* to find alternatives to the damaging pesticides, monocrops, and hybrid seeds promoted by the Green Revolution throughout the 60s and 70s by building on traditional practices that were adapted to the area — all while using new insights from organic farming to increase yields.

Unlike the urban poor in Mexico, farmers in San Pedro Coxcaltepec say that the post-NAFTA rise in the price of tortillas didn't affect them at all. "I raise all the corn I need," one of them told me.

Unfortunately, farmers also need cash to participate in the modern world and buy goods they can't produce themselves. So the challenge is to find something besides corn to sell on the market. That way young people will want to stay and farm there and, in doing so, keep their traditional economy alive. CEDICAM has helped farmers like Tío Joel use greenhouses from a failed development project in the valley to raise vegetables to sell — not on the world market, but in nearby towns, where people will pay for fresh, local produce. Another organization, Puente a la Salud Comunitaria (Bridge to Community Health), has helped several communities revive the cultivation of amaranth, a grain which originated in the Mixteca region and still grows wild there, but which was almost entirely eradicated by the Spanish, who thought it was associated with pagan practices. Amaranth has much higher protein than corn and, unlike corn in the modern market, still has a high market value in Oaxaca — thus it can serve dual purposes of improving village nutrition and providing a viable cash crop.

In Santo Tomas Mazaltepec, the availability of the high-protein grain has had a significant effect on nutrition in the community. Mothers who added small amounts of locally grown amaranth — less than an ounce a day — to their children's daily meals as an experiment said that the kids were clearly more energetic and growing better.

Food sovereignty isn't limited to farmers in rural areas. Most of the people in Oaxaca City are within one or two generations of living off the land and still know something about growing their own food. Given the steep rise in food prices in Mexico since NAFTA was signed, city-dwellers who grow at least some of their own food can supplement meager incomes to insulate themselves and their families from the effects of layoffs and low wages; this also increases their resilience during the frequent political struggles that occur in Oaxaca between the population as a whole and the corrupt government. The ability to eat during strikes may make the difference between winning or losing the struggle.

Growers María and Laurentina started raising oyster mushrooms two years ago; a year ago, they were working hard to explain to people in the produce markets how to cook the mushrooms; this year, the demand for mushrooms is enough that they're looking for ways to increase their production and capacity, like buying a refrigerator to store their own spores in, rather than having to buy them, and to store their crops for a few days. Another urban farmer talked about what a help it was to her household budget not to have to go to the market for tomatoes, cilantro, parsley, and celery.

These farmers and urban gardeners are not looking for hand-outs or foreign aid. What they need is a supportive environment for their survival and the rejuvenation of a once-sustainable rural economy. The United States can help by supporting trade policies that don't pit Mexican small-scale agriculture against U.S. agribusiness and create an economic environment that supports the rest of the world in growing its own food. NAFTA is up for renewal in a few years, offering us a chance to do exactly that.

"If you really want to combat hunger in the world," farmer Eleazar García told us as he showed us the difference between thriving cornstalks in a field that had been fertilized with cheap organic compost, and stunted corn in a field that had been fertilized with chemicals for too many years, "it's in the hands of *campesinos*. They live on what they grow."

Mike Wold wrote this article for *YES! Magazine*, a national, nonprofit media organization that fuses powerful ideas with practical actions. Mike is a regular contributor to *Real Change* newspaper in Seattle and a long-time activist on immigration and related social justice issues.

WE CAN FEED THE WORLD WITH THE FOOD WE WASTE

By Joanne Will

According to the Food and Agriculture Organization (FAO) of the United Nations, approximately one third of all food produced for human consumption goes to waste. As much as we fetishize food in North America, we also waste an incredible amount. One of the big paradoxes of our time is that, despite alarming global hunger statistics, the FAO found we throw out an estimated 1.3 billion tonnes of food annually — four times the amount required to feed the world's 795 million hungriest people.

In Canada, a 2014 report by Value Chain Management International Inc pegged the annual value of food waste across the country at $31 billion. And it's not just food that's wasted, it's also the labour, energy, machinery and natural resources required to produce, store and transport it.

Then there's the impact on the environment. "When you look at food waste globally, if it was a country, it would be third in terms of greenhouse gas emissions behind China and the United States. So, it's a huge climate change issue. There are emissions all the way along the path, from production — particularly for things like beef that are very greenhouse gas intensive — all the way through to disposal," says JoAnne Berkenkamp, Senior Advocate with the Food and Agriculture Program of the US Natural Resources Defense Council (NRDC).

In North America, the largest piece of the food waste pie, by value, occurs in households, followed by grocery stores, restaurants and institutional food service like hospitals, colleges and universities.

Much of our household waste is due to spoiled produce, languishing unused in refrigerators. We buy in mass quantities at warehouse-style supermarkets that offer super-sized shopping carts and too-good-to-be-true deals, which means we often overbuy. Since we've grown accustomed to abundance, we also tend to take it for granted. Nowadays, we waste about 50 percent more food than in the 1970s.

"What we found in our research is people are often extremely conscious of the cost of food when they purchase it, but they're oblivious to the cost when they throw it out. The average family of four spends $1,500 a year on food that they throw out," says Berkenkamp.

A number of factors contribute to that. "People often purchase more than they can eat. And that's driven by things like 55 percent of grocery purchases in the US are impulse buys, which is to say a person didn't have an intention about what they were going to buy when they got there. They're shopping without a list. It's also driven by two-for-one deals, and very large pack sizes of things. Boxes of lettuce that are three times what a family can use but it looks really cheap, so people are motivated by the prospect of getting a good deal to purchase more than they can utilize," says Berkenkamp.

Busy lifestyles are another factor. "We tend to be aspirational shoppers in the grocery store: we want to have more variety in our diet, we want to try new recipes, we want to get the healthy options, we don't want to run out, we want to get something all the members of our household will like. We're maybe trying to accommodate kids that have really different schedules so we're planning for multiple meals, maybe even in a given evening to accommodate family member's schedules. All of those things tend to spur us to purchase and prepare more food than we can eat."

Confusion over date labels and how to store food also has an effect. "In the research we did for the Ad Council's 'Save The Food' campaign, we had researchers go into people's homes and to the grocery store with them, and look in their refrigerator and their trash, and keep food waste diaries. We'd see things on the shelf that belong in the fridge and vice versa. Refrigerators at too high of a temperature, or milk being pulled out and left on the dinner table for an hour or two per day, which raises the temperature and causes it to not last as long. Things like fruits need to be at a low humidity so they belong in the low-humidity crisper drawer, whereas vegetables need higher humidity and they belong in the other drawer. Things like that are not widely understood."

Nor, says Berkenkamp, is the fact that produce should not be stored in the bags that it's typically purchased in. "Most fruits and vegetables need to breathe, so if you store [something] tied up in a plastic bag, you're going to get condensation in there, and more moisture, and it will not last as long as it otherwise might."

Other waste occurs in restaurants and at retail food businesses: the leftovers on our plates due to oversize portions we can't finish, or produce discarded because it doesn't look cosmetically perfect — even though it might be perfectly fine to eat.

Some good news is that food waste is rapidly becoming a subculture of haute cuisine, with a trickle-down effect to home cooks. Chefs and restaurants are providing inspiration about the possibilities for dishes that can be created with what we may be overlooking in our own refrigerators.

American chef and author Dan Barber took his popular pop-up restaurant wasteED across the pond to Selfridges in London this spring, for a dining experience even notorious curmudgeon Oscar the Grouch would have loved. wastED highlights edible ingredients that are often discarded or rejected, turning them into delicious dishes made from the likes of broccoli stalks, the ribs of kale leaves and fish bones.

Food rescue programs also make a dent in waste by gathering food that would otherwise be binned and redistributing it to food banks and shelters. There's even Transfernation, an "Uber for food rescue" organization based in New York City that uses an app to connect those who can transport leftover food to those who can use it.

Others, such as Tristram Stuart, founder of the UK charity Feedback and author of Waste: Uncovering the Global Food Scandal, are educating consumers with campaigns such as 'Feeding the 5000.' At each event, a communal feast for 5,000 people is served, made entirely from food that would otherwise have been wasted. Stuart has also created Toast Ale, beer made using surplus bread that was destined for a landfill.

So, what can average consumers and households do to reduce waste? Plenty. Plan meals, shop with a list, ignore "best before" dates, educate yourself and family members on how to store and use produce. The Waste Free Kitchen Handbook by Dana Gunders, a staff scientist and food-waste fighter at the NRDC, provides a plethora of tips. As does the site savethefood.com.

Another suggestion is to adopt some fresh thinking, and stop discarding food you previously considered inedible. Using up leftovers or overlooked ingredients can be a boon to creativity. On a recent particularly empty refrigerator day, necessity drove me to take the skin of a kabocha squash, which had been roasted previously and the innards used to make soup, and chop and fold it into an omelette. The sweet, nutty flavour of the squash-skin omelette turned out to be a delicious change from my usual onion/mushroom/spinach combinations.

To help realize the full extent of what we can do with the food we have in our homes, there are websites, columns and cookbooks focused on how to make meals with kitchen scraps. Food52's Lindsay-Jean Hard's biweekly column highlights recipes that include scraps (for example,

Use Chef Allison Mountford's Personal Food Waste Audit to get to the bottom of where your food waste comes from and how you can address it:

endsandstems.com/blog/how-to-conduct-a-food-waste-audit

homemade celery salt–crusted baked potatoes, and a soup that uses stale cornbread). Hard is currently working on a cookbook focused on cooking from scraps, due out from Workman Publishing in early 2018.

When it comes to treating food with respect, our food culture also plays a role.

"Clearly the primary driver in the US is that people feel badly about wasting money. The second thing they regret about wasting food is that they know that there are people that don't have enough to eat. So, there is some moral argument to be made. There is some data that asked parents in particular how they felt about food waste, and they said that one of the motivators was that they wanted to set a good example for their kids," says Berkenkamp.

"Most surveys don't ask that question, so you don't see it in the data. But Johns Hopkins University did a national survey in the US in the last 12 months, and they got some really interesting data. One of their observations was that parents didn't want to set a bad example for kids, so I think that's something to be leveraged."

Educating ourselves and the next generations on the value of food, where it comes from and the resources required to produce it, seems key to reducing waste. As Senegalese engineer and environmentalist Baba Dioum once said, "In the end we will conserve only what we love; we will love only what we understand; and we will understand only what we are taught."

Joanne Will has been a regular contributor to *The Globe and Mail* since 2009. In 2014, she was a Knight-Wallace Journalism Fellow at the University of Michigan.

ECOCHALLENGE: PUTTING IT INTO PRACTICE

Here are some ideas for putting what you learned this week into action. Find more ideas and commit to one Ecochallenge this week at **choices.ecochallenge.org**

Don't waste food, and eat what you buy. Check your fridge and plan your meals before you shop. Use up leftovers. Start with smaller portions. Food that is wasted and sent to the landfill creates methane, which is an extremely potent greenhouse gas. If you do need to throw food out, compost!

Buy organic when you can. Organic food is free of petroleum-derived fertilizers and pesticides, which is better for your health, the health of farm workers, and the health of the planet. See the "Dirty Dozen" and Clean Fifteen" lists in this session for ideas of where to start.

Eat less prepared food and more fresh, whole foods. Whole, fresh foods are generally healthier than pre-made and processed foods. Eating whole foods also reduces your packaging waste, an often overlooked contributor to greenhouse gas emissions.

Eat more seasonally. When you eat what's in season in your area, the food doesn't have to be shipped great distances or grown in a fossil fuel-heated hot house. You also do more to support your local economy. When you do buy out of season produce, go for foods with longer shelf lives that can be shipped by boat (apples, oranges bananas) instead of being shipped by plane (asparagus, berries) or grown in a hot house (tomatoes, lettuce).

Grow your own food. Even if it's just a small herb garden or one tomato plant, growing your own food connects you to the growing cycle in a tangible way. If you're growing organically and from seeds, the carbon footprint is negligible. And food from your own backyard (or balcony) is generally fresher, cheaper, and more nutritious than than other options.

Reduce your consumption of meat and dairy. Cows and sheep in particular emit methane as a by-product of their digestion. Methane is at least 20 times more powerful than carbon dioxide as a greenhouse gas. Sensible reduction in consumption of these food types can help you be healthier, save you money, and reduce your greenhouse gas emissions.

Drink water from the tap. Fossil fuels are used both in the transportation of bottled water from factories to stores and in the production of the plastic bottles themselves. The plastic bottle is used only once, and then disposed of in the landfill or recycled. Not to mention that tap water is hundreds of times cheaper than the bottled stuff! Take a reusable bottle with you, save money, and waste less by drinking tap water.

SESSION 4

WATER

"Nothing is softer or more flexible than water, yet nothing can resist it."

— Lao Tz

LEARNING OBJECTIVES

- Become familiar with the concept of a watershed and understand the global water cycle.
- Develop a focus on your local watershed(s).
- Gain a more in-depth knowledge of our water consumption habits, including the water used to make the foods we eat and the products we use.
- Understand how our personal and community choices affect the quantity and quality of water available both locally and in distant places.

Special thanks to Washington State University Extension for letting us adapt their work.

SESSION DESCRIPTION

Water is key to life. Life started in the ocean, and the ocean covers 71% of the planet. 97% of the planet's water is in the ocean, and less than one percent is freshwater (the remainder is stored in glaciers and polar ice). Throughout our existence, the availability of fresh, clean water has determined the success or failure of the human experiment. History shows that civilizations have evolved only with access to adequate water resources. When water supplies have been interrupted, populations have secured new sources, migrated to areas of greater abundance, or simply collapsed. Water is essential to our survival, and yet all too often we take this precious, limited resource for granted. We generally expect it to be there when we turn on our faucets and hoses, flush our toilets, and run our water-dependent appliances. We are largely unaware of the hidden water costs of our lifestyles. In this session, we will consider our own water consumption and the ways in which humans affect water resources both locally and globally.

REFLECTION

Find out more about your local watershed. You can locate your watershed using the link on page 77. Use the questions underneath the link to guide your learning. Post your Reflection to your Dashboard on **choices.ecochallenge.org**. If you are not using the Ecochallenge site, write your thoughts in a journal and then reflect with your group.

What item currently on your person do you think required the most water to produce, and why?

Reminder to the facilitator: The circle question should move quickly. Elicit an answer from each participant without questions or comments from others. The facilitator's guidelines are on page 10.

SUGGESTED DISCUSSION QUESTIONS

1. Where are your nearest natural bodies of water?
2. Name some of the human activities impacting the health of water systems, both locally (your watershed) and globally (freshwater and oceans). What can you do to improve the health of water systems?
3. How does our use of single-use plastic affect/interact with water, both freshwater and ocean water?
4. What single-use items (e.g. straws, coffee cups, vegetable bags, plastic bags) do you regularly use? What could be substituted instead?
5. How can you reduce the use of bottled water in your home/office/school?
6. How do you think climate change will affect your region's water supply? Think about the effects of weather, storms, salinity, and sea level rise, among other changes. How can you find out more about climate change's impact to your region?
7. How can your region/household prepare for changing water situations in order to become more resilient?
8. What would a sustainable water future in your region look like? What needs to change?

SUGGESTED GROUP ACTIVITY

If you would like to do an activity with your group, we recommend one of these.

- Determine how much water your lifestyle takes by using the Water Calculator at **watercalculator.org**
  Did anything surprise you about the water usage of your lifestyle? Share your results and ideas for reducing your water usage with your group.
- Take a tour of your local wastewater treatment plant as a group.

FURTHER RESOURCES

Interested in finding out more on the topics presented in this session?
Visit our website for further readings and resources: **ecochallenge.org/discussion-course-resources.**
Follow our blog at **ecochallenge.org/blog/**; we post links to new resources and inspiring stories regularly.

WATER IS LIFE

By Osprey Orielle Lake

I do not know exactly when it happened: perhaps during a summer swim as I weightlessly flew underwater, dreaming of curious sea lions who glided upstream with me from their ocean home. It might have been years later as I canoed miles upriver to catch a glimpse of a fledgling osprey. Somewhere, though, my body became a part of the Big River watershed in Northern California. The waters' spirit cracked open my heart, bidding me to always remember that this natural beauty is not only a luxury to revere, but also an indispensable key to our collective coherence as a species.

The simple and profound equation is this: Water is life. Yet the startling reality is that today, more than a billion people worldwide do not have access to safe drinking water, resulting in nearly 2 million fatalities a year — mostly children — due to waterborne diseases. With water scarcity increasing due to human population growth, pollution, and climate change, clearly our relationship to water must change.

First and foremost, we must secure access to clean and safe water as a basic human right for everyone in every country. This will require not only changing our detrimental use of water, but also ensuring that no institutions or corporations impede this life-giving right to water. Communities around the world are now engaged in critical struggles to protect their local waters, and it is time that we uphold water as a global commons for all. The United Nations took an important step toward this goal in 2010 with its adoption of a resolution recognizing the human right to safe and clean drinking water and sanitation.

To support efforts to protect and defend water, we also can look beneath the surface of the stream into the deeper currents of our understanding about it, and in this manner begin healing our relationship with this irreplaceable liquid.

Big River is part of the Mendocino watershed where I have spent much of my life. This gentle, sauntering body of water, whose sloping banks are adorned with willow, fir, and redwood trees, emerges just south of town to join the Pacific Ocean. The redwoods and the entire river's integrity have almost been lost on numerous occasions due to efforts to log even the last hoary stands. Taking in this beauty involves awareness of the river's story, her health, her wonders, and her battle — like that of rivers around the world — to survive.

Like many, I have always been enamored with water. This precious element seems the ultimate teacher of movement and shaping, both physically and spiritually. Everything has been touched by water. It has sculpted the landscape of our world, and we, too, are shaped by water. As we look upon the fluid-cut forms — mountains and gorges shaped by snowmelt rivers; craggy shorelines chiseled by waves — so, too, is our consciousness molded.

Not only is this fluid element able to carve and define form, it can also be shaped into any matrix. When water enters any crevice, container, or living entity it will round

DEFINITIONS

Watershed: A region or area bounded peripherally by a divide and draining eventually to a particular watercourse or body of water by means of ditches, streams, directly over the ground surface, or through the ground.

Stormwater Management: Stormwater management means to manage surface runoff. It can be applied in rural areas, but is essential in urban areas where runoff cannot infiltrate because the surfaces are impermeable. Traditional stormwater management was mainly to drain high peak flows away. Modern approaches aim to rebuild the natural water cycle, i.e., to store runoff water for a certain time, to recharge groundwater and to use the collected water for irrigation or household supply.

Acidification: Acidification occurs when carbon dioxide gas (or CO2) is absorbed by the ocean and reacts with seawater to produce acid that changes the chemistry of ocean water. This can interfere with the ability of some ocean species, like oysters, to form shells.

Dead Zones: "Dead zone" is a more common term for a hypoxic or anoxic area; that is, an area where there is a reduced level of oxygen in the water. Dead zones often occur when nutrient runoff from farming is carried downstream into rivers, and eventually large bodies of water like the Gulf of Mexico. The nutrient runoff causes massive patches of algae to "bloom," then decompose, starving other aquatic life of the oxygen they need to survive. Less dissolved oxygen in the water is often referred to as a "dead zone" because most marine species either die, or, if they are mobile, like fish, leave the area. Habitats that would normally be teeming with life become, essentially, biological deserts.

Water footprint: The amount of water an individual or group uses, including potable water, wastewater, and the water used to grow the food and make the things each individual or group consumes. This concept also considers the water cycle, and includes the idea that water does not vanish after use.

each corner, bending into every imaginable configuration. And water openly embraces the volume of all things that enter it, yielding to every surface and shape, enveloping a thing completely or, if it is in motion, gliding around it. As I walk Big River, I watch tumbling streams effortlessly flow around several large boulders and then just as easily accept a tossed stone. I think the unique properties of water have a lot to teach us about living in balance with the planet, each other, and our very own nature. After all, at an average of 70 percent liquid, we are primarily unmoored water strolling about this planet.

Humans are as much a part of the cosmic movement of Earth's lifeblood as are the plants, animals, and oceans. Water is moving through all of our bodies in one giant circulation. We, and I mean the big We of all growing, moving, living beings of Earth, are literally sharing Earth's water, and these are the same waters that existed millions of years ago.

As the most ubiquitous element of our physical embodiment and the very life force of our home in this galaxy, perhaps there is a message bubbling up from its depths that deserves our full attention at least for a moment: Given our makeup of 70 percent water, we are, in fact, more like each other than not. No matter our ancestry, ethnicity, religion, nationality, or DNA, we are most essentially water.

♦ ♦ ♦

The guiding ways of water can be found everywhere. There is an indigenous saying that the moon is the heart of the forest. Beyond just poetic imagery, the moon is, in fact, directly affecting the movement of water in all the trees and plants of the forest, gravitationally, pumping as a heart does. Biologists have studied how water moves and expands in trees and how, in addition to suction and ionic bonding, this movement might be linked to the cycles of the moon and the corresponding forces of lunar gravitational pull. While plants and trees devoutly look to the cycles of the moon for their rhythm in rise and fall, so, too, do the oceanic tides. Can we humans, as personal vessels of water, disbelieve that we are deeply influenced by these same lunar-water cycles?

Only modern humans have attempted to defile water's natural flow, straightening it into rigid pipes, suppressing mighty river gyrations behind huge walled dams, and subjugating waterways to linear cement canals.

Since 1950, as the demand for water globally has more than tripled, the number of major dams worldwide has grown from 5,000 to 45,000. Many rivers have been drained dry because water is lost through evaporation in dammed reservoirs, and then diverted and siphoned off all along the length of a river, drastically decreasing or altogether stopping the flow.

In her book Last Oasis, Sandra Postel of the Global Water Policy Project tells us, "The Nile in Egypt, the Ganges in South Asia, the Amu Dar'ya and Syr Dar'ya in Central Asia, the Yellow River in China, and the Colorado River in North America are among the major rivers that are so dammed, diverted, or overtapped that little or no fresh water reaches its final destination for significant stretches of time."

As a Californian, I am painfully aware of my state's participation in the hijacking and heartbreak of the Colorado River. What happens to the well-being and very spirit of the water when we stop its primordial, sacred flow?

Water must move to live; it is its nature to be in vibrant motion. I cannot help but think that damming rivers is a great offense to the wild rights belonging to water. We speak, as we certainly must, about the universal human right to water, but I wish to add that we need to address water having its own rights. I believe that an inherent benefit of respecting the right of water to remain as undisturbed as possible will be the rediscovery of our own ecological and spiritual equipoise with this sacred element.

Our ever-expanding industrial civilization uses water without restraint in almost every aspect of manufacturing and as a waste container for every contaminant imaginable. Today, due to chemical poisoning of waterways and waterborne diseases, millions of people die annually. A 2010 United Nations Environment Program study reports that at least 1.8 million of these fatalities are children under 5 years old — that is, one child every 20 seconds. Maude Barlow, director of the Blue Planet Project, warns us, "The destruction of aquatic ecosystem health, and the increasing water scarcity, are ... the most pressing environmental problems facing humankind."

Although in water-wealthy countries problems of scarcity are often hidden, most of the world is currently thirsting for pure, clean water to drink. People in many countries, most often the women, must walk for miles each day to collect water for their immediate needs, carrying containers that can weigh up to 50 pounds when they are full. Sadly, the hard-won water is often polluted and sickens the household. It is no wonder people in these regions are shocked to learn that other people flush their toilets with clean water.

Even though 70 percent of our Earth's surface is water, the main portion of it, 97 percent, is salt water. Much of the remaining 3 percent that is fresh is held in snow and glaciers, leaving about 1 percent available. Unabated pollution is reducing the purity of this invaluable 1 percent. Further, the impact of climate change is increasing hot spots around the planet, while watershed runoff is being reduced from shrinking glaciers and fewer wet snowpacks. The ways of water are increasingly reflecting our human actions through a multitude of extremes: from long-term droughts and unseasonable floods to rising sea levels.

As we look toward mitigating increasing water crises, we can no longer do so in isolation from the climate crisis, scientifically or politically.

At the same time, our human populations are rapidly growing, and scientists predict that by 2020, 35 nations will experience severe water shortages. Already, a third of Earth's population is struggling as a result of inadequate freshwater supplies. It is important to remember that there is the same amount of water on our planet now as there was thousands of years ago, but the number of people has greatly increased. We need to listen to what the water is telling us and develop a new consciousness about this life-giving element. Good water practices are at the core of a viable Earth etiquette.

The importance of working together as a world community is one of the messages that water seems to be telling us. Mikhail Gorbachev, former president of the Soviet Union and current president of Green Cross International, wrote in the foreword to *Water, The Drop of Life*: "Without water security, social, economic and national stability are imperiled. This is magnified where water is shared across borders — and becomes crucial where water stress exists in regions of religious, territorial or ethnic tension. Thus we are faced with a mighty challenge."

Water molecules do not exist individually, on their own; it is their very nature to be in continuous relationship with one another. At this poignant moment, can the global community, following water's example, address our challenges collectively and come together with a new understanding of water as a sacred commons?

We have an opportunity to respond now in a timely and creative manner with healthy community relations to successfully navigate cross-border water conflicts and to help people who are suffering from an immediate lack of water resources. There are myriad innovative water resource solutions. Villagers in the small Chilean coastal town of Chungungo, with the help of Canadian engineers, followed nature's example, installing huge mesh nets in the mountains above the village to act like the eucalyptus trees in the area and catch coastal fog. The droplets are funneled into pipes that carry the sky water into tanks for Chungungo. Similar fog-collecting projects have been developed in Mexico, Croatia, Nepal, and other countries, and in both urban and rural areas around the world rainwater catchment is a growing source of water conservation and collection.

New technologies will certainly be instrumental in resolving transboundary issues. Speaking at the eighth Stockholm World Water Symposium, Jerome Delli Priscoli, senior adviser at the U.S. Army Corps of Engineers Institute for Water Resources, explained that through satellite technologies, countries sharing watersheds have the ability to accurately view the water use in an entire region, leading to more openness and clarity in negotiations, as there is no longer the possibility of secreting data.

Priscoli went on to state, "The symbolic content of water as cleansing, healing, rebirth, and reconciliation can provide a powerful tool for cooperation and symbolic acts of reconciliations so necessary to conflict resolution in other areas of society. . . . Rekindling the sense of sacred water ... is one way to facilitate the escalation of debate on water cooperation to higher levels and thus impact the capacity to reach cooperation and to manage conflict."

Understanding that water is sacred and the very essence of life is universal to indigenous cultures. This is also true of people who live close to the land, as any farmer will tell you. Because of this respect, many societies have acknowledged water as a shared commons. In our consumer-market-driven world, however, water is increasingly becoming a commodity for sale, accessible only to those who can afford it. Citizens in communities worldwide are taking a stand to protect their local water basins from commoditization and are learning how best to defend and care for this irreplaceable source of life.

Around the world people continue to practice a multitude of life-honoring water ceremonies: Mongolians high in the Altai Mountains, Taoists in China, Aboriginal people in Australia, First Nations people in the Americas — and many other indigenous people. Aboriginal elders from diverse lands tell us that these water ceremonies are, in fact, keeping the world alive, while both Jews and Christians have rituals of water purification that are central to their beliefs. In Japan, the water ritual of the tea ceremony is practiced daily. The Koran says, "By means of water, we give life to everything" (21:30).

I need to remember these traditions and stories when I am bathing, cleaning, drinking, and washing at my home, bringing this respect to the water that touches my skin. I want to simply and unshyly say, I love water. It is a love that I find is universal among all people.

From snow-capped mountains to white-capped sea, there are multitudes of bodies of moving water, our Earth's lifeblood flowing through tens of thousands of veins. This yet-untamed liquid landscape moves through our hearts to the heart of the great ocean, and so I am hopeful because the heart is the most trusted place of power — it has the courage to be vulnerable, humble, and unafraid; strong, loyal, and unflinching.

In this way, we can make our stand by water.

Osprey Orielle Lake is the founder and director of the Women's Earth and Climate Caucus and an international advocate for the Global Alliance for the Rights of Nature. This article is excerpted from *Uprisings for the Earth: Reconnecting Culture with Nature* by Osprey Orielle Lake (White Cloud Press), the recipient of a 2011 Nautilus Book Award.

HOW YOUR DIET CONTRIBUTES TO WATER POLLUTION

By Paul Greenberg

If you were to go looking for a magnificent American body of water worthy of an epic end-to-end swim, Lake Champlain might be it. Carved out of high country by glaciers, fed by Green Mountain brooks and icy Adirondack springs, it stretches 120 miles, forming much of the border between New York and Vermont. It provides drinking water for 145,000 people. But in 2004, when clean-water activist Christopher Swain swam the full length, he was immediately confronted by the truth: Lake Champlain was anything but pristine. "I swam through clouds of manure runoff that were kind of slippery and sticky at the same time," Swain recalls. "I could smell the fertilizer, when it was pouring down rain. There was this lawn-and-garden chemically smell." In the northern reaches of the lake, he swam through blue-green algae. In the south, he encountered invasive aquatic weeds that entangled him. At another point, he felt a tingling on his leg, "like a cellphone buzzing in my pocket." It turned out to be a sea lamprey, an eel-like, parasitic fish, trying to suck his blood.

The stink, the animal feces, the algae blooms, even the lamprey were all "things that didn't belong here but now had the run of the place," Swain says. Many could be linked to nutrients that leach from farms upstream and fertilizers flowing from fields and lawns, making their way into streams and eventually the lake. This persistent ooze of waste has been steadily rising over the last century, changing the lake's ecology and stimulating the growth of blue-green algae, which can prove fatal to dogs and toxic to humans. Beach closures have become an annual summer event in part due to the toxic algae, setting up a conflict between those like Swain who prize Champlain for its recreational opportunities and those who make a living by growing food in the watershed.

But Champlain is just one lake in a much larger struggle. Today the U.S. Environmental Protection Agency rates nearly half of all American rivers and streams as "poor," with 46 percent of water bodies overloaded with phosphorus and 41 percent with nitrogen, much of which flows off farms in the form of fertilizers, manure and soil. These farm-born pollutants overwhelm the Susquehanna River and the Chesapeake Bay that it feeds; they choke the San Joaquin on down to San Francisco Bay; and they punish the Mississippi River ecosystem all the way south to the Gulf of Mexico, where excess nutrients stimulate the growth of oxygen-sucking algae, which in turn create an annual dead zone bigger than the state of Connecticut. The complex array of problems tied to this pollution not only pits die-hard greens against regulatory-averse farmers, but fishermen against dairy producers, neighbor against neighbor. With the Trump administration in Washington viewing clean water regulations as a symbol of regulatory overreach, these conflicts are poised to rise to a fever pitch.

LEGISLATING BETTER WATER

In today's political climate, it might be hard to believe that at one time the country was nearly unified in the fight for clean water. In 1972, Congress overrode President Nixon's veto and passed what is commonly called the Clean Water Act, one of the country's most significant environmental laws, which continues to shape water quality to this day. Ohio's Cuyahoga River no longer catches fire from dumped petrochemicals (the 1969 fire became a symbol that helped launch the environmental movement). A corporation can no longer dump oil in the ocean and walk away scot-free. The billions BP paid to settle claims from the 2010 Gulf spill are a direct result of the Clean Water Act's provisions. That's because the Clean Water Act subjected polluters that directly discharge waste into America's waterways to permitting, fines and potential lawsuits if they fail to comply with regulations. These were designated as "point source" polluters, because the sewer pipe, or wastewater plant, could be easily identified as the source.

But the act also defined "nonpoint source" pollution, which arises from diffuse sources, such as irrigation ditches that carry fertilizer into rivers, or dry streambeds that can channel cow manure into rivers after a heavy storm. Significantly, agriculture won an exemption under the Clean Water Act, which meant that nonpoint pollution from agricultural sources could continue unchecked. Attempts to limit or more precisely define this exemption are often framed as an attack on farmers by bureaucratic regulators and environmentalists. So progress in cleaning up water often stalls and conflict persists.

But Vermont, in its typically iconoclastic way, has tried to bridge the opposing camps. Starting a few years before Christopher Swain was stroking across Champlain's murky surface, state regulators sought common ground to take action and restore the lake. The resulting water-protection rules have been exemplary. If the Trump administration succeeds at rolling back federal water regulations, Vermont and Lake Champlain may well serve as an example for other states that want to clean up their local waters while keeping farmers solvent.

UPSTREAM ON THE FARM

Guy Choiniere is a third-generation Vermont dairy farmer based in the village of Highgate Center. His operation, which is certified organic, sits on 450 acres of rolling land that today is an incarnation of the well-managed farm. Grasses of a half dozen varieties flutter in the light breezes, 100 healthy cows loll in the fields and rest peacefully in the loafing barns, and a robust buffer of woods and shrubs guides the eye down to the Rock River, which meanders to nearby Lake Champlain. But 15 years ago, Choiniere's farm was an exposed swath of mud and manure — just the sort of farm that would be a source of nonpoint water pollution and a direct threat to Vermont's great lake.

"There wasn't a blade of grass on those riverbanks," Choiniere comments as he ambles over clover and vetch. "The cows were destroying it. There were landslides every other year. Conservation is about keeping your soil and your minerals on your own farm. And that's exactly what I wasn't doing. I attracted attention long before these rules were mandated" — because of fertilizers and manure he routinely spread on his fields that leached into the Rock River.

Guy Choiniere's farm shows how agricultural pollution built up not just over years but centuries. Choiniere is of Quebecois heritage and his French predecessors were the first white men to colonize the valley after Samuel de Champlain "found" it in 1609. The farm, like the rest of the Champlain Valley, had been covered in forest, which the settlers cleared, starting the first big pulse of pollution into the lake.

Cleared trees and dairy cows, however, weren't the only source of the lake's rising levels of nutrient pollution. An even more potent vector arose by the time Choiniere's father carved out his farm from the family land: "My dad took over in the '60s and that's when corn took over," Choiniere explains. His father followed conventional advice to rely on feed and reduce the time cows spent on pasture eating grass, with the goal of pumping more milk from the cows. "As cows' genetics improved we were milking heavier so we had to satisfy their energy needs," Choiniere says. "And corn became a nice energy source. Cows love it."

But corn — with all the fertilizers and pesticides it takes to produce — is an exceptional burden on waterways. Unlike pasture, which keeps ground covered in grass year-round and the soil intact, corn requires plowing and added nutrients to pump up yields. To supplement soil with nitrogen and phosphorus, farmers spread cow manure, never in short supply on a dairy farm, as well as chemical fertilizer on their plowed fields. Through the winter snow and spring rains, fields are kept bare — meaning that the exposed soil can wash away. Besides adding sediment to the watershed, the soil has phosphorus bound up in it, adding to the nutrient load. Until the early 2000s, most Vermont corn was grown this way. Even though their goal was to fertilize corn, farmers were inadvertently overfertilizing Lake Champlain.

AT WATER LEVEL

Phosphorus and nitrogen stimulate plant growth, which is why farmers spread them on their fields. But when rains wash fertilizers and manure into streams and lakes, these nutrients feed microscopic algae. During warm weather, they proliferate at a tremendous rate in "algae blooms."

They're an eyesore, turning lakes bright green and portions of ocean, such as the Gulf of Mexico, red. These algae consist of multiple species, some harmful, others benign. They foul shorelines, lakes and rivers. Particularly worrisome is blue-green algae, which is technically a bacteria known as cyanobacteria. These microorganisms can produce toxins that kill fish, mammals and birds. Across the country, dogs have died after swimming in lakes and rivers choked with blue-green algae. People have also been sickened, because under certain conditions, the algae emit toxins that can cause rashes, respiratory symptoms, diarrhea and intestinal pain, and with long-term exposure, may harm the liver and digestive system.

Preliminary research at Dartmouth College has linked cyanobacteria toxins to ALS (Lou Gehrig's disease). Researchers mapped higher-density clusters of people with ALS across northern New England near lakes with the lowest water quality that are likely to have harmful algae blooms. The researchers suspect that toxic algae blooms may play a causal role in clusters of the neurodegenerative disorder. But they warn against overreacting, saying that swimming in fouled water once won't cause the disease. If there is a connection between ALS and cyanobacteria it likely involves long-term exposure to cyanobacteria, as well as a genetic predisposition to the disease and other environmental or chemical triggers.

Though this research sounds scary, it is not conclusive at this point, and many other potential factors could have caused the ALS clusters. "We agree that there should be rigorous research into that devastating disease, but this hypothesis about a linkage with a particular amino acid in cyanobacteria is not supported," says Vermont state toxicologist Sarah Vose, Ph.D.

Although Vermont authorities say there are no records of serious human health effects from blue-green algae on Lake Champlain, beach closures occur every summer, impacting the $300 million in annual recreational revenue from vacationing families, watersports enthusiasts and fishermen. Cyanobacteria isn't the only culprit: E. coli from livestock, pets and untreated sewage can foul the lake too. By the early 2000s, beach closures were common — between 2012 and 2014, there were more than 60 closures.

Algae — both toxic and nontoxic species — are harmful in other ways too. In warm weather, the blooms shade out more benign aquatic plant life. Once the algae die off in winter, waterborne bacteria gobble them up and multiply, consuming oxygen from the water and choking fish and other species. By springtime, a pond suffering from nonpoint source pollution and algae blooms may be effectively dead. Were this just occurring in Lake Champlain, the concerns would perhaps not travel further than the state legislature. But the blooms occur in nearly every state, peaking in August and September, though no national agency tracks them — or the illnesses they cause.

The Gulf of Mexico's oxygen-poor "dead zone," for example, comes like clockwork each summer as nutrients flow from the heartland and out the mouth of the Mississippi River into the Gulf. This feeds the Karenia brevis algae that cause "red tide." State agencies closely monitor red tide, closing shellfish beds and limiting fishing to ensure contaminated seafood doesn't make it to consumers. The states surrounding the Chesapeake Bay have tried, for decades, to address nonpoint pollution and algae blooms, but annually receive failing marks on water quality, much to the chagrin of seafood lovers. In the Midwest, favorite summer lake-recreation spots suffer because visitors can't enjoy waters fouled with blue-green algae.

And then there's drinking water. In 2014, the city of Toledo shut down its water supply, forcing it to truck in bottled water, because of blue-green algae that engulfed the western end of Lake Erie. (Vermont, New York and Quebec have been mostly successful at treating the 20 million gallons of water that's drawn from Lake Champlain each day for algae and other pollutants.)

Des Moines, Iowa, faces a related crisis, spending millions of dollars each summer so its water utility can clear drinking water of nitrates, which arise from fertilizer runoff and can be especially harmful to infants and small children. "Look at the culverts discharging [agricultural runoff] into the Raccoon River" — the main source of drinking water for 500,000 people, says Des Moines Water Works utility manager Bill Stowe. "They have the exact same configuration as if they were coming out of a city storm-sewer system. But thanks to our friends at EPA, agriculture has an exemption for stormwater discharge under the Clean Water Act." The utility sued three northern Iowa counties to block upstream agricultural pollutants, but a federal judge dismissed the closely watched suit in March 2017. The judge said it was up to the Iowa state legislature to act.

SUING TO SAVE OUR WATERS

Guy Choiniere would never say that the Clean Water Act or any regulation caused him to completely rethink his way of farming. Like most good farmers, he senses, almost preternaturally, what his land needs. As the Clean Water Act's co-drafter Thomas Jorling notes, "Farmers tend to be much more knowledgeable about natural systems than people who've gotten a Ph.D."

But the aspirations of the Clean Water Act and the failsafe devices baked into the legislation made a radical change economically feasible in a state like Vermont — even when it involved rethinking agriculture. Jorling, then a Senate staffer, and the other drafters of the act recognized that "government agencies have a tendency to become paralyzed by complexity or funding." So they wrote the Clean Water Act in such a way that there was no legal wiggle room if water quality fell below an acceptable threshold. In other words, if the powers that be are not doing their job to keep the water clean, the act allows them to be sued. The "civil suits" provision in the act gave the people of New England legal recourse when the water in Lake Champlain became unacceptable. Which is exactly what happened.

In 2002, the state of Vermont proposed phosphorus limits for the lake to comply with the Clean Water Act, setting a "Total Maximum Daily Load" (TMDL) that marks a threshold for the maximum amount of pollutants that a body of water can handle each day. But the evolving science on the matter convinced the nonprofit Conservation Law Foundation that these limits were insufficient to stop the algae blooms and protect the ecology of the lake. So in 2008, the foundation sued the EPA, arguing that the Feds needed to step in, revise Vermont's limits and fund measures to reduce the flow of nutrients into the lake. The EPA and the state eventually agreed to set a lower TMDL for the lake, which was issued in 2016.

Since the bulk of the lake nutrients arise from farms, the state realized it had to focus on that source. Luckily federal conservation grants are available to farmers, paying for water-protecting measures, such as streamside vegetation buffers. These USDA grants, which increased from 2002 through 2014, can amount to hundreds of thousands of dollars for even small farmers. Funded every five years under the massive Farm Bill, they have a good chance of surviving in the Trump era because of support by Republican lawmakers in Congress. The money, after all, flows to farm-state constituents.

In Vermont, federal programs work in tandem with the state's water-cleaning Act 64. Passed in 2015, the law required all farms to start using specific farming techniques to reduce runoff by July 2017. Even farms with fewer than 50 animals must use practices like manure injection, underground catchments for stormwater runoff and extension of streamside forested buffers — all measures that are designed to protect the watershed and can often be funded under federal farm programs.

HOPE FOR THE FUTURE

The impact of well-placed farming subsidies and water-quality management laws are now evident on many farms in Vermont. At Lorenzo Whitcomb's conventional dairy farm just outside of Burlington, he sows winter rye as a cover crop over his harvested cornfield. In just 10 years, cover crops in Vermont have gone from 50 to 25,000 acres. On the southern end of the lake in Orwell, where 24-year-old Rachel Orr has taken over from her father to run their 200-cow dairy farm, the young farmer produces a dictionary-thick "nutrient management plan" that pinpoints her soil types down to the square foot and indicates precisely the amount of fertilizer that needs to be applied. All of these different efforts were co-funded by federal and state matching grants.

> "Being sustainable is money in my pocket. That's the name of the game for staying in business."
>
> — Guy Choiniere

But most impressive is Guy Choiniere's organic farm. When farm inspectors first started snooping around his property in the late 1990s, he admitted it was hard to take. "Someone coming onto your farm and telling you you've got problems is very insulting," Choiniere recalls, echoing a common complaint of farmers. "We had to get over that." Ten years later, strolling through his pastures, it is clear he is very much over it. Beneath his barn, catchments slow drain water and cause it to percolate slowly through the soil, filtering out nutrients. Up ahead is a cow path that had previously been a mudslide but has been reworked as a tidy, erosion-proof stone lane. And leading down to the river itself is a lush forest planted with the most efficient trees for absorbing nutrients before they can hit the river and fertilize an algae bloom. All this was partially financed by an active federal and state government grant program, including $250,000 from the USDA's Natural Resources Conservation Service. Choiniere chipped in around half of the bill for the improvements — eager to grow his business and lighten his farm's footprint.

Eventually Choiniere took a leap of faith and went a step further than the government required. He went organic and planted his cornfields back into native pasture. Since pasture is never tilled, it holds the soil and nutrients better than an annual crop like corn. And there are other benefits. His vet bills have plummeted now that his animals are 100 percent grass-fed. The price he earns from his milk has risen 15 percent and he spends nothing on tilling. "Being sustainable is money in my pocket," he says, as he looks out over his lush fields. "That's the name of the game for staying in business. Agribusiness will give you recommendations all day long. How much fertilizer to use. How much grain to feed... Me, I went with my instincts."

In other words, in a bid for water quality, measures were put in place that ultimately improved farming and, in Choiniere's case, profitability. But even farmers who have not gone organic or reverted to pasture have taken basic but effective steps. And those successful in controlling their nonpoint pollution have seen profits rise, says Ryan Patch, ag development coordinator for Vermont's Agency of Agriculture, Food and Markets. He oversaw many of the state's listening sessions with farmers leading up to Act 64 and recalled a number of "aha" moments when farmers would suddenly exclaim, after a nutrient-management training course, "You just saved me $10,000 in fertilizer!" Savings arose because nutrients were applied more judiciously and kept on the farm instead of washing into Lake Champlain.

Of course not everybody in the agricultural community is on board. Plans to reduce nutrient runoff hit roadblocks last year, when farmers sought more time to implement the kind of measures that Choiniere champions. Across-the-board change, it seems, won't come easily.

Nor will it come fast. Although some streams running into the lake show marked improvement, others continue to exceed their nutrient limits. And portions of the lake remain far above target levels for phosphorus, meaning a continued pattern of toxic algae blooms, summer beach closures and dead zones for aquatic life. But Patch, for one, takes a long view. "I am optimistic about the road map we've laid out," he says, speaking of the state's plans. "We'll do it with the help of the farms." He also notes that the lake is dealing with centuries of human impacts — all the latent pollution from logging, erosion and residential development — that "won't be able to be addressed until we shut the faucet off" from all the farms upstream. Patch and other officials estimate that it will take 20 years to close the tap for good, and once that's done, they can begin to reduce the residual nutrients in the lake.

Will the rest of the country, facing similar water-quality crises, follow suit? In these tumultuous times, with environmental regulations under siege from the White House, the paths that individual states and the federal government take on water quality may diverge. Vermont, as its most famous poet, Robert Frost, once wrote, is taking the road "less traveled by." Whether other states head down that road, too, will determine how clean our nation's water will be in the future.

Paul Greenberg is the *New York Times* bestselling author of *Four Fish and American Catch*. A regular contributor to the *Times* and many other publications, Mr. Greenberg is the featured correspondent and co-writer of the 2017 PBS Frontline documentary *The Fish On My Plate*. The winner of a James Beard Award for Writing and Literature and a National Endowment for the Arts Literature Fellowship, Mr. Greenberg has been featured on Fresh Air with Terry Gross and his TED Talk has over a million views to date.

YOUR VIRTUAL WATER FOOTPRINT

Often when people think about their water footprints, they only think about the water they use from the taps in their houses. But everything you touch uses water in the manufacturing process, from clothes, to electronics to food. This hidden water is called "virtual water," and, as award-winning environmental journalist and author Stephen Leahy says in *Your Water Footprint: The Shocking Facts About How Much Water We Use to Make Everyday Products*, "each of us uses far more virtual water than the 'regular' water we can see, feel and taste." On average, Americans use 100 gallons of regular water everyday, and 1980 gallons of virtual water. Below are the water footprints of some common things we use or consume every day.

Cutting back on consumption of manufactured goods reduces the number of products that are made, in turn reducing the amount of water used in factories. Additionally, recycling the products we've already used can have a positive effect. For example, you can save about 3.5 gallons of water just by recycling a pound a paper — the same amount found in a typical daily newspaper. By doing little things like eating lower on the food chain, buying only things we need and buying used whenever possible, recycling at home, reusing items when we can and using fewer plastic bags and paper towels, we can greatly reduce our virtual water footprints.

	Virtual Gallons of Water
It takes 24 gallons of water to make 1 pound of another everyday material: **plastic**. In fact, it takes at least twice as much water to produce a plastic water bottle as the amount of water in the water bottle.	24
Your morning cup of **coffee** (8 fluid ounces) requires 37 gallons of virtual water to produce.	37
One cup of **black tea** using one teabag, on the other hand, needs 9 gallons of virtual water to grow, process, and brew.	9
The water footprint of one **disposable diaper** is 144 gallons. A reuseable cloth diaper's footprint is just four gallons. (Though the cotton required for one of these diapers is 198 gallons, the simple fact that it will be reused up to 50 times brings that number down.)	144
It takes 2000 gallons of water to grow the cotton for and manufacture one pair of **jeans**. (Not included in that number is the water you'll use to wash your jeans throughout your time owning them.)	2,000
Producing two pounds of **bananas** requires 209 gallons of water (84 percent is for growing; the rest is accounted for in washings before sale). It works out to roughly 42 gallons per banana!	42
A 750-milliliter bottle of **whisky** requires 322 gallons of water.	322
It takes half a gallon of water to produce a **single pasta noodle**.	1/2
Making two pounds of **paper** requires 793 gallons of water — so think before you print!	793
Producing one **smartphone** — everything from mining metals to polishing the glass screens to making microchips — requires 240 gallons of water.	240
Making two pounds of **beef** requires 4068 gallons of water. Feed for the livestock accounts for 99 percent of that massive footprint.	4,068
It takes 75,000 gallons of water to produce one ton of steel. Since the average car contains about 2,150 pounds of steel, that means over 80,000 gallons of water is needed to produce the finished steel for **one car**. The gasoline that fuels a car also requires water consumption: approximately 1 to 2.5 gallons of water is used in the process of refining a gallon of gasoline.	80,000

Sources: http://mentalfloss.com/article/59480/surprising-water-footprints-15-common-things
http://www.gracelinks.org/285/the-hidden-water-in-everyday-products

WATER AND CLIMATE CHANGE

By the Union of Concerned Scientists

Water in its various forms is always on the move, in a complex process known as the water cycle. Global warming is already having a measurable effect on this cycle, altering the amount, distribution, timing, and quality of available water. Water users — from communities, to industries, to ecosystems — are in turn affected: their activities and functions depend, either directly or indirectly, on water.

CHANGE IS UNDERWAY

With climate change, the water cycle is expected to undergo significant change. For example, a warmer climate causes more water to evaporate from both land and oceans; in turn, a warmer atmosphere can hold more water — roughly four percent more water for every 1°F rise in temperature. Changes like this are expected to lead to specific, and in many cases negative, consequences. Some parts of the U.S. — in particular, the Northeast and Midwest — can expect increased precipitation and runoff, especially in winter and spring, leading to increased flooding. Other areas — notably the Southwest — can expect less precipitation, especially in the warm months, and longer, more severe droughts as storm tracks shift northward leaving arid areas increasingly dry.

RAIN VERSUS SNOW CAN MAKE A CRITICAL DIFFERENCE

The form that precipitation takes is also subject to change in response to warming: climate projections

WATCH THIS VIDEO!
Learn more about watersheds by watching "What Is a Watershed?" by Caring for Our Watersheds.
tinyurl.com/whatisawatershed

You can find out more about your own watershed at **water.usgs.gov/wsc/map_index. html**

Then, answer the following questions:

1. In what watershed do you live?
2. What are the most prominent water concerns in your area: drought, flooding, pollution, access, security, privatization?
3. What are your watershed's geographic boundaries?
4. What bodies of water and geological features are in your watershed?
5. Where do the boundaries of your watershed differ from town, city, county or state boundaries? Does your tap water come from this watershed?
6. If not, what watershed does it come from?
7. Does the water from your watershed drain into the ocean? Where does your wastewater go?

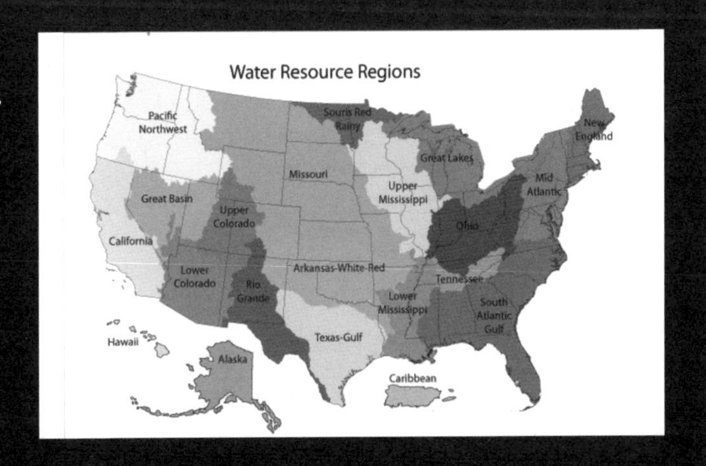

for many regions of North America suggest less snow, overall, and more rain. In areas dependent on the gradual melting of snowpack to supply surface water through the warm months, this means lower flows and greater water stress in summer — a trend already in evidence in parts of the western U.S. While the effects of climate change on groundwater are not fully understood, rising water competition and stress at the surface are likely to drive greater use — and overuse — of this resource.

Overall, wet areas are expected to become wetter and dry areas drier, placing additional stress on the nation's over-taxed water systems as well as water-dependent sectors.

WATER QUALITY AFFECTS PEOPLE AND ECOSYSTEMS

Declining water quality is another consequence of climate change. Water temperature, for example, will generally rise in streams, lakes, and reservoirs as air temperature rises. This tends to lead to lower levels of dissolved oxygen in water, hence more stress on the fish, insects, crustaceans and other aquatic animals that rely on oxygen. As more — and more intense — precipitation leads to increased runoff in certain regions, we can also expect more pollution to be washed into our waterways: sediments, nitrogen from agriculture, disease pathogens, pesticides, and herbicides. Naturally, the pollution load in streams and rivers will tend to be carried to larger bodies of water downstream — lakes, estuaries, and the coastal ocean — where one of the more dramatic consequences of heavy runoff can be blooms of harmful algae and bacteria.

THE TIDE IS RISING

One of the starkest effects of climate change is the anticipated rise in sea level worldwide. This occurs for two main reasons — the expansion of the ocean as it warms, and the increased melt from ice sheets, ice caps and glaciers. Along with alarming threats to coastal communities, infrastructure, economies and ecosystems, this rise has implications for available freshwater, as rising sea levels drive saltwater into freshwater aquifers. To be useful for drinking or irrigating, more water from our aquifers, then, would need to be treated, usually by energy-intensive processes. Given the wide range of human activities that depend — directly or indirectly — on water, future climate-driven changes in water resources will affect many aspects of our lives.

The Union of Concerned Scientists (UCS) was founded in 1969 by scientists and students at the Massachusetts Institute of Technology. UCS put rigorous science to work to build a healthier planet and a safer world.

THE OCEANS ARE DROWNING IN PLASTIC — AND NO ONE'S PAYING ATTENTION

By Dominique Mosbergen

Imagine an area 34 times the size of Manhattan. Now imagine it covered ankle-deep in plastic waste — piles of soda bottles and plastic bags, takeout containers by the mile, drinking straws as far as the eye can see.

That's a total of about 19 billion pounds of garbage. And according to one of the best estimates available, that's how much plastic waste ends up in our oceans every year.

"We're being overwhelmed by our waste," said Jenna Jambeck, an environmental engineer who led the 2015 study that determined this staggering number. According to Jambeck's research, this figure is on track to double by 2025 unless something is done, swiftly and at a global scale, to stem the tide of garbage.

Plastic — a versatile, durable and inexpensive material — has in many ways been a boon to humanity, used in everything from medical equipment to parts of airplanes. But some of the very traits that have made plastics so popular (they're cheap, and therefore easy to throw away) have also made them a growing problem in our landfills and oceans. Today, plastics are the No. 1 type of trash found in the sea. Ocean Conservancy, a nonprofit that organizes an annual coastal cleanup event in more than 150 countries worldwide, said plastic debris makes up around 85 percent of all the trash collected from beaches, waterways and oceans — and that's just the stuff we can see.

There are also untold numbers of extremely small plastic fragments in marine waters. Plastics are non-biodegradable and merely break down into smaller and smaller pieces with exposure to sunlight. These fragments, known as microplastics, are less than 5 millimeters long, or about the size of a sesame seed. Some are microbeads, tiny pieces of plastic that are added as exfoliants to health and beauty products, while others come from larger plastic pieces that have degraded over time.

Recent studies have found that microplastics can also get washed out of synthetic clothing, like those made of polyester or acrylic. A 2016 paper concluded that a single cycle of a washing machine could release more than 700,000 microplastic fibers into the environment.

The United Nations Environment Programme says there could be as many as 51 trillion microplastic particles in our seas. Many of them have accumulated in five enormous swirling ocean convergences known as gyres. Marcus Eriksen, a co-founder of the 5 Gyres Institute, an organization dedicated to reducing plastic pollution, describes marine microplastics as a "plastic smog throughout the world's oceans."

FROM LAND TO THE SEA

So, how does all this plastic waste end up in the oceans?

Some of it comes from ships and offshore oil and gas platforms, but more than 80 percent of plastic waste in the oceans comes from land. Activities like the deliberate dumping of garbage into waterways and water pollution by plastic manufacturers contribute to some of this ocean trash, but mismanaged waste disposal appears to be the primary culprit.

In 2010, according to Jambeck's research, over 50 percent of waste in more than 60 countries worldwide was found to be inadequately managed, mostly due to a lack of waste management infrastructure coupled with ballooning populations. In China, Indonesia, Vietnam, Thailand and the Philippines — which were identified in a 2015 Ocean Conservancy report as the top five plastic-polluting nations in the world — the amount of mismanaged waste was closer to 75 percent or more.

Developing nations don't bear all the blame: The United States has an ocean pollution problem, too. The main issue in this country is littering, according to Jambeck. "Even though we do have robust and effective waste management systems, we have litter," she said. "And because our per-person waste generation rate is so high in the U.S., even that small amount of litter contributes to this problem." The United States is one of the world's top five waste-generating developed countries, according to the World Economic Forum.

Litter that consists of single-use plastic products is a particularly troublesome source of ocean garbage — the plastic bag wafting in the wind that finds its way to a storm drain; the potato chip bag forgotten on a beach; the plastic soda bottle washed away in a stream that leads to a river and, finally, the sea.

Worldwide, "single-use packaging is the biggest source of trash" found in or near bodies of water, said Ocean Conservancy's Nick Mallos. In 2015, volunteers in the group's International Coastal Cleanup event collected almost 1 million plastic beverage bottles, 800,000 plastic bottle caps, and about half a million each of plastic bags and drinking straws — and this was in just a single day. The internet's best stories, and interviews with their authors.

THE NOT-VERY-LONG HISTORY OF PLASTICS

Though it seems now that the world couldn't possibly function without them, consumer plastics are a remarkably recent invention. The first plastic bags were introduced in the 1950s, the same decade that plastic packaging began gaining in popularity in the United States.

"What I think many people aren't aware of is just how

quickly the amount of plastic in the world has increased," said Jambeck, speaking from her home in Athens, Georgia, earlier this month. According to her research, global plastic resin production has increased by about 620 percent since 1975.

This growth has happened so fast, in fact, that science is still catching up with the change. Plastics pollution research, for instance, is still a very early science.

"We put all these plastics into the environment and we still don't really know what the outcomes are going to be," said Susanne Brander, an ecotoxicologist at the University of North Carolina at Wilmington who studies the impact of plastic pollution on humans and wildlife.

What we do know, though, is disturbing.

Ocean Conservancy says plastics are believed to threaten at least 600 different wildlife species. One in three leatherback turtles, which often mistake plastic bags for edible jellyfish, have been found with plastic in their bellies. In February, a dead whale beached on Norway's coast had 30 plastic bags in its stomach. Ninety percent of seabirds, including albatross and petrels, are now eating plastics on a regular basis. By 2050, that figure is expected to rise to 100 percent.

And it's not just wildlife that's threatened by the plastics in our seas. A growing body of evidence suggests humans are consuming plastics through the seafood we eat.

In one study, 1 in 4 fish that researchers purchased from fish markets in Indonesia and the United States during the second half of 2014 were found to have plastic in their guts. It appears that some fish are mistaking plastic fragments coated in bacteria and algae for normal food sources.

Studies have also found microplastics in the digestive systems of shellfish, including oysters, mussels and lobsters. Two Belgian researchers, looking at the amount of microplastics in some shellfish, concluded in 2014 that the average European seafood consumer could be eating 11,000 microplastics every year.

For now, the potential risks to human health posed by this plastic consumption are not totally clear — although preliminary research suggests some plastics could be toxic to humans, and could potentially increase the risk of cancer and liver damage, reproductive problems, and other negative health effects.

With this in mind, experts say that all of us have a critical role to play in mitigating the issue — in ways both big and small.

At a global level, several countries have recently committed to reducing the amount of plastic they send into the oceans. At the Economist World Ocean Summit this week, 10 nations — including Uruguay, Costa Rica, France and Indonesia — vowed to reduce plastic marine litter as part of U.N. Environment's new #CleanSeas initiative.

As part of the campaign, Indonesia, one of world's top plastic polluters, committed to slashing its marine litter by 70 percent by 2025. Uruguay said it will introduce a tax on single-use plastic bags later this year. The United States has yet to join the U.N. campaign.

But it's not just countries that need to do their part. Corporations also have a role, as do individuals (yes, you).

We can all start by thinking twice before we use single-use plastic products — and when we do use them, we should take care to properly dispose of them or recycle.

"The one thing I've learned in doing my research is that population density is a huge driver of ocean pollution, so especially in places with high population densities, our individual choices really do matter," Jambeck said. "Things that may seem mundane, like using a reusable bottle or a reusable bag — when taken collectively, these choices really do make a difference. I think it's empowering as a citizen to know that your choices can make an impact."

Dominique Mosbergen is a reporter at HuffPost covering climate change, extreme weather and extinction. Send tips or feedback to dominique.mosbergen@huffingtonpost.com or follow her on Twitter.

WATCH THIS VIDEO!
The Story of Bottled Water
storyofstuff.org/movies/story-of-bottled-water/

In five minutes, The Story of Bottled Water tells the story of manufactured demand — how you get Americans to buy more than half a billion bottles of water every week when it already flows virtually free from the tap — and explains how we can avoid bottled water and support public investment in clean, available tap water for all.

The Story of Stuff's nine award-winning animated movies have garnered more than 50 million online views around the world and encouraged viewers to support hundreds of environmental projects and campaigns with their time, energy and money.

A SEA OF PLASTIC

- A million plastic bottles are bought around the world every minute and the number will jump another 20% by 2021.
- 80 per cent of all litter in the oceans are made of plastic.
- As much as 51 trillion microplastic particles — 500 times more than stars in our galaxy — litter the seas.
- Animals can get tangled up in this trash or ingest it — either because they mistake it as prey or because the plastic has been broken down into tiny particles by seawater.
- Around 80 percent of marine litter actually originates on land — either swept in from the coastline or carried to rivers from the streets during heavy rain via storm drains and sewer overflows.
- It is projected that by 2050 there will be more plastic than fish in the ocean.

WHAT CAN WE DO?

- Stop intentional littering.
- Use reusable bags.
- Recycle.
- Clean up beaches and shorelines.
- Advocate for, enforce and strengthen legislation to stop marine litter.
- Ban smoking on beaches.
- Ban plastic bags.
- Invest in research to develop non-toxic material.
- Invest in waste management infrastructures.
- Show the true cost of plastic disposal on products.

Sources:
UN Environment
www.nrdc.org/stories/10-ways-reduce-plastic-pollution
www.theguardian.com/environment/2017/jun/28/a-million-a-minute-worlds-plastic-bottle-binge-as-dangerousas-climate-change

OCEAN ACIDIFICATION

By the Climate Reality Project

Climate change isn't the only consequence of carbon pollution from fossil fuels. If driving global temperature rise wasn't enough, increased carbon in our atmosphere is also behind the rapid acidification of our world's oceans.

But what exactly is ocean acidification? And what does it mean for marine ecosystems and for humans? The answers can be complicated. But before we get into the details, here are some quick facts that show why ocean acidification is a really big deal for our planet — and why we need to keep dirty fossils in the ground:

- Ninety-seven percent of the Earth's water is in the ocean. And the ocean covers more than 70 percent of the planet's surface.
- Since the beginning of the Industrial Revolution, oceans have absorbed an estimated 525 billion tons of carbon dioxide from the atmosphere.
- The Great Barrier Reef is bleaching rapidly due to climate change and ocean acidification, with only 7 percent of the reef unaffected by the most recent mass bleaching event.

SO, EXACTLY WHAT IS OCEAN ACIDIFICATION?

Our oceans are an incredible carbon sink — they absorb about 25 percent of the carbon dioxide humans produce every year. But this is changing sea surface chemistry dramatically: when carbon dioxide is absorbed by the ocean, it dissolves to form carbonic acid. The result, not surprisingly, is that the ocean becomes more acidic, upsetting the delicate pH balance that millions and millions of organisms rely on.

Since the Industrial Revolution, our seas have become about 30 percent more acidic, a rate not observed in 300 million years. This has a wide range of consequences for marine ecosystems, as well as for the billions of people who depend on the ocean for food and survival.

Oceans becoming more acidic after the Industrial Revolution is no accident. As humans burn more and more fossil fuels, the concentration of carbon dioxide in our atmosphere continues to rise, driving climate change and making both air and sea temperatures hotter and hotter.

But climate change isn't the only consequence of carbon pollution — so is ocean acidification. With more and more carbon dioxide in the atmosphere, oceans absorb more and more of it, becoming — you guessed it — more and more acidic.This is happening at an unprecedented rate and will continue unabated if we don't stop burning dirty fossil fuels.

WHAT ARE THE CONSEQUENCES OF OCEAN ACIDIFICATION?

Ocean acidification doesn't just threaten marine ecosystems. It also puts pressure on human food systems and affects the livelihood of people who depend on the ocean for their income in every way from fishing to tourism.

One reason why? Because as oceans become more acidic, some sea creatures have a more difficult time forming shells, including coral polyps. These are the "tiny builders" of coral reefs — when a polyp attaches to a rock on the seafloor, it divides into many clones and eventually creates a reef. Ocean acidification can slow the growth of coral skeletons, and make reefs more brittle and less resistant to stressors like warming water temperatures.

Keeping coral reefs healthy and growing is vital. Reefs protect our coastlines from erosion and flooding, support local economies through tourism and fisheries, and host vastly productive ecosystems. The US National Oceanic and Atmospheric Administration, for example, estimates that about half a billion people live within 100 kilometers of a coral reef and benefit from the protection and natural resources it offers. Globally, coral reefs may provide goods and services worth $375 billion each year, which means threats to reefs have profound ripple effects.

WHAT'S HAPPENING WHEN CORAL BECOMES BLEACHED?

You've probably heard a lot lately about mass coral bleaching events in places like the Great Barrier Reef. As NPR explains, "Coral bleaching occurs when the living organisms that make up coral reefs expel the colorful, photosynthetic algae that normally live inside their bodies, and provide them with food. Those algae give coral reefs their color and disappear when the reefs are exposed to stressful climatic conditions, such as temperatures even a few degrees higher than normal."

Coral reefs are considered to be the most biodiverse ecosystem on the planet. When coral is hit hard by both ocean acidification and climate change, so too are the many species that humans rely on for food. According to the United Nations Environmental Programme, "fish, including shellfish, contribute 15 percent of animal protein for 3 billion people worldwide. A further 1 billion people rely on fisheries for their primary source of protein."

IT'S EASY TO SEA: WE NEED TO TAKE CLIMATE ACTION FOR OUR OCEANS

Just like climate change, ocean acidification is already dramatically impacting people (and species) around the world. To save our oceans and stop climate change, we must transition away from burning dirty fossil fuels.

The Climate Reality Project's mission is to catalyze a global solution to the climate crisis by making urgent action a necessity across every level of society. The founder, Nobel Laureate and former US Vice President, Al Gore got the world talking about climate change with the Academy Award-winning film *An Inconvenient Truth.*

THE RACE TO SAVE FLORIDA'S DEVASTATED CORAL REEF FROM GLOBAL WARMING

By Chris Mooney

PICKLES REEF, Fla. — Twenty feet under water, Nature Conservancy biologist Jennifer Stein swims over to several large corals and pulls several laminated cards from her dive belt.

"Disease," reads one, as she gestures to a coral that exhibits white splotches. "Recent mortality," reads another card. Along the miles of coral reef off the Florida Keys, Stein and her fellow divers have found countless examples of this essential form of ocean life facing sickness and death.

The pattern of decay is shaping up as one of the sharpest impacts of climate change in the continental United States — and a direct threat to economic activity in the Keys, a haven for diving, fishing and coastal tourism.

The debate over climate change is often framed as one that pits jobs against the need to protect the planet for future generations. In deciding to exit the Paris climate agreement and roll back domestic environmental regulations, the Trump administration said it was working to protect jobs.

But what is happening here — as the warming of the sea devastates the coral reef — is a stark example of how rising temperatures can threaten existing economies.

The 113-mile-long Overseas Highway between the mainland and Key West — linking islands that themselves emerged from an ancient coral archipelago — is lined with marinas, bait and tackle shops and an abundance of seafood restaurants.

From the visitors who fill dive charters out of Key Largo to the local fishing industry's catches of spiny lobsters, grouper, snapper and other species, nearly everything in the Florida Keys is tied in some way to the reefs.

Diving, snorkeling, fishing, and eating seafood are among the key tourist activities that could be harmed if the reef continues to suffer damage.

Cece Roycraft and a partner own the Dive Key West shop, which sells scuba gear and runs boat charters. Their operation depends on a healthy reef system, because divers naturally are not as interested in exploring dead or damaged reefs, which do not attract as many fish and can be covered in algae. It is an economic reality accepted by residents of the Keys but not yet widely recognized by other Americans, she said.

"It's equal to the Yellowstone Park, okay?" said Roycraft, who worked to help create a federal program that certifies vessels that train their crews in proper coral protection practices, including following proper mooring rules and ensuring that divers do not poke and prod the reefs.

Tourism "is the economic engine of the Florida Keys. There is no other way for people to make money," Roycraft said.

Three and a half million people visit the Keys each year — nearly 47 for each of the area's 75,000 full-time residents. Tourism supplies 54 percent of all island jobs and fuels a $2.7 billion economy, according to Monroe County, which includes the Keys and a significant portion of Everglades National Park.

The importance attached to the reef system defies the usual political divides. Here in the Keys, people voted 51 percent to 44 percent in favor of Donald Trump in the presidential election — but they seem to differ from the president in their support for government-funded programs to protect the environment.

In March, amid fears that the administration might try to defund Environmental Protection Agency programs that protect the reef system, Monroe County's board of commissioners called for sustaining the EPA's role and declared in a board resolution that "a healthy marine environment is essential and the most important contributor to the economy of the Florida Keys."

The EPA's South Florida program, which received $1.7 million in federal funds in fiscal 2017, conducts coral surveys, studies of the health of sea grasses and carries out more general water-quality assessments. Trump's proposed 2018 federal budget seeks to eliminate the allocation.

In recent years, the islands have spent millions of dollars, including some federal money, to convert to central sewer systems, ending the damaging practice of allowing human waste to seep into the ocean from septic tanks.

But what is coming into focus is that the threats to the

reef system cannot be countered locally.

Ecologists describe the 360-mile-long Florida Reef Tract as a global treasure. It is the world's third-largest barrier reef, although much less famous than Australia's Great Barrier Reef.

But less than 10 percent of the reef system is now covered with living coral. Scientists anticipate that as early as 2020, it could be in line for almost yearly bleaching events, in which heat stresses upend the metabolism of corals, in some cases killing them. The reefs experienced back-to-back major bleaching events in 2014 and 2015.

An influential 2016 study in the journal Scientific Reports found that coral declines were just as likely to occur in remote, pristine reefs, such as the northern sector of the Great Barrier Reef, as they were to occur in non-remote reefs, such as the Florida Reef Tract. That is despite the fact that reefs closer to human communities probably experience a lot more pollution, overfishing and poor water quality.

The researchers suggested that the main reason for a decline of coral was a uniform global cause — warming.

"It's not only me feeling compassion for the actual coral, but for the entire ecosystem and how that's going to affect it in the years to come, unforeseen things that we just don't know are going to happen," Stein said after the dive. "It's frustrating and sad at the same time."

In the Keys, longtime residents say there's just no parallel between the reef of today — which still impresses inexperienced tourist divers — and what locals saw decades ago.

Mimi Stafford is a Key West-based master of all trades — commercial fishing, massage therapy, marine biology — who has lived here for decades. Over that time, the ocean has swallowed 25 feet of beach in front of her home, where iguanas thrash through the mangroves and military jets blast by regularly from nearby Naval Air Station Key West.

"When I was a child in the '60s, the water was so clear I used to think of it as being Coke bottle blue," said Stafford, citing the colored glass some Coke bottlers used. "And the reef was so healthy, all the coral was very alive. I don't recall even thinking about bleaching or coral death or coral diseases back then."

For most, those worries didn't arrive until the late 1990s.

The threat of climate change to coral reefs first garnered major attention during the strong El Niño event of 1997-1998, which triggered widespread bleaching and coral death around the world. The topic has become even more urgent amid an even-worse global bleaching event that began in 2014 and may be winding down only now.

The unrelenting ocean heat in 2014 and 2015 caused many of Florida's corals to turn white and lose key metabolic functions from heat stress.

The heat episodes in 1997-1998 and in more recent years "have been the worst events on record for bleaching events and have had devastating effects and losses of coral cover," said Rob Ruzicka, who heads the coral research program at Florida's Fish and Wildlife Research Institute.

Florida enjoyed a respite last year, but the reef system still suffered from a protracted outbreak of deadly diseases that often follow bleaching.

"This is different in that the extent and number of species of corals that have been affected have been dramatic," said Esther Peters, a coral reef ecologist at George Mason University in Virginia. Twenty-one coral species in the Florida Reef Tract are suffering from multiple diseases, according to reef surveys by the Nature Conservancy. Seven of those species are listed as threatened under the Endangered Species Act, among them staghorn and elkhorn corals.

A 2017 study led by the Nature Conservancy's senior marine scientist, Mark Spalding, estimated that coral reefs are worth $36 billion annually to tourism industries in key tropical coastal regions such as Florida and Hawaii, the Queensland coast in Australia and the coast of Kenya on the Indian Ocean.

Research from the World Resources Institute has found that 94 countries rely on reefs for tourism and in 23 of them, tourism related to reefs provides more than 15percent of gross domestic product.

Back in the Keys, scientists are trying radical new approaches to restoring the reefs.

Twenty feet under water at Pickles Reef, the Coral Restoration Foundation, based in Key Largo, has implanted endangered staghorn corals across the reef.

The implants, raised in undersea nurseries, are small but are growing steadily.

"A little piece the size of your pinkie can grow to be a piece the size of the diameter of a grapefruit in just six months on one of those trees," said Kayla Ripple, the foundation's science program manager, referring to the submerged PVC frames from which coral fragments are suspended to grow. "And after six months, we can take them to the reef."

The question now is whether these reefs will stand up to climate change — and whether experimental solutions such as the restoration approach or global strategies such as the Paris climate agreement can make enough of a dent in time.

"My children saw it right before it really started to decline," said Mimi Stafford. "But you know, I don't think their children will unless we can do something."

Chris Mooney writes about energy and the environment at *The Washington Post*. Chris previously worked at *Mother Jones*, and spent a decade prior to that as a freelance writer, podcaster and speaker, with his work appearing in *Wired, Harper's, Slate, Legal Affairs, The Los Angeles Times, The Post* and *The Boston Globe*. Chris also has published four books about science and climate change.

WATCH THIS VIDEO!

In this short video, Ocean Conservancy envisions a pristine Gulf of Mexico teeming with life, despite the impacts of the 2010 BP oil disaster. That's the future Ocean Conservancy works to achieve each day.

tinyurl.com/healthyseaturtles

ECOCHALLENGE: PUTTING IT INTO PRACTICE

Here are some ideas for putting what you learned this week into action. Find more ideas and commit to one Ecochallenge this week at **choices.ecochallenge.org**

- Use reusable bottles. Reduce your plastic and water waste by using a reusable bottle instead of purchasing bottled water.
- Say "no" to plastic straws. Small plastic pieces are some of the plastics most likely to make their way into our oceans. Say "no" to plastic draws in all of your drinks, and explain to your waiter or bartender why that choice is important.
- Say "no" to plastic bags. Plastic bags float down our waterways and are often mistaken for food by sea creatures. Take reusable bags with you wherever you go, and explain to your cashier why that choice is important.
- Get to know your local watershed. Find local resources for learning about your watershed and the particular water issues you region faces.
- Install a toilet tank bank. Reduce the amount of water flushed and save up to 11 gallons (41 L) of water per day by installing a toilet tank bank.
- Collect rainwater. Create a rain garden or bioswale, or use rain barrels to collect water for outdoor watering needs.

"If
the ocean
can calm itself,
so can you.
We
are both
salt water
mixed with
air."

— MEDITATION, NAYYIRAH WAHEED

SESSION 5

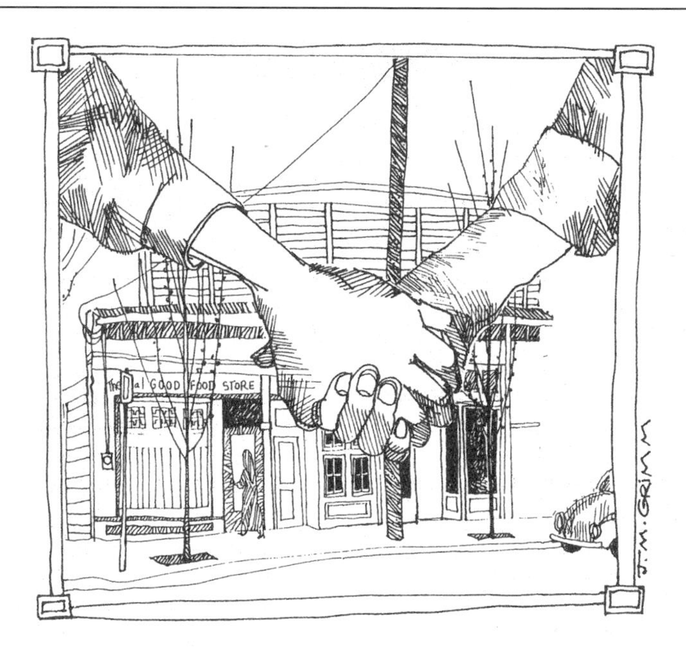

COMMUNITY

"Community's not a sentiment. It has to do with necessity — with people needing each other. If you allow the larger industrial system to remove the pattern of needs that is the force holding people together, then you lose the community."

— Wendell Berry

LEARNING OBJECTIVES

- **Envision what sustainable communities look like, including geographic place, physical infrastructure, decision making, and human relationships. Consider which factors indicate the health of a community.**
- **Envision how multiple factors (e.g. geographic place, physical infrastructure, decision making, and human relationships) influence sustainability and health at the community level.**
- **Compare and contrast innovative solutions developed by local communities to support their members and reduce their impact on Earth.**
- **Commit to specific actions to make your community more sustainable, more participatory, and more just.**

SESSION DESCRIPTION

This session explores the role of community in creating a more sustainable world. At the scale of local communities, individuals can often see the power of their collective actions more clearly. In our neighborhoods, towns and cities where we are connected by both infrastructure and relationships, building supportive, interdependent communities can move us toward a more sustainable way of living.

REFLECTION

How can you be more involved in nurturing a sustainable and just community where you live? Where could your deep passion meet your community's needs? Post your Reflection to your Dashboard on **choices.ecochallenge.org**. If you are not using the Ecochallenge site, write your thoughts in a journal and then reflect with your group.

Circle Question

What does community mean to you?

Reminder to the facilitator: The circle question should move quickly. Elicit an answer from each participant without questions or comments from others. The facilitator's guidelines are on page 10.

SUGGESTED DISCUSSION QUESTIONS

1. What makes you feel connected to your neighborhood, your neighbors, or another kind of community in your life?
2. In your opinion, how do social inequalities diminish a strong sense of community?
3. How can community design influence social interactions in positive and negative ways? For example, what type of design features make you feel safe in your neighborhood or city?
4. How do residents get involved in community decision making in your area? What stakeholders are involved in the economic aspect of planning decisions in your community?
5. How can your community support inclusive decision making?
6. How does environmental quality influence your sense of community?
7. What does a sustainable community look like?
8. What is one thing you can do to help create a sense of community where you live? What is one thing you can do to help your community become more sustainable?

SUGGESTED GROUP ACTIVITY

If you would like to do an activity with your group, we recommend these.

- Look at a few maps of your local region that show land use (Google or another search engine can help you locate some). Use the maps to answer the following questions:
  - Where are the most densely populated residential areas?
  - What features help community come together (e.g., parks, sidewalks)? Where are these features located?
  - What features divide people from each other or other parts of the city (e.g., highways)? Where are these features located?
  - Where are zones in transition (e.g., gentrification — see definitions on page 88)?
  - How do each of these things contribute to or detract from a sense of community among the people who live in your region?
- Imagine that you and your neighbors are asked to join a participatory budgeting process, where you give input into how a part of your neighborhood, community, or municipal budget will be spent. How might your personal interests differ from the community's priorities? How can you find a compromise or common ground? Is there an opportunity for you to be involved in participatory budgeting in your community?

FURTHER RESOURCES

Interested in finding out more on the topics presented in this session?
Visit our website for further readings and resources: **ecochallenge.org/discussion-course-resources.**
Follow our Facebook page to continue the discussion online:
facebook.com/Ecochallengeorg/

THIS IS WHAT DEMOCRACY LOOKS LIKE

By Fred Kent

The events, marches, and peaceful uprisings we have witnessed [in 2016 and 2017] — in this country and abroad — have made us all think closely about the value and function of public space. It's clear that now, as ever, public space is the prerequisite for democracy.

The size and number of our public spaces, their distribution across a city or town or nation, and our ability to exercise our rights in them, must surely be important measures for judging how "public" our space actually is. Trying to improve a public space may be a worthy cause, but there is always the threat that it can become less public in the process, less open to everyone, less open to "non-conforming" uses, whether it's a protest, a march, or something subversive but apolitical, like sleeping on a bench or bathing in a fountain.

Bryant Park, for example, might be a great spot to play ping pong, but Washington Square Park is still where New Yorkers go to hold a rally. Pershing Square ought to be the heart of Los Angeles, but one of the largest Women's Marches in the country couldn't spill into this would-be symbolic center because of its fortress-like design. On the other hand, places that were never public spaces, like the loading zones of airports or privately-owned public spaces like Zuccotti Park during Occupy Wall Street, can suddenly become public when citizens decide to take them back. In reality, public space is not where the public sector ordains it, but where the public demands it.

True placemaking is not just about the creation of places where we want to go and spend our time. It's about creating communities that have a greater capacity to self-organize — to pilot their own destinies, to express outrage, solidarity or celebration, to exchange and innovate and incubate new ideas, and yes, to bathe in the fountain. When communities come together to shape their public spaces, these commons can be a platform for democratic life of all kinds.

For Americans, placemaking is a direct, local form of democracy that is sorely needed in a time when our representative democracy is ever more divided, distant and dysfunctional (or perhaps in decline, depending on who you ask). For all of us, in these times of fear and anger, placemaking can be a process for mediating difference and perhaps even peacemaking within and between our communities.

Public space may be the prerequisite for democracy, but its presence alone is not enough. Only the People can ensure the publicness of our public spaces and the vitality of our democracy.

Fred Kent is the founder and president of Project for Public Spaces. He is a leading authority on revitalizing city spaces and one of the foremost thinkers in livability, smart growth and the future of the city. He offers technical assistance to communities and gives major talks across North America and internationally.

DEFINITIONS

Resilience: The ability to recover from or adjust easily to difficulties or change.

Equity: Fairness or justice in the way people are treated. Equitable treatment includes eliminating barriers that prohibit or limit access to opportunities and resources.

Gentrification: Gentrification occurs when wealthier individuals, families, or developers purchase and renovate properties in deteriorated or struggling urban neighborhoods. When upper- or middle-income residents move into these neighborhoods, property values rise, but low-income families and small businesses that were historic residents of the neighborhoods are often displaced, and the character and culture of the neighborhood changes.

Participatory budgeting: A democratic decision-making process in which community members directly decide how to spend part of a public budget.

Participatory design: An approach to design attempting to actively involve all stakeholders (e.g. employees, partners, customers, citizens, end users) in the design process to help ensure the result meets their needs and is usable.

Green infrastructure: Stormwater management that uses natural principles to protect communities against flooding or excessive heat, or to help communities improve air, soil and water quality, biodiversity, and quality of life.

Green space: An area of grass, trees, or other vegetation set apart for ecosystems services, recreation, or aesthetic purposes in an otherwise urban environment.

Gray infrastructure: Stormwater management that uses conventional structures like concrete, piped drainage and water treatment systems designed to move urban stormwater away from the built environment.

SIX FOUNDATIONS FOR BUILDING COMMUNITY RESILIENCE

By Daniel Lerch

Communities across the United States are talking more and more about resilience. They're spurred by recent natural disasters like Hurricanes Katrina and Sandy, weather extremes like the harsh Northeast winter of 2014-15, and long-term drought in the West.

Efforts to build community resilience often focus on growing the capacity to "bounce back" from disruptions, like those caused by climate change. But climate change is not the only crisis we face, nor is preparing for disruption the only way to build resilience. Truly robust community resilience should do more. It should engage and benefit all community members, and consider all the challenges the community faces — from rising sea levels to a lack of living wage jobs. And it should be grounded in resilience science, which tells us how complex systems — like human communities — can adapt and persist through changing circumstances. This report describes how communities can approach the full scope of the 21st century's challenges equitably and sustainably.

WHAT IS THE PROBLEM WE'RE TRYING TO SOLVE?

Global interconnection is the dominant factor of our modern world. If the aim of community resilience — at minimum — is to safeguard the health and well-being of people in the face of the 21st century's many complex challenges, those challenges need to be understood in a global context. We organize them as a set of four distinct but intertwined "E4" crises: ecological, energy, economic, and equity. Community resilience building should aim to keep the community from irrevocably changing for the worse as the result of these crises — and ideally change the community for the better.

WHAT IS RESILIENCE, REALLY?

Resilience is the ability of a system (like a community) to absorb disturbance and still retain basic function and structure. Building resilience means intentionally guiding the system's process of adaptation in an attempt to preserve some qualities and allow others to fade away, all while retaining the essence — or "identity" — of the system. In a human community, identity is essentially determined by what people value about where they live. However, what a community of people collectively values is open to interpretation and subject to disagreement. This suggests that people — and the ways they come to rough consensus — are necessarily at the center of community resilience building.

WHY COMMUNITIES?

In the United States, state and local governments have significant regulatory and investment power over many of the issues affecting everyday life. This — together with the many ways community members can self-organize and engage in civic life in the U.S. — allows for the kinds of innovations, experimentations, and even failures that are necessary in resilience building, but are not always possible at larger scales. Moreover, because everyone in a community is a stakeholder, it is both ethical and effective for everyone to participate in resilience building and have some responsibility for it: democratic communities have an inherent right to self-determination, and critical community resilience-building processes like social cohesion and system feedback are richest at the local level. Local decision-making doesn't always lead to equitable outcomes, however; one of the weaknesses of decentralization is that parochialism and local prejudice can flourish if unchecked. This suggests two requirements for building community resilience if it is indeed to be organized at the local level:

1. The responsibility for resilience building and the power to decide how it is done must rest with community members.
2. The process of resilience building must equitably address both the particular situation of the community and the broader challenges facing society.

THE SIX FOUNDATIONS

Although many resilience frameworks and tools for building community resilience are now available, no single approach will likely work for all communities and their varied social and economic contexts. Therefore we have identified six foundations that, in our view, are essential — no matter where or how resilience-building efforts are undertaken, or which challenges are of most concern locally. The foundations support building community resilience, rather than achieving resilience as a fixed goal, so as to emphasize resilience building as an ongoing process.

The six foundations are:

1. **People.** *The power to envision the future of the community and build its resilience resides with community members.*

Communities are products of human relationships. What the community is now and what it will be in the future both result from decisions made by people interacting, negotiating, and working together. Trust and deep relationships are crucial to holding communities together year after year and making resilience durable — but they can be challenging to build, especially in diverse communities.

Resilience building cannot turn a blind eye to the political and economic processes that determine what gets done, how it gets done, who decides, and who benefits. People of all interests and means must be able to participate in and benefit from resilience building; indeed, if they are to build true resilience, communities must embrace dissent and diversity.

The goals of community resilience-building efforts are best set by and focused on the needs of the people who make up the community — not just the needs of the most politically engaged or powerful individuals, businesses, and external stakeholders. Also, community members must collectively have power and responsibility for cultivating the resilience of their community as active participants and leaders — rather than only the local government or business leaders holding power and responsibility.

2. **Systems thinking.** *Systems thinking is essential for understanding the complex, interrelated crises now unfolding and what they mean for our similarly complex communities.*

   Our communities are thoroughly integrated sub-systems of a single global socio-ecological system. They're connected to or influenced by external factors like regional water supplies, national energy policy, and global climate change. Our communities are also complex systems in their own right, with innumerable components constantly changing and interacting with each other, the larger whole, and outside systems. Local economic activity, relationships among different social groups, local cultural patterns… they all influence the community from the inside out.

   The challenges we face are complex, so we can't approach them as if they were linear problems. Systems thinking helps us understand the complex E4 crises, as well as how our complex societies and communities work. It is also the basis of resilience science.

3. **Adaptability.** *A community that adapts to change is resilient. But because communities and the challenges we face are dynamic, adaptation is an ongoing process.*

   When complex systems are resilient in the face of disruption it is because they have the capacity to adapt to changing circumstances, thanks to system characteristics like diversity, modularity and openness. In human systems, resilience-building efforts aim (in part) to cultivate such characteristics — but if those efforts themselves don't adapt to changing circumstances, they may unwittingly cultivate the resilience of things that aren't desired. (Poverty, drought, and authoritarian governments can all be resilient in their own ways.)

4. **Transformability.** *Some challenges are so big that it's not possible for the community to simply adapt; fundamental, transformative changes may be necessary.*

   Communities generally adapt as the world around them changes. But if adaptation happens too slowly or is constrained, challenges can outpace the ability to cope and eventually threaten overall resilience. When automobile manufacturing started moving out of the Midwest, for example, many communities were so dependent on the industry that mere adaptation wasn't an option: they needed to radically rethink their economic basis (and the social and governance implications of radical change) if they hoped to maintain any ability to chart their futures. In other words, these communities needed to change some part of their identity (while retaining their most valued qualities) and transform to a new state that could be resilient under the new circumstances.

   Resilience building usually tries to maintain the basic function and structure of a system in the face of disruption. Transformational efforts are purposefully disruptive to the system, changing some of its functions and structures so that it can build resilience in ways more suited to the new reality.

5. **Sustainability.** *Community resilience is not sustainable if it serves only us, and only now; it needs to work for other communities, future generations, and the ecosystems on which we all depend.*

   Sustainability and resilience are distinct concepts that complement each other. Resilience helps us understand the nuts and bolts of how socio-ecological systems work and how they might adapt (or fail to adapt) to changes over time. Sustainability helps us understand in a more general sense our extremely complex relationship with the natural world, and the consequences of getting that relationship wrong. Where resilience is process-oriented and, in ways, value-neutral, sustainability forces us to confront deep questions and uncomfortable potential futures.

   Sustainability is a guiding light for resilience building, where there can be a danger of getting overwhelmed by endless system factors and dynamics. Its tools help us make sense of the torrent of information that systems thinking requires us to explore. The perspective we get from it informs the long-term goals of resilience building. But we also need to be careful in our pursuit of sustainability that we don't mistake what we want for what's actually possible.

6. **Courage.** *As individuals and as a community, we need courage to confront challenging issues and take responsibility for our collective future.*

   Community resilience building is not an engineering problem solvable just by knowledge and skill. It is a social undertaking, involving thousands or even millions of people and their most meaningful relationships, hopes, and fears. It confronts us with the worrying threats of the E4 crises and compels us to engage with people with whom we may disagree — perhaps quite strongly.

   We need motivation and emotional strength to take on such personally challenging work. Individuals need courage to speak out about their views and needs, and make themselves personally vulnerable. Communities, too, need courage to create space for difficult conversations, make far-reaching investments and policy changes, and risk sharing political and economic power.

   Courage is the ability to do something you know is difficult, and building community resilience in the face of the E4 crises can be difficult indeed. Resilience-building efforts need to cultivate courage in both individuals and the community as a whole to confront challenging issues and take responsibility for their collective future.

♦ ♦ ♦

Resilience is, in a way, the original aspiration of human communities. Since the dawn of civilization we have banded together for long-term mutual well-being and betterment in the face of future stresses and shocks. History is full of communities — even highly complex ones — that persisted for thousands of years: they found ways to be resilient despite natural disaster and internal discord, embedding their wisdom and practices in place-based cultures. Of course, history is also full of communities and civilizations that succumbed to external or internal crises, often far larger than they had any possibility of anticipating. While we should heed the warnings of that history, we can also consider ourselves fortunate in the modern era to have a broader view of what crises we might face, and access to countless examples of community resilience both ancient and contemporary.

Daniel Lerch is is Publications Director of Post Carbon Institute, serving as lead editor and manager of the Institute's books and reports. Post Carbon Institute's mission is to lead the transition to a more resilient, equitable, and sustainable world by providing individuals and communities with the resources needed to understand and respond to the interrelated economic, energy, ecological, and equity crises of the 21st century. This is an excerpt from their 2015 report, "Six Foundations for Building Community Resilience." postcarbon.org | resilience.org

THE URBAN COMMON SPACES THAT SHOW US WE BELONG TO SOMETHING LARGER

By Sarah van Gelder

An American friend living in Germany told me a story about when she first arrived. She and her German boyfriend were out walking when she heard a noise that got louder as they approached the town's main square. Puzzled, she asked her partner about the unfamiliar sound.

"That's the sound of people talking to each other," he told her.

People outside, not drowned out by the noise of cars or amplified music. Imagine!

On my recent trip to Europe, where I was speaking about my new book, *The Revolution Where You Live*, I, too, found people everywhere outside, enjoying common spaces.

Jane Jacobs, the author and activist who revolutionized urban planning, wrote often about the outdoor spaces where people encounter each other. Even in large, gritty cities such as New York and Berlin, these urban commons connect us to each other and to the land, water, plants, and animal life of our home. We experience what it means to belong to something larger, to be welcome simply because we are alive.

But common spaces have to be protected, especially as powerful private interests seek to increase private wealth.

In Berlin, I visited Elisabeth Meyer-Renschhausen, author of several books on urban gardening who fought for decades for garden space. We walked together to her favorite outdoor market, where we admired the massive displays of tulips and sampled chocolates made by a family-run business. She spoke to friends, asked farmers about their early spring greens, and recommended a coffee truck run by a Turkish family whose business gave these immigrants a foothold in the larger community. Going to market was as much about enjoying the company and savoring the tastes, smells, stories, and sights as it was about shopping for dinner.

We also visited a large park near to Berlin's Potsdamer Platz, a part of the center city once bisected by the Berlin Wall. The park land had been owned by the East German railway, but after the wall came down, city planners pressed for a freeway through this rare green space. The railroad company wanted to sell the land to developers.

A local citizens' movement pushed back, though, on behalf of those who had small garden allotments on the land, neighbors, and others who wanted green space in what was becoming a dense and crowded city. Meyer-Renschhausen was among the group that succeeded, after 15 years, in getting the land made into Gleisdreieck, a permanent park named after the old train junction.

She took me to see the gardens where she and dozens of others grow food and flowers in tiny fenced-in lots, many with sheds or tiny cottages.

"People are poor, and they need open spaces, places to garden for health reasons and because it's boring to be inside in small flats all the time," she said. "We have a huge rate of unemployment in the cities, and gardens offer one possibility for people to see that you can help yourself."

Walkers and cyclers explore the gardens via narrow pathways. Nearby, a shipping container, converted into a coffee stand, offers espresso drinks, fresh carrot/apple/ginger juice, and pastries. Couples and families gather around tables made from brightly painted pallets and other found objects. Truck tires, trees, and tiny furniture keep the children busy while their parents sip coffee and read the paper.

Further on, people gather at a skateboard park, picnic on open lawns, and care for the beehives at a community garden space used by Bosnian refugees.

Such scenes are harder to find in the United States, where isolation has reached that point that it is literally killing us via addiction, mental illness, and suicide. According to the recent World Happiness Report, Americans' well-being declined substantially over the past 10 years, in large part because of the erosion of the social fabric. Inequality reduces our sense of social solidarity. The fetish for privatization devalues open spaces along with other commons, like public education, a stable climate, and clean air and water. Powerful corporations profit by "enclosing," or taking for themselves, a commons that actually belongs to all of us (or, as in the case of water and the atmosphere, by using it as a dump). It takes tenacious people's movements to push back — like the ones Meyer-Renschhausen helped lead.

It's worth it, though, for many reasons. Common spaces offer chances for the everyday encounters that help to weave the social fabric. And when that fabric is strong and resilient, there is little we can't do.

Sarah van Gelder wrote this article for *YES! Magazine*. Sarah is a co-founder and columnist at *YES!* Her new book, *The Revolution Where You Live: Stories from a 12,000-Mile Journey Through a New America* is available now from *YES!* Read more about her road trip and book here and follow her on Twitter @sarahvangelder.

CONNECTING THE LOTS

By Diana Budds, Photography by Justin Fantl

City planners may shape streets and devise green spaces, but building community really starts where the pavement ends. Participatory design is a diplomatically driven method of development that listens to both stakeholders and local voices to create a neighborhood where stories and streetscapes are shared.

On a larger scale, New York City is in the process of redesigning Flushing Meadows Corona Park — 897 acres of open space in the borough of Queens. Originally built for the 1939-1940 World's Fair, seven million people now annually visit the park despite the fact that it hasn't been seriously updated for the past 50 years. To find out how to best bring the park into the 21st century, the Design Trust for Public Space, a nonprofit advocacy group, has been engaging in participatory design initiatives with the surrounding communities. Sam Holleran, a participatory design fellow at Design Trust, has been working on visual materials to aid the process and has designed the curriculum for community learning sessions. He thinks that participatory design, when implemented at the right time and in a meaningful way, unites people and builds better results for the end users. "Involving community is not just about taking an approach that brings in equity and social justice," he says. "It's about making spaces that are durable. There's less objection to the design and less revision."

Some of the more apparent benefits of participatory design can be seen in master-planned neighborhoods. A 2008 study from California Polytechnic State University researcher Esther Valle showed that residents living in places that were built using participatory design methods felt a stronger sense of community and a deeper connection with their neighborhood. The residents of Bernal Gateway Apartments in San Francisco and Oak Court Apartments in Palo Alto, two enclaves built using participatory methods, were interviewed about their satisfaction with their living environments. The study found that they use their neighborhoods' communal meeting spaces for socializing and feel more comfortable asking their neighbors for a favor, such as borrowing a cup of sugar, than residents of New Urbanist neighborhoods, which are built using another contemporary design method that promotes walkable environments but without participatory design efforts. The study concluded that while it's difficult to unequivocally say that either method alone is a primary contributor to creating community, involvement with the design creates attachment to a place, which in turn brings a stronger sense of community. Because people are encouraged to work together during the planning process, it sows the seed for interaction afterward.

Participatory budgeting is another strategy that builds community. This concept sets aside part of a civic budget and allows citizens to vote by committee on how to use it. In open forums, local leaders and their constituents meet, propose projects and decide what should get funded. "Participatory budgeting processes always focus on in-person meetings that bring people into rooms with their neighbors," says Josh Lerner, executive director of theParticipatory Budgeting Project, a nonprofit that empowers people to collectively decide how to spend public money. "By creating new conversations, the community comes together around shared needs. The best way to understand what a community needs is to ask them, and the best way to meet those needs is to give the community real power to make the solutions happen through direct control over a budget."

In Vallejo, California, a $3.2 million participatory budgeting allotment rallied 4,000 people around community gardens, new streetlights, road repairs, park improvements and senior citizen programs, among others. Prior to the process, city council members thought the residents wanted more police and public safety. But after engaging with the community, they found that while safety was a concern, it wasn't the only thing. People voiced their desire for parks, saw what needed to be done to get them and took action. "Some of the gardens have turned blighted, unused lots into vibrant gathering spaces in residential neighborhoods, while other green spaces have paved the way for new education and training programs in public schools and churches," says Ginny Browne, West Coast Project Manager at the Participatory Budgeting Project. The new gardens provide a much-needed "third place" for residents to enjoy and nurture. With home referred to as the "first place" and work as the "second place," third places are important social areas for spontaneous interactions, such as coffee shops, bars and parks.

In addition to jump-starting civic projects, participatory budgeting also builds stronger trust between the city and citizens. "It was a time when Vallejo's residents' trust in city government was at an all-time low, and residents themselves were deeply divided over the reasons for the municipal failure," Browne says. "Through participatory budgeting, residents were able to sit across the table from city staff to talk through project ideas, learn about costs and feasibility and share their own knowledge about what was and wasn't working in their communities. We saw learning on both sides of the table, and both residents and city staff came away with a new sense of the value of collaboration." Coming together made the planning process transparent to the community, taught them how to get their voices heard and helped them arrive at a shared vision for what their neighborhoods could become.

In his work with The Better Block, Roberts travels the world to share what he has discovered through speaking with people about their worries concerning a diminishing sense of neighborhood kinship and togetherness. What he's learned is that because of the fast pace of modern living and the detachment from communal social structures, people have slowly drifted apart from each other and are searching for ways to find their way back by working together in their neighborhoods. "There's an overall sense that we're not engaged as a community," Roberts says.

"There's a void, and that void comes back to the fact that we used to do things together, craft our places together and look after each other, and we're not doing that anymore. People feel like they're missing their tribe because of this."

Perhaps the way to reverse the years of disbanding is to take an active role in building and designing communities that reflect our shared desires, whether it's a park, streetscape or neighborhood that promotes a connected, slower life. Think of the difference between knitting a scarf versus buying one in a shop: the former is a point of pride you'll take care of to ensure it'll last a lifetime, whereas the latter will never earn the same regard. We should be living in neighborhoods we're proud of contributing to and reflect who we are. We should want to cherish them and pass them down to the next generation like a well-loved heirloom. The way to maintain that legacy — or to even build one from scratch — is not through having one voice heard; it's through a chorus of community involvement.

Gazing at a city from 1,000 feet above the ground reveals a fascinating — and complex — narrative of modern-day urbanism. Based on the shape of streets, the layout of houses, their density and the dominant colors, a city's character comes into focus — as do the lives of the people who live there.

Take these aerial photographs of Phoenix, Arizona, as an example. Ambitious residential developments such as Arrowhead Lakes in the Glendale neighborhood are built around a sea of blue water. Lush green lawns lay adjacent to arid desert. Highway off-ramps lead to nowhere and paved street grids eagerly await neighborhoods to sprout up around them. While the lined-up houses each have their own postage stamp yards, there's not a park to be seen, nor a café or corner pub. These omissions reflect the actions of planners and developers who build cities based on speculation, not people. While the signs of civilization are there, the citizens themselves are noticeably absent, and this lack of interaction diminishes the sense of community. And this is all by design.

The United States had a major growth spurt in the 20th century when policymakers and developers formed cities with industry and efficiency at the heart of decision making: It was about expanding the highway system, getting cars from point A to B, building parking spaces for those vehicles and designing sprawling intersections for them to safely cross paths. Architects proposed "visionary" projects that, on paper, would improve urban life. However, the polar opposite occurred as they based their objectives on assumptions of what people required, not what communities desired.

As we consider what makes a place desirable, it boils down to championing people. The good news is that decades of top-down planning have given way to bottom-up innovation as the community is now welcomed at the table. Much of this formal community involvement is called participatory design, an umbrella term for workshops, activities, surveys, visioning sessions and interviews that call upon experiences and input from all stakeholders in a project — including the government, neighborhood members, developers and designers — not just the traditional decision makers at the top. The hope was that involving the community affected by a project would yield a stronger design.

Also called cooperative design or co-design, the participatory concept originated in Scandinavia and made its way to the United States in the 1960s. During this decade, pioneering activists like the great Jane Jacobs issued a rallying cry for planners to listen to people, take the pulse of a successful neighborhood and try to reverse engineer it for new initiatives instead of imposing predetermined master plans. In fact, it's thanks to Jacobs that New York City did not demolish parts of the West Village and SoHo, two of the city's most iconic enclaves, in favor of an expressway: While it would have supposedly improved traffic flow from Brooklyn to the Holland Tunnel, construction of the four-lane freeway would have razed Washington Square Park, which is a beloved public space and the heart of the community to this day. Her neighborhood-saving endeavors illustrate the root of the issue: As cities hold the purse strings for capital projects, rezoning and permitting development, bad design fundamentally boils down to bad policy.

"Many of our policies are built out of fear," says Jason Roberts, co-founder of The Better Block. His organization leads grassroots exercises on ways the community can improve their neighborhoods and also consults with local governments on how to incorporate citizen-led design into the bureaucratic process. "Rules are typically put in place because of the fear that something horrendous could happen — which could be valid, I don't want to minimize that — but once you start constructing your community based on fear, your byproduct will be these structures that are inhumane," Roberts says. A classic example of this notion of "hostile" or "defensive" architecture is park benches that people can't lie on: Spacing the seats a certain way is a subtle modification intended to prevent homeless people from sleeping on them, but it also restricts how the seats are used by the rest of the population. "Your options are fear or love," he says. "When you look at an environment built on love, you get an entirely different ethos: You get an area with a high quality of life that shines and is very human-centered."

The Better Block started in 2010 when Roberts gathered a few friends together to stage a pop-up intervention in a section of Oak Cliff, a rougher neighborhood in Dallas, Texas. They banded together and spent an afternoon painting bike lanes, bringing in potted plants and trees, propping up a few café chairs and creating mock-ups of businesses in the empty storefronts. Once they were set up, they used the neighborhood like it was just another vibrant street. The hope was that by showing how easy it was to create a welcoming space in an area that was previously abandoned — thereby altering the psychology of the block — the city would take note and change some of its policies.

While the project was ephemeral (Roberts likens it to an art project), its effects weren't. Their act of building an attractive and vibrant city block sparked community. Since then, his team has replicated this process of faux-placemaking across the country. "Time and time again, I see people come out to these projects and say, 'I just want to work with my hands and do something,'" Roberts says. "Humans are made to move and made to be social. When people do some kind of physical activity together, it benefits the broader community and brings a sense of engagement."

Diana Budds is a design writer living and working in New York City. She is currently a writer for fastcodesign.com and formerly a senior editor at Dwell. She wrote this article for *Kinfolk*.

WHAT IT LOOKS LIKE WHEN COMMUNITIES MAKE RACIAL JUSTICE A PRIORITY

By Zenobia Jeffries and Araz Hachadourian

MISSOURI

In the weeks following the 2014 shooting of Michael Brown, Wellspring Church in Ferguson became a space for protestors to meet, talk about issues, and strategize for change. Two years have passed, but Wellspring's pastor, The Rev. F. Willis Johnson Jr., wants to keep those conversations going.

He teamed up with another local church to create The Center for Social Empowerment, hoped to be an incubator for social justice solutions in Ferguson. The center stems from the idea that while policy changes are needed — like those recommended in a 2015 U.S. Department of Justice report — they don't address the problem of racism within the community. To do that, Johnson says, the experiences of individual community members need to be considered.

The center holds monthly conversations that are open to the community and partners with organizations and schools to bring discussions to them. The meetings engage participants in reflecting on their own experiences with race and hearing the stories of others. This creates a shift from "debate rhetoric" to dialogue, says Nicki Reinhardt-Swierk, one of the program's coordinators. "When we can get people to realize that the world as they understand it is not the world as experienced by other people, that's how you start seeding change and sprouting action."

In these forums, participants discuss actions they can implement in their own lives to change the role race plays in their community. Those actions don't always include protesting, explains Reinhardt-Swierk. They might be recognizing the racist connotations of the word "thug" or changing the way an elderly woman interacts with a cashier.

"From [conversations] we can raise a healthy and loving challenge," adds Johnson. "Now that I know better, I can push myself to do better. I can see my role in reconciliation and in my community." — Araz Hachadourian

MISSISSIPPI

After living in Cleveland and Chicago, Iya'falola H. Omobola says she had never seen anything like what she's witnessed over the past several years in Jackson, Mississippi, where homes have been allowed to "deteriorate and just stay there."

Unlike other cities that use the threat of taxes or demolition to clean up derelict properties, Jackson appeared to have a pattern of neglect, says Omobola. In response, Cooperation Jackson, a grassroots organization co-founded by Omobola, is working to thwart gentrification and subsequent displacement of residents by buying as much property as it can to make land and homes affordable.

Decay, abandonment, and plunging property values are pervasive in many U.S. urban centers that are predominantly African American, like Jackson. Meanwhile, nearly 20 percent of these neighborhoods with lower incomes and home values have experienced gentrification since 2000, according to Governing magazine. In cities such as Seattle, Portland, and Washington, D.C., those changes have pushed out many residents. Cooperation Jackson members are determined to prevent the same thing from happening in Jackson, where about 80 percent of the population is African American.

The group has established a community land trust as part of its Sustainable Communities Initiative, which includes building co-ops (three operate today), purchasing land, and building affordable housing on the west side of town. So far, Cooperation Jackson has purchased more than 20 parcels of land for as little as $800 apiece. The land trust was part of former Mayor Chokwe Lumumba's vision before he died in 2014; Omobola, Lumumba's media director, and Kali Akuno, who also worked for Lumumba's administration, formed Cooperation Jackson and opened the Chokwe Lumumba Center for Economic Democracy and Development.

The goal is to enable as many people as possible in Jackson to own their own resources, Omobola says. Now, the organization is focused on acquiring property within a 3-mile radius over the next two years. "We're looking at creating self-sustainability," she says. — Zenobia Jeffries

MICHIGAN

To outsiders like Donald Trump, Detroit is like "an urban dystopia of poverty, crime, and blight." But to Detroiters and those committed to the city's revitalization, it's a city full of promise — with the notable exception of its school system. Following multiple state takeovers, the largest school district in Michigan continues to suffer teacher layoffs, crowded classrooms, and financial mismanagement. And longtime residents and activists have had enough, turning to a legacy of the civil rights movement's Freedom Schools to serve their children.

In February, parent Aliya Moore's call to boycott schools on Count Day — when the state uses student attendance to calculate per-pupil funding — prompted a local group, Detroiters Resisting Emergency Management, to reimagine education for Detroit schoolchildren and launch the Detroit Independent Freedom Schools Movement.

Organized by African Americans in the 1960s around sociopolitical and socioeconomic issues, the Freedom Schools presented an alternative setting for all ages centered mostly on voter registration and social change, as well as academic components — mainly reading skills — for young people. Since then, civil rights and racial justice organizations, along with grassroots movements, have resurrected the Freedom School model for their work in African American communities still faced with inadequate education, disenfranchisement, and racial discrimination.

The organizers of DIFS created a program that was piloted this summer at a local recreation center, where volunteer teachers provided cultural activities and lessons in the core subjects of math, science, English/language arts, and social studies. Other institutions, including the Charles H. Wright African American Museum, have signed on to host the DIFS program at their facilities this fall.

Gloria Aneb House, a former member of the Student Nonviolent Coordinating Committee and a member of D-REM, helped to organize the local Freedom Schools movement. "Our intention is to do as much in outreach around the city and get into as many churches and community centers where they're happy to have us," House says. — Zenobia Jeffries

---

Zenobia Jeffries and Araz Hachadourian wrote this article for *50 Solutions*, the Winter 2017 issue of *YES! Magazine*. Zenobia is the racial justice associate editor. Follow her on Twitter @ZenobiaJeffries. Araz is a regular contributor to *YES!* Follow her on Twitter @ahachad2.

HOW TO TURN NEIGHBORHOODS INTO HUBS OF RESILIENCE

By Taj James and Rosa González

Think of it as a silver lining to the gathering dark clouds. We live in an era of extraordinary disruption, from the serial crises of a changing climate to the wrenching shifts of a globalized economy. But in that disruption lies the potential for positive transformation.

Addressing climate change requires adapting to the impacts that are already here — heat waves, droughts, superstorms and more — while preventing and mitigating future impacts. Taking these challenges seriously calls for radical changes in the way we live. It calls us to zero out our carbon emissions, and to rethink the systems that shape our lives, including the economy, food and power. It calls us to fundamentally transition from a world of domination and extraction to a world of regeneration, resilience, and interdependence.

It's a tall order, no doubt, but that transition is already underway. In our work with movement builders on the front lines of the transition, we've identified two key guideposts — connectedness and equity — that point us toward the world we want.

Connectedness is the recognition that our well-being is inextricably tied to that of other people and the planet itself. It means there are no throwaway people, no throwaway places, no throwaway anything. In fact, there's no "away"; there's just here. In practice, connectedness is about lifting up the voices of the marginalized, and it means regenerating forgotten places, from industrial brownfields to hollowed-out rural towns and Rust Belt cities. The second guidepost, equity, is about recognizing and repairing the harm generated by situations of extreme power imbalance. Equity is about building power from the bottom up.

When communities are fully engaged in problem-solving, they come up with holistic solutions that address complex, interlocking challenges. Here are three.

SUNSET PARK, BROOKLYN, NEW YORK

When Superstorm Sandy ripped through the Eastern Seaboard in 2012, the waterfront neighborhood of Sunset Park was hit hard. Power lines toppled and businesses were shuttered. The neighborhood's industrial district flooded, washing toxic residue into nearby residential areas.

But as the people of Sunset Park worked together to rebuild, a hopeful possibility emerged. What if the neighborhood rebuilt in ways that made the local economy more resilient and equitable, while limiting the impact of climate change? That's the vision of UPROSE, a grassroots environmental justice group that took root in Sunset Park 50 years ago.

"Superstorm Sandy was a real wakeup call for our

community," says UPROSE director Elizabeth Yeampierre. "Climate change is here now, and waterfront communities like ours are extremely vulnerable." The neighborhood's low-income, immigrant residents were especially at risk, so in the aftermath of Superstorm Sandy, they turned to UPROSE for a community organizing effort to prepare for a wetter, more uncertain future.

The plan they came up with builds climate resilience while protecting the environment, health, and — crucially jobs.

The point is not simply to rebuild what was there before; UPROSE members don't want more jobs in the same dirty industries that had polluted the neighborhood for decades. "We have a lot of businesses on the waterfront, and we want to keep them here because people need places to work," Yeampierre says. "But we want safe places to work." To that end, UPROSE has joined forces with labor unions, the Center for Working Families, and business owners to transform Sunset Park's industrial space into a manufacturing hub that produces environmentally friendly building and construction materials, powered by renewable energy. And they are encouraging these industries to hire locally.

It's a plan that addresses many problems at once. In a city with skyrocketing inequality and rampant gentrification, it could help preserve the blue-collar jobs that once anchored the middle class. At the same time, it could reduce toxic hazards and make Sunset Park a safer, healthier place to live. And it could reduce the carbon emissions that are driving that change.

The process of developing the plan was as transformational as the plan itself. UPROSE consults with residents on the future they want, then arms them with the tools they need to make that vision a reality. Some residents take on the role of block captains and gather input and educate their neighbors on city planning processes. Through partnerships with researchers, residents conduct participatory action research on issues of concern. It's a deeply democratic, holistic approach that builds local power and increases community control over resources — key elements of community resilience.

BUFFALO, NEW YORK

Left behind by the globalized economy, Buffalo has lost more than half its population since 1950. By 2005, when the community group People United for Sustainable Housing (PUSH) Buffalo was founded, residents of the West Side neighborhood were struggling with unemployment, rampant blight, and high energy costs.

At that time, there were an estimated 23,000 vacant homes in Buffalo. PUSH took on a state housing agency that was using vacant buildings to speculate on Wall Street, and got the buildings turned over to the community — with funding to fix them up.

Next, PUSH brought together hundreds of community residents to craft a plan for a large, blighted area. The result is a 25-square-block Green Development Zone(GDZ), which is now a model of energy-efficient, affordable housing. PUSH and its nonprofit development company rehabilitate homes in the GDZ, installing efficiency upgrades, like insulation and geothermal heating, that dramatically lower residents' utility bills. The organization won a New York state grant to build 46 new homes, including a net zero house, which produces as much energy as it consumes.

The GDZ doubles as a jobs program. Through its construction projects, PUSH has cultivated a growing network of contractors who are committed to hiring locally. And PUSH successfully advocated for New York's Green Jobs-Green New York program, which seeks to create 35,000 jobs while providing energy upgrades and retrofits for 1 million homes across the state.

Across the West Side, PUSH has transformed the urban landscape. In partnership with Buffalo Niagara Riverkeeper and the Massachusetts Avenue Project, PUSH has turned trash-strewn, vacant lots into state-of-the-art rain gardens, small urban farms, and aquaponics greenhouses. These urban oases bolster food security, while providing much-needed green space.

RICHMOND, CALIFORNIA

A predominantly low-income community of color is challenging the oil giant that has long dominated their city.

WATCH THIS VIDEO!
Real Money, Real Power: Participatory Budgeting
vimeo.com/162743651
Participatory budgeting (PB) is a different way to manage public money, and to engage people in government. It is a democratic process in which community members directly decide how to spend part of a public budget. It enables taxpayers to work with government to make the budget decisions that affect their lives. Find out more in this short video.

In Richmond, the 3,000-acre Chevron refinery looms over the city with towering smokestacks and tangled pipes going in every direction. The largest of its kind in California, the Chevron refinery showers Richmond with unpronounceable toxic chemicals and periodic fiery explosions that put residents at risk. As a major source of jobs and tax revenue, Chevron has long held outsized influence on the city's politics. But, fed up with their toxic neighbor, residents are working to counterbalance the company's political muscle.

The first step was to activate community power. A coalition of local nonprofits including the Asian Pacific Environmental Network (APEN), Communities for a Better Environment (CBE), the Alliance of Californians for Community Empowerment(ACCE), the Richmond Progressive Alliance, and Faith-Works brought residents together to devise solutions to community problems.

The coalition organized forums and rallies, held regular learning institutes for decision-makers, and encouraged public participation at planning commission meetings. In this way, residents reshaped their city's General Plan to make Richmond less reliant on Chevron. The new General Plan emphasizes green industries, anti-displacement policies, and better mass transit systems. Now, the coalition is at work translating the plan into projects, programs, and laws.

At the same time, the Our Power campaign in Richmond is working to build community control over essential resources, such as food, land, water, and energy. Our Power partners with Cooperation Richmond, a local co-op incubator and loan fund that helps low-income residents create their own cooperatively owned businesses. The group holds the annual Our Power Festival, which brings together residents, small businesses, and the public sector to envision a transition to local energy management.

Despite this groundswell of community organizing, Chevron continued to hold sway on the City Council. So the organizers switched to electoral tactics to supporting progressive candidates who would stand up to the oil giant. And it worked. In 2014, despite millions of dollars invested in the election by Chevron, residents voted in candidates aligned with community values and renewable energy.

"Winning political power, especially in this political moment, is critical for communities at the intersection of poverty and pollution," says APEN Action executive director Miya Yoshitani. "If we are going to win back our democracy from the hands of corporations, and win the powerful vision we have for living local economies, we need to invest in organizing the power of the people and the polls in all our neighborhoods."

Taj James and Rosa González wrote this article for *YES! Magazine*. Taj James is the founder, executive director, and a board member of Movement Strategy Center, a national nonprofit that promotes movement-building strategies and supports organizations to work more collaboratively and sustainably. Rosa is the center's director of applied practice and leads the Community Climate Solutions program to advance transformative resilience strategies that accelerate the emerging transition to a regenerative and interconnected world.

HOW LIVABLE IS YOUR COMMUNITY?

Check out your community's livability score at **livabilityindex.aarp.org/**

ECOCHALLENGE: PUTTING IT INTO PRACTICE

Here are some ideas for putting what you learned this week into action. The following page also offers several ideas for how to build community. Find more ideas and commit to one Ecochallenge this week at **choices.ecochallenge.org**

- Meet your neighbors. Set a goal to meet a certain number of neighbors each week. Find out where they work, who their kids are, what they care about.
- Get involved. Join your neighborhood association.
- Attend a meeting. Attend a local event or meeting concerning a current issue in your community that you'd like to know more about. This could be an informational session, a planning meeting, a town hall, or a training on taking action.
- Connect with a nonprofit. Connect with a local nonprofit, environmental or otherwise, and find out how you can get involved or become a member.
- Build relationships with those who are different than you. Invite a refugee family, an international student, or someone from a different religion than you over for dinner, ask them about their interests, and get to know them as people.

How to Build Community poster by SyracuseCulturalWorkers.com. This is available as a poster from Syracuse Cultural Workers.

SESSION 6

TRANSPORTATION

"Two roads diverged in a wood, and I — I took the one less travelled by, and that has made all the difference."

— Robert Frost

LEARNING OBJECTIVES

- **Discuss the impacts of current transportation systems, including both the transportation of people and of goods.**
- **Recognize transportation choices and infrastructure as land use and quality of life/livability issues, as well as environmental issues.**
- **Identify the various viable transportation options available in different communities, including your own.**
- **Advocate for transportation systems which minimize environmental impact while meeting human needs.**

SESSION DESCRIPTION

Most travel in the United States is by car, often with a single occupant — the driver. Planners and engineers have built city streets and road systems to meet our transportation demand and in doing so have encouraged even more traffic without providing options for other modes of travel. About 28 percent of all greenhouse gas emissions in the US are from transportation, including both transportation of people and goods. Greenhouse gas emissions, congested roads, noise, polluted runoff and rising gas prices point to the unsustainability of our current transportation system. This session looks at some of the transportation-related problems we face and how some places are re-designing their communities for the benefit of people instead of cars.

REFLECTION

What are the different ways you get around your neighborhood, city and region? What alternatives are available to you? Purposefully choose a mode of transportation you don't use very often to get somewhere you go regularly this week — work, school, the grocery store, or the park. How was your experience different? Post your Reflection to your Dashboard on **choices.ecochallenge.org**. If you are not using the Ecochallenge site, write your thoughts in a journal and then reflect with your group.

What is your favorite mode of transportation, and why is it your favorite?

Reminder to the facilitator: The circle question should move quickly. Elicit an answer from each participant without questions or comments from others. The facilitator's guidelines are on page 10.

SUGGESTED DISCUSSION QUESTIONS

1. Andy Murdock outlines "The Environmental Cost of Free 2-Day Shipping." How often do you purchase things online instead of at a local store? What factors influence your online shopping and which shipping methods you choose?
2. How do your transportation choices affect your engagement in your community? Does your experience differ while walking, riding transit, biking or driving?
3. What effects has the invention of the automobile had on the design of cities? How does the design of cities influence the kinds of transportation choices people have?
4. How does an emphasis on pedestrians help to improve the quality of life in a community? For example, why are sidewalks important in communities?
5. Describe your early experience with transportation. Did you have access to effective public transit? How has your early experience influenced your current attitudes about transportation and your transportation behavior?
6. Other than re-establishing commuter rail lines, what are some ways that suburbs could be retrofitted to encourage more sustainable transportation?
7. How could you collect information in your community that would help city planners promote safer and more sustainable transportation?
8. What stereotypes do you think might discourage more diversity in bicycle ridership? How could you challenge these stereotypes in your community?

SUGGESTED GROUP ACTIVITY

If you would like to do an activity with your group, we recommend these.

- Use Google Maps or another map service to determine what services and stores (i.e. library, grocery store, post office, farmer's market, bakery, park) are located within a 20 minute walk from where you live. What services and stores are located within a 20 minute bike ride? A 20 minute bus/train ride? Try to prioritize frequenting the places that you can access without using a car.
- On a map of your region, plot the places each person in your group lives. Is there a way to carpool or bike together more often?

FURTHER RESOURCES

Interested in finding out more on the topics presented in this session?
Visit our website for further readings and resources: **ecochallenge.org/discussion-course-resources.**
Follow our blog at **ecochallenge.org/blog/**; we post links to new resources and inspiring stories regularly.

REIMAGINING OUR STREETS AS PLACES: FROM TRANSIT ROUTES TO COMMUNITY ROUTES

By Annah MacKenzie

Streets are our most fundamental shared public spaces, but they are also one of the most contested and overlooked. Today, and for most of the last century, we have taken for granted the idea that our streets are primarily zones for cars, parking, and the transporting of goods. This has not been the case, however, throughout most of history. Across many cultures and times — since the beginning of civilization, in fact — the street has held vast social, commercial, and political significance as a powerful symbol of the public realm.

The street was "the first institution of the city," as architect Louis Kahn once wrote, and even if we don't always recognize it, streets are still a powerful force in shaping our physical and mental landscapes. We name them after our idols and fallen heroes — in remembrance of presidents or literary figures, civil rights leaders or old Hollywood stars. In many of our own lives and experiences, they are sites for both celebration and rebellion: Stages for summer block parties and holiday parades, they are also the place we gather to express public dissent — as with recent demonstrations following the grand jury decisions in St. Louis and New York, where millions took to the street in protest of widespread police brutality and racial injustice. When streets function well on the level of

DEFINITIONS

Complete Streets: Streets designed and operated to enable safe access for all users, including pedestrians, bicyclists, motorists and transit riders of all ages and abilities.

New Urbanism: An urban design movement which promotes environmentally-friendly habits by creating walkable neighborhoods containing a wide range of housing and job types.

Smart Growth: An approach to development that curbs urban sprawl by encouraging a mix of building types and uses, diverse housing and transportation options, development within existing neighborhoods, and community engagement.

Transit Oriented Development: A type of community development that creates compact, walkable, pedestrian-oriented, mixed-use communities centered around high quality public transportation.

everyday experience, they provide opportunities for people to connect in a way that no other public space can.

Despite the central role they continue to play in each of our lives and memories, today's streets are failing us on multiple scales. Our streets once functioned as multiple-use town centers, as places where children could play and where neighbors and strangers would stop for conversation; today they have become the primary and near-exclusive domain of cars.

Beyond traffic and safety issues, many of our generation's most pressing challenges are bound in some way to our relationship with streets and the built environment: Reduced physical activity is a leading culprit of our current epidemics of obesity and chronic disease; lack of access to good places has led to widespread social isolation and depression (particularly amongst older populations); increased vehicle emissions have degraded air quality and contributed to the greenhouse gases causing climate change; and a lack of transportation options for many communities has caused uneven access to jobs, social services, healthy food options, and community interaction.

Clearly, we need to start thinking seriously about how we can reverse these trends and begin turning streets back into places — into destinations for culture, creativity, and community. If streets have "lost their importance in terms of their share of land," and their "prominent role in shaping the culture and history of cities," as indicated in a 2013 UNHabitat report, then how did we move so far away from this ideal?

MAKING ROOM FOR CARS: A BRIEF HISTORY OF THE MOTOR-CENTRIC CITY

When we build our landscape around places to go, we lose places to be. — Rick Cole

Traffic and road capacity are not just inevitable fallouts of progress and growth. Rather, they are the results of deliberate plans to design and organize communities around the private automobile. When modernist architect Le Corbusier envisioned the urban street as a "machine for producing traffic" in 1924, congestion had already begun to cause serious problems in major cities like Paris and New York. "The congestion is so complete," he wrote, "that in New York businessmen leave their automobiles in the outskirts and take the subway to the office. An amazing paradox!" His solution? Design streets solely around the car — eliminate pedestrians, wide boulevards, and sidewalk cafés altogether. Not only would this alleviate unwanted congestion, so his theory went, but it would also reduce social ills such as crime and public revolt.

In the United States, similar concerns about increasing traffic congestion in cities, which reached a climax after World War II, led to a mass expansion of national road systems. Plans for a high-speed freeway system would culminate a decade later with the 1956 Interstate Highway Act, which would erect a 42,500-mile network of high-speed, limited-access highways that linked cities from coast to coast.

As history has shown, the "freeway rush" of the following two decades would leave lasting, sometimes devastating, marks on the physical and social landscapes of the nation. Not only would highway construction actually *increase* traffic in residential and commercial areas, but it would also drive development away from cities. In the process, established residential neighborhoods would be divided, often destroyed in the name of "slum clearing," and the availability and value of urban housing would decline as much of the middle-class population migrated to the suburbs. These shifts, along with the de-concentration of economic activity as it moved to the suburban periphery, worked to further disenfranchise poor and largely nonwhite inner-city communities.

In short, because of single-minded assumptions that the car was and always would be king in America, for most of the past century cities and communities have been designed to meet *mobility* needs rather than *human* needs like social interaction, physical activity, or a connection to place. We still need highways, of course. Roads that facilitate efficient travel from point A to point B are essential for the national economy, for our mobility, and for modern life writ large. But some of our streets — especially those in our cities, neighborhoods, and downtowns — need to become more multifunctional to accommodate a greater variety of activities and users.

Even though our values and demographics have shifted dramatically over the past 70 years, the planning and engineering principles we are using to design and regulate our streets and cities, by and large, have not. Unless we make some significant changes, we will continue to get the same results: a few isolated great places linked by car-dominated streets, placeless sprawl, poor physical health, social isolation, and disinvested low-income communities.

That's the bad news.

The good news? It doesn't have to be this way! Streets can once again become thriving, livable environments for people, not just cars. Downtown streets can become cultural destinations, not just monotonous routes to and from the workplace. Neighborhood streets can become safe play zones for children, and commercial areas can become grand boulevards that welcome pedestrians, vendors, cyclists, and drivers alike. How? By focusing on creating great places, and centralizing this process in our policy and planning frameworks. This is where Streets as Places comes in.

THE PLACEMAKING MOVEMENT STARTS WITH STREETS

When the revolution starts, there should be no question of where to go. — Charles Moore

Streets as Places — as both an organizing concept and a strategy — can help make way for these transformations. Taking an integrative approach to the planning, design, and management of our shared public spaces, the growing Streets as Places movement is helping people begin to see streets in their entirety: not just their function in transporting people and goods, but the vital role they play in animating the social and economic life of communities. It's not a streetscape design, it's a process — it's about communities owning and reclaiming their streets, participating in civic life, and having a direct impact on how their public spaces look, function, and feel.

In the last two decades, with the mobilization of numerous alliances and coalitions, we have made great strides towards improving our streets. The Smart Growth, Complete Streets, and Active Transportation movements have been instrumental in moving transportation policy to better encourage multi-modal street designs that safely accommodate a range of users. Because of the efforts of these and other groups, nearly 700 communities in the U.S. have passed Complete Streets policies and the U.S. Department of Transportation has made it a major priority to create safer streets for bicyclists and pedestrians.

This is a huge step in the right direction! Making streets safe for all modes of transport — automobile, public transit, bicycle, pedestrian — is the first step in turning streets into *destinations* in their own right. But for streets to truly function as public places, they have to do more than allowing people to safely walk or bike through them. When streets are great places, they encourage people to linger, to socialize, and to truly experience the unique culture and character of a particular street.

With a growing number of examples from around the globe, more and more people and institutions are realizing that access to good places is a right, not an option or privilege that only a fortunate few can enjoy. Whether it's through the adoption of transportation initiatives (such as road diets and rightsizing, Vision Zero, or the Shared Space concept), through efforts to boost the local economy by revitalizing Main Streets and experimenting with block makeovers, or through creative Placemaking projects involving public art and community programming (like City Repair and "Paint the Pavement" projects), cities everywhere are beginning to move away from a narrow perception of streets as mere conduits for cars. On local and national levels, designers and planners, government agencies, nonprofits, community organizations, and ordinary citizens are thinking of the potential of streets to once again be livable and productive places — for bicycles, for markets, for businesses, for people.

Even in our own backyard, out the window of our Manhattan office, we at PPS watched in excitement over the past year as Lafayette Street underwent some significant transformations. A block away, one of our favorite lunch spots has just applied with the NYCDOT for a Street Seat — a 6'x25' platform that replaces several parking spots to enable seasonal public open spaces where sidewalk seating isn't available. We can't wait for spring, when, if all goes according to plan, we can stroll down our street to share a meal with co-workers and neighbors, lingering together on our impromptu island as we watch the vibrant life of the street on either side of us.

As the energy surrounding Placemaking continues to gain momentum, the time is ideal for rallying around the Streets as Places movement! Together, we can turn our streets — our most vital public resources — into interactive, functional, and fulfilling places for everyone. Here are some ways you can get involved:

1. **Make your own street a place.** Think about ways you can improve the block where you live or work. Small measures, like planting a tree or flowers, putting out a Little Free Library in your front yard, or organizing a block party are great ways to start. Remember, if your house or building faces out onto the street, it's part of the street and people's experience as they pass by it.

2. **Organize an Open Streets.** Dozens of cities across the country now regularly close their streets to cars for special events, allowing people to take advantage of the whole right-of-way. It's a great way to help people see streets in a new light, and to open a conversation about how our streets should be used.

3. **Consider "Lighter, Quicker, Cheaper" strategies** to improve and activate your streets. There are many relatively low-cost, quick ways to transform your streets, from layering in public art or benches, building street seats or parklets, rightsizing projects that prioritize pedestrians, holding special events or concerts on the street, to lighting displays. For more inspiration, check out the Better Block and Tactical Urbanism projects.

4. **Support small businesses that activate streets.** Local shops, like hardware stores, bakeries, and coffee shops are vital places in our communities. When they're located along a Main Street, they help encourage people to walk, enhance the local economy, and encourage neighborly interaction. Shop local, and encourage these businesses to think about how they can help enhance the street to benefit their bottom line and the neighborhood through creative window or outdoor merchandise displays, a bench or seating on the sidewalk, attractive landscaping, hosting local events, or getting involved in the local Main Street or merchant's association.

5. **Advocate for safe streets.** To make people feel comfortable walking and spending time on a street, it

needs first and foremost to be a safe place. Too many Americans, particularly seniors and children, are killed and injured on our streets every year. Reducing vehicle speeds and safe infrastructure for those walking and biking — sidewalks, protected bike lanes, crosswalks, and medians — are critical to making a street a place for people. Learn about the role of local transportation agencies in street design and how you can effectively impact these processes by downloading PPS's "Citizen's Guide to Better Streets" here. It's free!

6. **Ask your local transportation departments and elected officials to support measures that recognize streets as places for people.** Streets should be safe for people to walk and to bike; they can have places to gather together; they should highlight local talent and can close to vehicles during special celebrations or for market days. Check out PPS's 'What Makes a Great Place?' to help diagnose how your community's streets stack up.
7. **Think Beyond the Station.** Bring life to local transit stops! People waiting for the bus or metro deserve better than standing next to a pole without any seat or shelter. With some basic amenities and creative design, transit stops can be places where people actually want to spend time.
8. **Get involved in local projects and groups.** There are efforts in every community across the country already working to create better streets for people, including biking and walking organizations, smart growth groups, and Main Street associations. Join one and ask how you can help.
9. **Celebrate success!** Nominate a "Great Street" to our updated Great Public Spaces web resource. Is there a street in your community, or that you've encountered in your travels, that deserves recognition? Let us know! Help us in generating an ongoing conversation about the important role of Streets as Places in communities across the world.

What do streets mean to you, and what are the features that make a street truly great? By taking small steps to activate the streets in our own cities and neighborhoods, together we can affect real change in reclaiming our right to this dynamic public space. To the streets, everyone!

Dr. Annah MacKenzie is the VP of Communications at the Project for Public Spaces. Annah holds a PhD in American Culture from the University of Michigan, specializing in 20th century visual and material culture.

For more information about placemaking and taking back public spaces, see the Community Session in this course.

THE ENVIRONMENTAL COST OF FREE 2-DAY SHIPPING

By Andy Murdock

It's easy to see why online shopping is so popular. Just a couple of clicks and that new pair of socks is winging its way to you at breakneck speed. And they can get it to you in two days for free? Click.

But we care about the planet, so should we really be shipping individual pairs of socks? Or should we just drive to the closest store?

There are lots of good arguments for buying local, but if you're trying to reduce your impact on the climate, local isn't always best. If you compare online shopping with driving to the store, in many cases online shopping can have a smaller carbon footprint: Trucks have to deliver goods to stores, just like they do to your house.

Problems start when we opt for speed: We don't just want things delivered to our door, we want them delivered to our door right now. If we can get a pair of socks delivered in two days instead of five, we're going to choose the faster option, especially if it's free.

"Before, companies were able to consolidate, to optimize their distribution. Now, because some of them are offering really fast and rushed deliveries, that disintegrates the consolidation," said Miguel Jaller, from the Institute for

Transportation Studies at the University of California Davis. "Every individual is buying more and wanting those goods to be at their home really fast. That creates more vehicles, more traffic, and potentially more emissions."

From a logistical perspective, the ability to get a pair of socks delivered to your door in less than a day is something of a triumph. But from a climate perspective, that speedy pair of socks takes us in completely the wrong direction, putting more of the most polluting vehicles on the road.

"If you look at passenger vehicles, they're pretty darn clean at this point," said Matt Barth, director of the Center for Environmental Research and Technology and a professor at UC Riverside. "Trucks are a different animal."

Unlike passenger vehicles in the US, the focus of the bulk of emissions regulations to date, most trucks still run on diesel fuel, which produces larger amounts of air pollutants. Swapping clean car traffic for dirty truck traffic is a big step backward.

This doesn't mean you have to throw out your holiday shopping list from climate guilt: There are things we can do right now to make online shopping cleaner. On the consumer side, we can opt for slower shipping times and try to consolidate our orders. From the company side, they could be doing a lot more to nudge us in that direction by providing incentives and simply alerting us to the fact that slower is greener — and it saves companies money, on top.

Delivery companies have been working on efficiency for decades, mostly to reduce costs. Since the 1970s, UPS has worked on ways to encourage drivers to take fewer left turns, reducing their emissions by around 100,000 metric tons of carbon dioxide every year. New technologies, from smart traffic lights that communicate with delivery vehicles to trucks that can drive in tight platoons to reduce wind drag and save on fuel, are also speeding our way in the coming years to help solve this problem.

Andy Murdock is a writer, editor and content strategist. His writing has appeared in the *San Francisco Chronicle, Washington Post, CNN, Vox, Discovery, USA Today, BBC Travel, Gadling, Thrillist, Savvy Sugar*, and more, as well as in several Lonely Planet books.

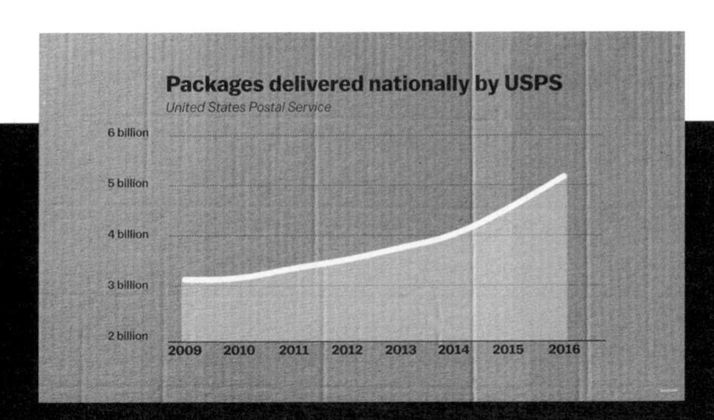

AIR TRAVEL

If you are like many people in developed nations, flying may be a large part of your carbon footprint. Air travel currently contributes around 2.5% to total carbon emissions in the world, and 11 percent of all transportation-related carbon emissions in the United States.

Although no other human activity pushes individual carbon emission levels as fast and as high as air travel, most of us don't know much about — and don't take the time to think about — its impact on climate change. If you travel by airplane, you will add a significant amount of greenhouse gases to the atmosphere — there's no way around it. But there are some ways to reduce the carbon footprint of your air travel. Here are a few suggestions:

1. **Figure out the carbon impact of your air travel.** Start out by using a carbon calculator to learn about the carbon impact of your jet setting. Awareness is the very first step in knowing how to make your carbon footprint smaller.

WATCH THIS VIDEO!
Climate Lab: The Environmental Cost of Free Two-Day Shipping

tinyurl.com/voxshipping

Find out more about how making two-day shipping the default option affects the planet and what you can do about it in this fun and informative video created by University of California's Climate Lab team.

2. **Fly less often.**
   This is the most effective way to reduce your carbon footprint. More people taking fewer flights would mean that airline companies wouldn't burn as much jet fuel.

   Flying becomes more efficient the longer the distance covered because cruising requires less fuel than other stages of flight. So flying cross-country is a better idea than driving that distance solo. If your trip is short, however, it may be better to drive.
3. **Choose nonstop flights.**
   Flying nonstop can help reduce your carbon footprint, too. The more times you take off, the more fuel you use: according to a 2010 report from NASA, about 25 percent of airplane emissions come from landing and taking off, including taxiing.
4. **If you fly, offset it.**
   Buying carbon offsets lets you pay to take a certain amount of carbon dioxide out of the atmosphere to balance out the planet-warming greenhouse gases your lifestyle puts into it. For example, you can put money toward replanting trees, which absorb carbon dioxide from the atmosphere.

   Some airlines — like Delta, United and JetBlue, among others — offer the ability to purchase carbon offsets. You might have to search a little bit -- they aren't usually offered as an options during the booking process, and some airlines only offer offsets on separate sustainability pages. You can also buy offsets through other organizations like Terrapass.
5. **Fly coach.**
   A World Bank study estimates that the emissions associated with flying in business class are about three times as great as flying in coach.

   In business class and first class, fewer people take up more room, so fewer people are being moved by the same amount of fuel. A first-class seat could use as much as nine times the carbon as an economy seat.
6. **Be intentional in your airline choice.**
   You can check the fuel efficiency of the airlines you fly. A report from the International Council on Clean Transportation shows Alaska Airlines and Spirit Airlines were the most efficient domestic carriers in 2010. American Airlines and Allegiant Air were at the bottom of the list of the 15 largest airlines.

Sources: https://www.nytimes.com/2017/07/27/climate/airplane-pollution-global-warming.html?_r=0
https://theconversation.com/its-time-to-wake-up-to-the-devastating-impact-flying-has-on-the-environment-70953
http://www.theicct.org/sites/default/files/publications/U.S.%20Airlines%20Ranking%20Report%20final.pdf

AMERICA'S 'WORST WALKING CITY' GETS BACK ON ITS FEET

By Jay Walljasper

The US gave up on walking in the mid-20th Century — at least planners and politicians did. People on foot were virtually banished from newly constructed neighborhoods. Experts assured us that cars and buses (and eventually helicopters and jet packs) would efficiently take us everywhere we wanted to go.

But thankfully, Americans refused to stop walking. Today — even after seventy years of auto-centered transportation policies — more than 10 percent of all trips are on foot, according to Paul Herberling of the US Department of Transportation. That number rises to 28 percent for trips under one mile.

Indeed, we are in the midst of a walking renaissance as millions of people discover a daily stroll can prevent disease, boost energy, ease stress, connect us with our communities, and is just plain fun. The number of us who regularly take a walk has risen 6 percent in the last decade, according to the US Centers for Disease Control and Prevention. Eighty four percent of Americans–even higher for those under 35 –want to live in a place that's walkable, according to a new study from the National Association of Realtors.

Walking's popularity now reaches beyond older city neighborhoods into suburbs and the Sun Belt. Even Oklahoma City — which was named as the "worst US walking city" in a 2008 study of 500 communities by Prevention magazine and the American Podiatric Medical Association — is embarking on big plans to become more walkable. This is no small task in a community whose land area is the 4th largest of any US town outside of Alaska, and its population density close to the lowest of any major US city.

"Bleak" is how Jeff Speck, urban planner and author of Walkable City, describes walking in Oklahoma City seven years ago. "Traffic sped too fast...for pedestrians to feel comfortable on the sidewalks...oversized traffic lanes encouraged highway speeds," he wrote in Planning magazine. Speck went on to note "street trees were in short supply" in a place where summer temperatures regularly hit 100 degrees, and that three- and four-lane one-way streets without parking meant pedestrians walked exceedlingly close to roaring traffic. He calculated that the city had twice as many car lanes as it needed.

The city also suffered from perhaps the worst sidewalk network in America. Most other towns conscientiously built sidewalks until the 1950s, but Oklahoma City abandoned the effort as early as the 1930s in some neighborhoods. As an oil town on the sparsely settled plains, people here embraced autos ahead of other cities, explains AJ Kirkpatrick, Director of Planning for the local downtown business improvement association. "We forgot what it meant to be a city," Kirkpatrick says.

Mick Cornett, the city's Republican mayor since 2004, notes, "We built a great community if you were a car, but if you were a person you were combating the car all day."

"We probably were last in the country for walking," Cornett admits.

This rock-bottom rating really stung in a community that had earlier been passed over by United Airlines as the site for a new maintenance facility because, despite the city's generous financial incentives, the company's CEO said he couldn't imagine asking his managers to move to Oklahoma City.

Then, a year after the walk rankings, the city again found itself in the harsh glare of unwanted media attention. This time Men's Fitness magazine stigmatized Oklahoma City as the "#2 fattest city" in America. Among the country's 100 largest cities, only Miami was more corpulent.

"People are 14 percent less likely than average to go for a walk, the 4th lowest rate of any city in our survey," Men's Fitness reported. "Oklahoma City residents are 28 percent less likely to participate in fitness walking than average, the 2nd lowest overall participation rate among cities in our survey."

But that's all changing. Speck notes that many cities on the worst walking list merely shrugged at their low rank. But in Oklahoma City, he reports, "the City and its leading institutions responded to this wake-up call in an unprecedented way. The outcome of this effort constitutes nothing less than the complete rebuilding of all streets in the downtown core."

Also, an ambitious $18-million sidewalk improvement fund was approved by voters as part of a tax increase that also included money for parks, transit, bike trails and senior wellness centers around town. Four busy streets heading into downtown are now being narrowed, with new "smart intersections" that provide walkers more safety with "refuge island" medians in the middle of streets and clearly marked crosswalks.

So what's driving all this pedestrian progress?

For one thing Mayor Cornett, a former sportscaster, bristled at his city being called fat and sedentary. Yet he knew that he couldn't credibly deny these charges since he'd gained enough extra pounds while in office to be labeled obese, thanks to endless rounds of breakfast and lunch meetings. So Cornett launched an initiative to get the city back in shape, which he announced in front of the elephant exhibit at the city zoo.

Over the past seven years, Cornett notes, Oklahoma City has added 400 new miles of sidewalks, built 7.5 miles of bike lanes on the streets (there were none in 2008), added 100 more miles to the recreational trail network, built new gyms at many public schools, created a public rowing center and started work on an whitewater kayak and rafting course on the Oklahoma River. Low-income neighborhoods, where health and obesity issues are most severe, are the biggest focus of the city's programs for healthy eating and active living.

Cornett also issued a successful Challenge for Oklahoma Citians to lose one million pounds. Forty-seven thousand people signed up, and lost on average 20 pounds. Cornett himself shed 38. One major thrust of this campaign was working with fast food restaurant to offer healthier menus. Cornett is proud of this partnership and during our interview slipped into his office closet to fetch a life-size cardboard cut-out of himself posing with Taco Bell's low-fat options, which was displayed in the chain's 40 Oklahoma City restaurants.

This all seems to be making a difference — the growth in Oklahoma City's obesity rate has slowed significantly from six percent annually to one percent, with the stage set for reductions in the future.

The mayor is quick to share credit. First and foremost, he applauds local citizens, who voted for a penny more in sales tax over seven years to pay for health initiatives. Oklahoma, he points out, is a very conservative state —

the only one where Obama did not carry a single county in either 2008 or 2012. Yet Oklahomans are willing to raise taxes when they know where their money is going. "They like projects where they can see the results," he points out. "And this is not debt and it's not a permanent tax — it's up for renewal every few years."

Cornett views this spending as a smart business move, noting that the 2010 tax referendum, and two earlier ones under previous mayors focusing on downtown revitalization and public education, amassed $2 billion in public investment which in turn spawned $6 billion more in private development.

"Ever since we decided to make this a great place for people to live, the jobs started coming here and young Millennials, who want to bike and walk, are arriving in numbers we've never seen before," he says. "We are creating a city where your kids and grandkids will choose to stay. They used to go to Dallas or Houston."

That was the goal that Jeff Speck laid out for the city in a 2009 walkability study:

"As cities compete to attract corporations, citizens, and especially young, entrepreneurial talent, the winners will be those places that can claim the sort of environment and culture that is favored by creative class and millennial workers. Studies document how these workers favor communities with street life, the pedestrian culture that arises from walkablity."

"It turned out that one thing people–especially young people–wanted was better sidewalks," Cornett explains. That's why the city now builds new sidewalks as part of most repaving projects and kicks in half the cost for any homeowner or neighborhood that wants them. Developers are now required to provide sidewalks in all new projects. As for the $18 million earmarked for sidewalks from sales tax revenue, "most of it goes where we know we need sidewalks, connecting schools and shopping centers with neighborhoods," the mayor says.

While most people consider walking essential to a good neighborhood, there's still of opposition. "We hear from those who say, 'We don't need sidewalks, because no one walks here,'" Cornett says, noting that the absence of sidewalks is a big reason people don't walk.

A Safe Routes to Schools program, making it possible for more school kids to walk or bike, and a Vision Zero campaign, aimed at eliminating all traffic fatalities in the city, are both in the works, says John Tankard of the city's planning department. The city also holds Open Streets events — festivals where a street is blocked off to vehicles so people of all ages can feel what it's like to be kings of the road.

"We've come a long ways in a short time," says Cristina Fernandez McQuistion, who moved from Santa Monica– one of the most walkable communities in California — for an executive position at a local firm. "But we still have a long ways to go."

Walkscore, which rates the walkability of any address in America, still ranks Oklahoma City in the lower 15 percent of cities over 200,000, which is nonetheless a big improvement over last place. The city's low score can be partly explained by the fact that sprawling subdivisions, which would be classified as separate municipalities elsewhere, are inside the city limits here.

The epicenter of walking in Oklahoma City is downtown and nearby neighborhoods, which exhibit all the signs of urban vitality: sidewalk cafes, new loft apartments, refurbished old neighborhoods with local business districts, indy shops and restaurants, nightlife, sports and entertainment venues, well-populated parks, riverside bike trails, and sidewalks alive with people of all ages walking between these spots.

An old warehouse district with a pedestrian promenade along a canal thrums with activity. A 70-acre central park is being developed that will connect downtown with a largely Latino neighborhood on the South Side via a new pedestrian bridge. A streetcar line debuts later this year that will loop through many of these neighborhoods. Protected bike lanes, which physically separate bicyclists and pedestrians from rushing traffic, will soon appear on major arteries coming in and out of downtown.

Oklahoma City's mission now is to widen the walkable heart of the city outward. Local transit service has been improved (including new Sunday and evening buses), resulting in an eight percent jump in ridership, according to the planning department's John Tankard (whose wife Elizabeth writes a blog Carless in OKC). The Wheeler District, a new pedestrian-focused infill neighborhood south of downtown, breaks ground this year with plans to create 2000 homes.

North of downtown, things are already picking up. "You have a lot of young people moving into the area because they can walk," says Fernandez McQuistion, who lives in the Crown Heights neighborhood. Business districts scattered throughout this part of town, some of which once harbored crack houses and brothels, now flourish with restaurants and shops catering to local residents. She, her husband and kids are still waiting for sidewalks on their street but already are walking more "because there are now more places to walk to." An attractive streetscape to improve the pedestrian ambience of the Western Avenue business district near their home makes walking more fun. "When we go anywhere in the neighborhood now, we usually go on foot," she says.

Jay Walljasper is a Senior Fellow at Project for Public Spaces. He writes, speaks, edits and consults about creating stronger, more vital communities. Jay is the author of *The Great Neighborhood Book* and *All That We Share: A Field Guide to the Commons*.

MILLENNIALS IN TRANSIT

By Derek Prall

Since automobiles were invented over a century ago, they have shaped the way we think about and order our lives. And with the advent of the interstate highway system after World War II, and the subsequent explosion of suburbs, cars have become the linchpin of American modernity. However, this a *priori* assumption that to thrive in America you have to drive is being questioned like never before.

For myriad reasons, Millennials — the 83 million people born between 1982 and 2003 — are rejecting cars in favor of alternative modes of transportation. As these young people are the next generation of innovators and up-and-comers in the workforce, it's no surprise that communities offering viable and multiple alternative transportation options are growing. If our cities want to experience similar growth trends, they are going to have to fundamentally rethink their transportation structures.

HOW DID WE GET HERE?

There are numerous reasons for the shifts we're seeing today, Darnell Grisby, director of policy and research at the American Public Transportation Association (APTA), says. "[Millennials] definitely want to live in communities that are walkable and have transit nearby," he says. "[According to APTA data] it's about 10 points higher than you'll find with baby boomers — 41 percent to 33 percent."

The reason for this sudden uptick, Grisby explains, is that Millennials increasingly see themselves as multimodal. "They are pragmatic consumers of mobility," he says. "They consider the best trip option… and consider these options for every time they decide to go somewhere, whereas earlier generations had a predilection for getting in the car for every trip they took."

Al McWilliams, a millennial that sits on the Ann Arbor, Mich., Downtown Development Authority Board, agrees that transportation options are important, and by addressing transit responsibly and realistically, a great many social ills could be assuaged.

"Transportation is affected and affects everything from equity to housing problems to infrastructure costs to safety," he says, pointing out that tens of thousands of Americans die traffic accidents every year — a figure he finds unacceptable. "If you tried to invent the car today, you'd be put in jail," he jokes.

Overall, for a millennial considering their transportation methods, optimization is the biggest consideration, McWilliams says, but this doesn't necessarily mean taking the fastest route — it's about the optimization of time, the optimization of money and the optimization of life in general.

One of the biggest considerations is for Millennials is cost, Nick Helmholdt, the acting director of Comprehensive Planning at the Chatham County — Savannah Metropolitan Planning Commission, says. Simply put, cars cost a lot of money, and there is a growing desire among Millennials to live frugal, debt free lives — imposed by internal or external factors. When other transportation options are available and cheaper, cars are increasingly seen as a luxury item rather than a necessity.

Technology is also a considerable factor — not only does technology allow for the optimization of time while on public transportation (checking work email, reading the news, socializing online, etc.), but telecommunications and e-commerce have diminished the need for people to actually go to physical places, and city planners seem to be ignoring how disruptive these technologies will be, Helmholdt says.

"Technology is changing the prioritization of the locations people need to be," he explains. "If you can access [any number of] services from your phone, you won't need to go to the post office to drop off the mail, you don't need to go to these places that might be inconvenient. It's definitely changing travel behaviors." Even the traditional work commute is being upended by a technologically facilitated ability to work from anywhere. Fewer Millennials are driving to traditional offices, as a result.

Environmental considerations also play a key role in our shifting transportation patterns. "We know that Millennials care about the environment," says Grisby. "About half of them in our survey (Millennials & Mobility: Understanding the Millennial Mindset) said that one of the reasons they take public transit is because it's good for the environment. That is, in fact, a core value that they have."

WHERE ARE WE GOING?

These changes in desires and values are generating a dialogue about whether automotive dependency should be a foregone conclusion in our nation's cities, but in order to offer what Millennials are demanding, our cities will need to change in both structure and ideology.

As with anything in local government, funding is the first — and often seemingly insurmountable — hurdle in providing the transit options Millennials are looking for. Fitting subway tunnels with the infrastructure to provide WiFi on trains, for example, is an extremely expensive, time-consuming task, Grisby says. "We want to be responsive," he says, "but we're facing headwinds when it comes to funding."

However, the responsibility doesn't fall squarely on the government's shoulders. Rideshare programs and even app-based companies like Uber and Lyft can work into the mobility fabric of an urban environment. "We find that ridesharing does, in fact, expand the catchment area of public transportation service," Grisby says. "People are using ridesharing to get to a train stop or bus rapid transit station, which helps our transit systems serve more people." Grisby adds some transit systems are actually partnering with rideshare apps to increase their reach.

Ultimately though, it comes down to priority. "If you look at the evolution of our cities, there was a period where there was a disinvestment," Grisby says. "Now the cities are coming back and the question now is how do you update those transit systems to reflect that growth."

It starts by convincing public leaders that diverse transportation modalities are important to the success of our cities — a fact on which most experts agree. "It's getting over the mental road block that cars are the only way to get around," Helmholdt says.

This fight played out in downtown Ann Arbor recently, McWilliams says, in the form of a proposed parking structure. He and others argued that the structure was unnecessary and would only exacerbate downtown traffic. "We're dealing with a limited geographical area… and if we're going to be sustainable we need to get more people into that geographic area every day. We simply cannot do so one at a time, each in their own car."

McWilliams said the now-scrapped plan for the parking structure was that it would pay for itself over 20 years, but he questions if that parking would even be necessary 10 years from now. "If we play the game right," he says, "It won't be."

The good news, Helmholdt says, is that nothing new needs to be invented. "We have all of the tools and strategies needed to solve these issues readily available," he says. "We know the answers already, the question is how do you implement them, how do you do them in a manner that is logical and sequential and fiscally stable."

Derek Prall is a multiple award-winning international journalist whose held numerous positions with a variety of print and online publications including the *New Jersey Herald, The Public Manager Magazine* and *TD* magazine. He's a 2008 graduate of Furman University holding bachelor's degrees in both English Literature and Communications Studies.

CITY PLANNERS RESPOND TO DEMANDS FOR BETTER NEIGHBORHOOD MOBILITY AND BICYCLING INFRASTRUCTURE

By Araz Hachadourian

TENNESSEE

North Nashville was once a "mobility desert": A highway dissected the neighborhood, and public transportation left many areas without service. For young people, the burden was especially heavy.

"When you get dropped off of the school bus, you're pretty much confined to your neighborhood," says Dan Furbish, who runs Oasis Bike Workshop, which provides students with bicycles and mentoring. He finds that many kids have not visited parks just 2 miles from their homes.

To make the case for better neighborhood mobility, Furbish's class of middle and high school students mapped their movements around North Nashville, tracking the spaces they visited most and the barriers that kept them from getting around, such as the lack of crosswalks and paths. They developed suggestions for connecting North Nashville to the rest of the city, eventually sharing their findings with urban planners.

After meeting with the class, city planners incorporated a new bicycle lane along Rosa L. Parks Boulevard. Although the lane stretched only 2 miles, it created a bicycle route across the interstate, connecting North Nashville to downtown.

ILLINOIS

Studies show that improving city bike infrastructure isn't just good for reducing traffic congestion. More sidewalks and bike lanes also boost health, generate business for local merchants, and help people feel more connected to their communities. The reason is simple: Moving through a city at 10 miles per hour allows for taking in more than if zooming by in a car.

With those benefits in mind and inspired by a community bike project in Detroit, Jamal Julien and Oboi Reed launched Slow Roll Chicago in 2014. Every Wednesday night, they lead group members — sometimes a few, sometimes a few hundred — on bike rides to introduce them to Chicago neighborhoods. "People don't patronize the local businesses here because of this narrative that there's crime and violence and you'll get killed," says Julien. "So what we found is that taking these people on the slow-based community rides, they can enjoy the local culture despite what the media says."

The program yielded an additional result. After riding through the South Side, cyclists were most alarmed by traffic, not violence, Julien says. Despite Chicago's commitment to being one of the most bikeable cities in the country, the South Side and West Side neighborhoods lacked a network of bike lanes.

Later that year, Slow Roll Chicago, together with other local cycling groups, published an open letter to Mayor Rahm Emanuel calling for the equitable distribution of bicycle resources across Chicago. They attended city meetings and cycling forums, spoke with officials, and organized with other cyclists to push the city to expand infrastructure.

Emanuel ultimately issued a revised plan promising every neighborhood a bike lane that connects to a greenway. Additionally, Slow Roll Chicago worked with the Department of Transportation to expand Divvy, the city's bike sharing system, to the South Side and to establish a subsidized annual fee and the ability to sign up without a credit card.

Araz Hachadourian wrote this article for *50 Solutions*, the Winter 2017 issue of *YES! Magazine*. Araz is a regular contributor to *YES! Magazine*. Follow her on Twitter @ahachad2.

POSSIBILITIES FOR CARS

By Project Drawdown

There are times and places where using a car is the only practical way to get from one place to another. Even if you are dependent upon a car to transport you, there are still ways to reduce your negative impact and increase your positive impact on your community, your health, and the planet. Consider these findings from Project Drawdown:

RIDESHARING

In 2015, the Oxford English Dictionary added ride-share to its pages. Ridesharing is the act of filling empty seats by pairing drivers and riders who share common origins, destinations, or stops en route. When trips are pooled, people split costs, ease traffic, and lighten the load on infrastructure, while curtailing emissions per person.

A wave of technologies has accelerated ridesharing's popularity:

- Smartphones allow people to share real-time information about where they are and where they are going.
- The algorithms that match them with others and map the best routes are improving daily.
- Social networks are buoying trust, so individuals are more likely to hop in with someone they have not met.

Getting people to double or triple up in their cars is not always easy. When fuel is cheap, carpooling declines. An abundance of free or cheap parking also steers people to journey solo. So does the desire for autonomy, privacy, and expedience.

For many, cars have seemed indispensable to day-to-day life. But, increasingly, mobility is seen as a service to access. When cars are used collaboratively, you can catch a glimpse of the future — one with fewer cars overall.

Potential Impact: 0.32 gigaton reduction of CO2. Our projection for ridesharing focuses solely on people commuting to work in the United States and Canada, where rates of car ownership and driving alone are high. We assume that carpooling rises from 10 percent of car commuters in 2015 to 15 percent by 2050, and from an average of 2.3 to 2.5 people per carpool. Ridesharing has no implementation costs and can reduce emissions by 0.3 gigatons of carbon dioxide.

ELECTRIC VEHICLES

Since the first electric vehicle (EV) prototype was built in 1828, the central challenge has been making good on a lightweight, durable battery with adequate range. In its absence, internal combustion engines have dominated the automotive landscape since the 1920s, and the atmosphere has paid the price.

Luckily, there are now more than 1 million EVs on the road, and the difference in impact is remarkable. Compared to gasoline-powered vehicles, emissions drop by 50 percent if an EV's power comes off the conventional grid. If powered by solar energy, carbon dioxide emissions fall by 95 percent. The "fuel" for electric cars is cheaper too. EVs will disrupt auto and oil business models because they are simpler to make, have fewer moving parts, and require little maintenance and no fossil fuels.

What is the catch? With EVs, it is "range anxiety" — how far the car can go on a single charge. Typical today is a range of 80 to 90 miles, long enough for most daily travel. Carmakers are closing in on ranges of 200 miles, while keeping batteries affordable.

The rate of innovation in EVs guarantees they are the cars of the future. The question is how soon the future will arrive.

Potential Impact: 10.8 gigaton reduction of CO2. In 2014, 305,000 EVs were sold. If EV ownership rises to 16 percent of total passenger miles by 2050, 10.8 gigatons of carbon dioxide from fuel combustion could be avoided. Our analysis accounts for emissions from electricity generation and higher emissions of producing EVs compared to internal-combustion cars. We include slightly declining EV prices, expected due to declining battery costs.

COMING ATTRACTIONS: AUTONOMOUS VEHICLES

The convergence of motion sensors, GPS, electric vehicles, big data, radar, laser scanning, computer vision, and artificial intelligence is hastening the arrival of autonomous vehicles (AVs) — cars that drive themselves. Experts predict they will make up 75 percent of road vehicles by 2040. Whether AVs will have a benign, neutral, or negative impact on society and the planet is unclear.

How cars are owned and utilized today could not be less efficient: They are driven 4 percent of the time. If mobility comes to be viewed as an on-demand service — rather than private ownership of expensive, two-ton assemblages of steel, glass, plastic, and rubber — the material savings would be immense. The U.S. auto fleet could decline by 50 to 60 percent. But it would require a massive cultural shift.

There are other potential advantages. For starters, AV concept models are smaller and more aerodynamic. In dedicated lanes, they can form platoons and draft, as cyclists do in a peloton. Autonomy is likely to accelerate the adoption of electric vehicles because most trips are local and in battery range. Still, big questions remain: Will AVs be used for ridesharing or single occupancy? Will their convenience drive miles traveled up, rather than down?

Project Drawdown is a nonprofit organization and coalition of scholars, scientists, entrepreneurs, and advocates from across the globe that is mapping, measuring, modeling, and communicating about a collective array of substantive solutions to global warming. It's research program has developed realistic, solution-specific models, technical assessments, and policy memos projecting the financial and climate impacts of existing solutions deployed at scale over the next thirty years.

RETROFITTING SUBURBIA: COMMUNITIES INNOVATE THEIR WAY OUT OF SPRAWL

By Erin Sagen

The suburbs have lost a lot of luster in the past 70 years. What was once hailed as a refreshing alternative to the grittiness of city living has been tugged and pulled and paved into a series of brownfields and vacant parking lots that stretch for miles and miles. Public planners have been predicting "the end of suburbia" for at least a decade now, saying that peak oil will starve out those towns and subdivisions that subsist on sprawl.

Saddled with traffic congestion and infrastructural erosion, can suburbia be retrofitted into a sustainable model of development and adapt to a post-oil world?

When they emerged 150 years ago, suburban developments sat on the peripheries of cities like New York and allured the wealthy, who commuted by train to enjoy fresh air and privacy. Suburban train stations brimmed with activity and fed commercial centers around them. But when the automobile rolled off factory floors in the 1910s, it quickly seduced an eager public and transformed suburban downtowns built around the trains. Car ownership exploded, the concept of the suburban downtown disappeared, and Americans designed new communities around driving.

Today, the cost of that so-called freedom is clear: Suburbanites have twice the carbon footprint as city dwellers; they spend more on housing and transportation combined; and they're more likely to struggle with obesity or die in car crashes. These realities paint a far less rosy picture than the days of early commuters. But today an enthusiastic network of designers, city planners, lawmakers, and longtime locals are envisioning a new era for suburbia.

Transportation, specifically automobile traffic, is the most important reason to retrofit, because it directly impacts public health, affordability, and climate change, says Ellen Dunham-Jones, professor of architecture at Georgia Tech and author of Retrofitting Suburbia. Between 1990 and 2013, the number of people who drove to work alone increased by 25 million, and, in 2013, highway vehicles used 83.2 percent of total transportation energy, with personal vehicles accounting for 71.1 percent, according to the Bureau of Transportation Statistics.

"Development is pushing us farther and farther out, sometimes 10 to 12 miles outside a city. Savings get eaten up," Dunham-Jones says. "Transit helps people walk more, and they spend less money. But [in the suburbs], those people who can't commute — who can't afford rising gas prices and car expenses — are out of luck because there's limited access to transit."

Most of this hasn't eluded city-flocking millennials — almost two-thirds would prefer to live where driving is optional — nor has it eluded more than half the country — 54 percent of adults say it is too far to walk to shopping and entertainment, and 50 percent say that walkability is a top or high priority, according to a 2015 report by the Urban Land Institute.

But people live in the suburbs for many different reasons, despite the negative effects of sprawl. For one, rent is generally cheaper than in increasingly gentrified cities, especially in commercial centers; and two, it's more spacious and closer to nature.

Because so many people, both young and old, value walkability, communities must invest in smarter, denser infrastructure, Dunham-Jones says. How ironic, then, that the future of suburban development seems to be pointing backward — to the pre-automobile, train-based model.

The birthplace of modern suburbia is Long Island, New York, where the first mass-produced suburb, Levittown, started it all. Twenty minutes away in the town of Babylon lies a hamlet called Wyandanch. Conduct an Internet search, and you'll come across a pretty bleak scene there — stories of gang violence, poverty (13.4 percent), and unemployment (12.2 percent) run down the screen. But Wyandanch is more than a small, distressed suburb where even a McDonald's had to shutter. After all, it has a train station.

The train ride from downtown Wyandanch to Manhattan is only 50 minutes long. That is an incredible asset, says former Babylon Township Supervisor Steve Bellone, because it allows lower- and middle-income residents to work in the city but live in the suburbs, thereby financing their communities and bolstering their local economies.

Bellone had worked with community groups, and knew that, despite its boarded-up buildings and deadened parking lots, Wyandanch had a lot to offer. But he knew they couldn't wait for private investors to swoop in and save the day.

"The only way to make this successful is to get the community involved," says Bellone, whose team partnered with nonprofit Sustainable Long Island to kick off a three-day weekend of meetings and workshops with residents, planners, and local government officials.

After years of losing their younger residents to Brooklyn or Manhattan, dynamic places with walkability and abundant transit, the community concluded that what they needed was an affordable, transit-oriented downtown. The transformation would center around their train station, which required major upgrading. The 19th century septic system begged for some serious attention too. So with a low-interest federal loan and a state grant, in 2011 the community began construction on a 2-mile-long sewer line, with hopes of eventually attracting more investment. The sewer was step one in a plan called "Wyandanch Rising." The $500 million project is backed by federal funds, state tax credits, grants, and low-cost financing and is expected to enhance the original business district, which dried up years ago.

Today, construction of the new train station is almost finished. Next door, ground has been broken on Wyandanch Village, a pair of five-story mixed-use buildings that will house 177 apartments, from studios to three bedrooms — 123 reserved for lower-income tenants. The ground-floor commercial spaces will be no larger than 5,000 square feet each to discourage big-box stores, according to Sustainable Long Island's website.

There's still a long way to go — retrofitting doesn't fix poverty or gang violence overnight — but there is hope.

"We'll gain the benefits eventually," says longtime local Phyllis Henry. She's lived in Wyandanch for 43 years and has been actively involved with community development for much of that time. "But people are excited. It's come a long way, it really has. It's not just developing the brick and mortar, but also the people."

Bellone says he wants to see a community where innovation doesn't push people out but lifts them up. Whether Wyandanch can retrofit itself into a model of equitable and sustainable suburban development is uncertain, but one thing is sure: A new era has been born, and driving it is no longer the car but the community. Soon, rather than "the end of suburbia," planners may be predicting "the end of sprawl."

Erin Sagen wrote this article for *Life After Oil*, the Spring 2016 Issue of *YES! Magazine*. Erin is an associate editor at *YES! Magazine*. She lives in Seattle and writes about food, health, and suburban sustainability. Follow her on Twitter @erin_sagen.

ECOCHALLENGE: PUTTING IT INTO PRACTICE

Here are some ideas for putting what you learned this week into action. Find more ideas and commit to one Ecochallenge this week at **choices.ecochallenge.org**

- Use muscle power. Commit to only use muscle-powered transportation (like walking, biking or skateboarding) within a certain distance from your home this week.
- Use public transit. Reduce your carbon (and other emissions!) footprint by using public transit instead of driving this week.
- Research better transportation. Research one of the solutions presented in this week's session and see if there are any groups in your community already doing this work.
- Improve a bus stop. Improve a bus stop in your neighborhood by posting the stop schedule, adding seating or shelter, adding art or flowers, picking up litter, or some other small improvement.
- Find a Safe Route to School. With your children, plan a Safe Route to School for walking or biking.
- Opt out of 2-day shipping. If you purchase something online and don't immediately need it, choose the standard shipping option instead of 2-day shipping.

TRANSIT ORIENTED DEVELOPMENT

Transit Oriented Development (TOD) is the creation of compact, walkable, pedestrian-oriented, mixed-use communities centered around high quality train systems. TOD implies high quality, thoughtful planning and design of land use and built forms to support, facilitate and prioritize not only the use of transit, but the most basic modes of transport, walking and cycling.

The 8 Principles of the TOD standard for designing better streets and better cities:

1. **WALK**. Develop neighborhoods that promote walking.
2. **CYCLE**. Prioritize non-motorized transport networks.
3. **CONNECT**. Create dense networks of streets and paths.
4. **TRANSIT**. Locate development near high-quality public transport.
5. **MIX**. Plan for mixed use.
6. **DENSIFY**. Optimize density and transit capacity.
7. **COMPACT**. Create regions with short commutes.
8. **SHIFT**. Increase mobility by regulating parking and road us.

Source: Institute for Transportation and Development Policy, Transit Oriented Development Institute.

SESSION 7

CONSUMPTION & ECONOMY

"Only population growth rivals consumption as a cause of ecological decline, and at least population growth is now viewed as a problem by many governments and citizens of the world. Consumption, in contrast, is almost universally seen as a good — indeed, increasingly it is the primary goal of national economic policy."

— Alan Thein Durning

LEARNING OBJECTIVES

- **Describe the links among our economic systems, consumer culture, our consumption patterns, and environmental degradation.**
- **Examine some basic assumptions and principles of our current economic systems, such as economic growth.**
- **Develop your own ideas of alternatives to our current economic system and consumer culture.**
- **Envision your power as more than a consumer: a citizen, a community member, a creator, a change agent.**

SESSION DESCRIPTION

Of the three factors that determine the scope of human impact on Earth — population, technology, and affluence — the latter is where daily choices can make the greatest difference. For decades, increasing material consumption has been heralded by government and business as the key to economic progress and an indication of "the good life." Economic assumptions like this — and the public policies based on them — have far-reaching consequences. In this session, we challenge the ethos of consumer culture and offer suggestions for living more simply and justly on Earth.

REFLECTION

During this week, what did you notice about the consumption behaviors of yourself and those you know? How are consumption and economics tied together in your own life and/or where you live? Post your Reflection to your Dashboard on **choices.ecochallenge.org**. If you are not using the Ecochallenge site, write your thoughts in a journal and then reflect with your group.

In "What Isn't for Sale" by Michael Sandel, which example of what is for sale surprised you the most?

Reminder to the facilitator: The circle question should move quickly. Elicit an answer from each participant without questions or comments from others. The facilitator's guidelines are on page 10.

SUGGESTED DISCUSSION QUESTIONS

1. Do you agree with Michael Sandel, that GDP (a measurement of a nation's economic activity) has become detached from our morals? Is this a concern? If so, why? Give examples.
2. What do you see as the difference between a market economy and a market society?
3. What appeals to you most in the "How We Live" video? What steps are you able to take to help transition to this way of living?
4. Vandana Shiva talks about the subsidization of the fossil fuel economy. What do you think should be subsidized?
5. What are some cultural assumptions that feed consumerism? What can you do to examine and transform these assumptions in your own life?
6. How does it make you feel to know that obsolescence is built into the things you buy? Why has this practice changed over time?
7. What reusable items are easy to share? What natural resources can be saved by sharing reusable items?
8. Why is it important to support local businesses? What happens if you don't?

SUGGESTED GROUP ACTIVITY

If you would like to do an activity with your group, we recommend these.

- Avoid shopping online this week and shop locally for anything you need. Specifically, try to support businesses owned and operated by people who live in your neighborhood. Or, take it a step farther and avoid shopping altogether this week. Share your experiences and recommendations with the group.
- As a group, schedule a visit to your local landfill or transfer station. Where is the station located? Who is affected by its location? What do you notice about the things that people have thrown away?
- Talk to someone at least 20 years older than you about what they used to buy, make, throw away and repair. How is today's world different than it used to be?

FURTHER RESOURCES

Interested in finding out more on the topics presented in this session?
Visit our website for further readings and resources: **ecochallenge.org/discussion-course-resources.**
Follow our Facebook page to continue the discussion online:
facebook.com/Ecochallengeorg/

DETROIT SPEECH

By Robert F. Kennedy

Let us be clear at the outset that we will find neither national purpose nor personal satisfaction in a mere continuation of economic progress, in an endless amassing of worldly goods. We cannot measure national spirit by the Dow-Jones Average, nor national achievement by the gross national product.

For the gross national product includes air pollution and advertising for cigarettes, and ambulances to clear our highways of carnage. It counts special locks for our doors, and jails for the people who break them. The gross national product includes the destruction of the redwoods and the death of Lake Superior. It grows with the production of napalm and missiles and nuclear warheads and it even includes research on the improved dissemination of bubonic plague. The gross national product swells with equipment for the police to put down riots in our cities; and though it is not diminished by the damage these riots do, still it goes up as slums are rebuilt on their ashes. It includes Whitman's rifle and Speck's knife, and the broadcasting of television programs which glorify violence to sell goods to our children.

And if the gross national product includes all these, there is much that it does not comprehend. It does not allow for the health of our families, the quality of their education or the joy of their play. It is indifferent to the decency of our factories and the safety of our streets alike. It does not include the beauty of our poetry or the strength of our marriages, the intelligence of our public debate or the integrity of our public officials. It allows neither for the justice in our courts, nor for the justness of our dealings with each other. The gross national product measures neither our wit nor our courage, neither our wisdom nor our learning, neither our compassion nor our devotion to country. It measures everything, in short, except that which makes life worthwhile; and it can tell us everything about America, except whether we are proud to be Americans.

This speech was delivered by Robert F. Kennedy, May 5, 1967.

DEFINITIONS

Capitalism: An economic system in which investment in and ownership of the means of production, distribution, and exchange of wealth is made and maintained chiefly by private individuals or corporations,especially as contrasted to cooperatively or state-owned means of wealth.

Consumer culture: A form of capitalism in which the economy and culture are focused on the buying and selling of consumer goods and the spending of consumer money. Most economists agree that the United States is a consumer culture.

GDP: GDP stands for Gross Domestic Product and is the measurement of market value of all officially recognized goods and services produced within a country in a given period. GDP per capita is often considered an indicator of a country's standard of living.

Globalization: The process of international integration arising from the interchange of world views, products, ideas and other aspects of culture. This ongoing process has many effects and causes, and has particularly been both criticized and praised for the spread of free-market capitalism around the globe.

Life cycle assessment: A tool or technique used to assess the environmental impacts of all the stages of a product's life, from raw material extraction, to production, to transportation, to use, to disposal or recycling.

Neoliberalism: Neoliberalism is an ideology and policy model which emphasizes the value of free market competition. It views sustained economic growth as the means to achieve human progress and free markets as the most efficient allocation of resources. Neoliberalism emphasizes minimal state intervention in economic and social affairs and the freedom of trade and capital around the globe.

BEYOND THE GDP

The most common measure of economic progress is the Gross Domestic Product (GDP). It measures a nation's economic activity. It can go up in times of wealth, as well as in times of crisis: when a country is hit by a natural disaster the GDP goes up because of spending on reconstruction and medical treatment for the victims. For the past 60 years, GDP has been the main method for the measurement of people's well-being. But it has no way to measure how money is distributed within a country or how economic activity contributes to production and services that contribute to the health of a society and the environment.

Rather than a simple mathematical equation of GDP, many people have been calling for a set of measures that not only includes financial cost but other costs as well, such as costs to the environment and to the society. There is growing awareness among governments and economists for a need to measure the subjective well-being of a country's inhabitants and resources in addition to economic progress. As this awareness of the need for alternative economic indicators grows, so does the discussion of what those indicators should be.

The folks at Demos — a research and advocacy organization focused on a more equitable economy, a robust democracy and a strong public sector — outline some of the main problems with GDP measurements (demos.org):

- **GDP does not distinguish between spending on bad things and spending on good things.** Events like hurricanes and wars increase GDP because of increased spending for clean up, supplies, government contracts, etc.
- **GDP doesn't account for the distribution of growth.** While our total national income has doubled in the past thirty years, average households have seen little or no income gains. Nearly all of U.S. national growth since 1980 went to the top 20 percent, and in the six years preceding the 2008 recession, nearly two-thirds went to the top 1 percent alone.
- **GDP doesn't account for depletion of natural capital and ecosystem services.** With GDP measurements, the value of ecosystem services like carbon absorption and erosion control is ignored. When these things are destroyed, the losses are not counted.
- **GDP doesn't reflect things that have no market price but are good for our society**, like volunteer work, parenting in the home, and public investments in education and research.

If GDP leaves so much out, how can we really measure our progress? Experts have developed many types of alternative indicators that bring us closer to reality. One is the Genuine Progress Indicator, or GPI, which starts with GDP but adjusts the level growth for as many as 26 factors of household, social, and environmental change. GPI was developed based upon green economics theories, which recognize the economy as part of the ecosystem. Over the last 50 years, a large and growing gap has emerged between GDP and GPI, indicating that a growing economy does not automatically mean improved well-being.

Additionally, the Himalayan Kingdom of Bhutan has famously chosen to measure Gross National Happiness (GNH) instead of GDP. GNH has four foundational pillars: sustainable and equitable socio-economic development; conservation of the environment; preservation and promotion of culture; and good governance.

Check out these other alternatives to GDP measurement:

- Social Progress Index: **socialprogressindex.com/**
- Happy Planet Index: **happyplanetindex.org/**
- The Good Country Index: **goodcountry.org/index/results**
- Global Slavery Index: **globalslaveryindex.org/**
- Global Peace Index: **visionofhumanity.org/indexes/global-peace-index/**
- Environmental Performance Index: **epi.yale.edu/**
- World Happiness Report: **worldhappiness.report/**

Information compiled by Betty Shelley and Lacy Cagle.
Visit www.demos.org for more information.

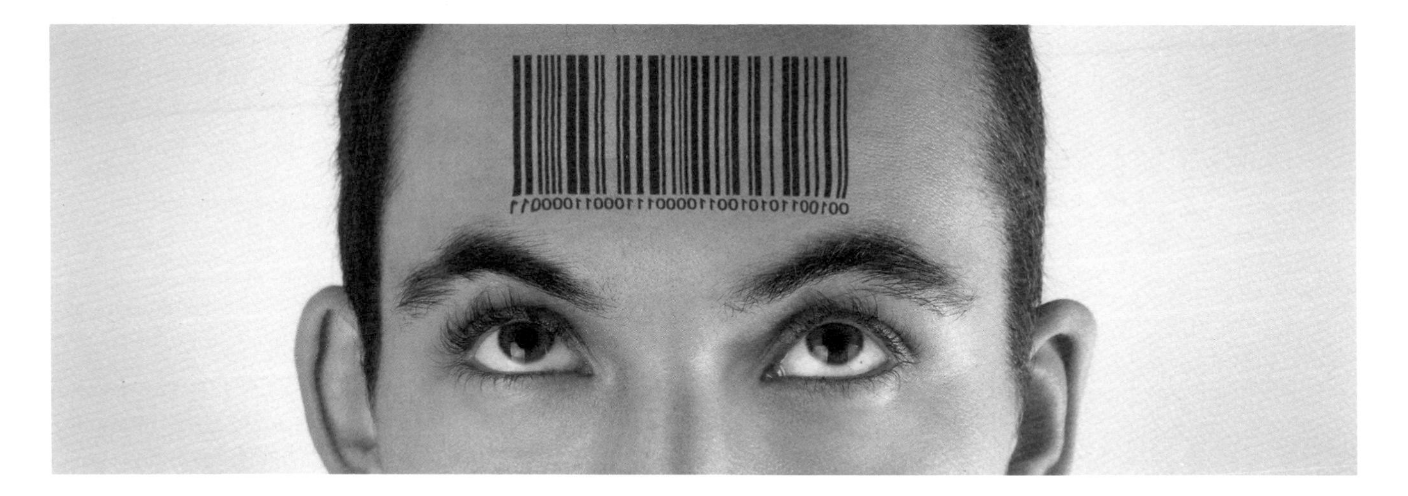

WHAT ISN'T FOR SALE?

By Michael J. Sandel

There are some things money can't buy — but these days, not many. Almost everything is up for sale. For example:

- *A prison-cell upgrade: $90 a night*. In Santa Ana, California, and some other cities, nonviolent offenders can pay for a clean, quiet jail cell, without any non-paying prisoners to disturb them.
- *Access to the carpool lane while driving solo: $8.* Minneapolis, San Diego, Houston, Seattle, and other cities have sought to ease traffic congestion by letting solo drivers pay to drive in carpool lanes, at rates that vary according to traffic.
- *The services of an Indian surrogate mother: $8,000.* Western couples seeking surrogates increasingly outsource the job to India, and the price is less than one-third the going rate in the United States.
- *The right to shoot an endangered black rhino: $250,000.* South Africa has begun letting some ranchers sell hunters the right to kill a limited number of rhinos, to give the ranchers an incentive to raise and protect the endangered species.
- *Your doctor's cell phone number: $1,500 and up per year.* A growing number of "concierge" doctors offer cell phone access and same-day appointments for patients willing to pay annual fees ranging from $1,500 to $25,000.
- *The right to emit a metric ton of carbon dioxide into the atmosphere: $10.50.* The European Union runs a carbon-dioxide-emissions market that enables companies to buy and sell the right to pollute.
- *The right to immigrate to the United States: $500,000.* Foreigners who invest $500,000 and create at least 10 full-time jobs in an area of high unemployment are eligible for a green card that entitles them to permanent residency.

Not everyone can afford to buy these things. But today there are lots of new ways to make money. If you need to earn some extra cash, here are some novel possibilities:

- *Sell space on your forehead to display commercial advertising: $10,000.* A single mother in Utah who needed money for her son's education was paid $10,000 by an online casino to install a permanent tattoo of the casino's Web address on her forehead. Temporary tattoo ads earn less.
- *Serve as a human guinea pig in a drug-safety trial for a pharmaceutical company: $7,500.* The pay can be higher or lower, depending on the invasiveness of the procedure used to test the drug's effect and the discomfort involved.
- *Fight in Somalia or Afghanistan for a private military contractor: up to $1,000 a day.* The pay varies according to qualifications, experience, and nationality.
- *Stand in line overnight on Capitol Hill to hold a place for a lobbyist who wants to attend a congressional hearing: $15–$20 an hour.* Lobbyists pay line-standing companies, who hire homeless people and others to queue up.
- *If you are a second-grader in an underachieving Dallas school, read a book: $2.* To encourage reading, schools pay kids for each book they read.

We live in a time when almost everything can be bought and sold. Over the past three decades, markets — and market values — have come to govern our lives as never before. We did not arrive at this condition through any deliberate choice. It is almost as if it came upon us.

As the Cold War ended, markets and market thinking enjoyed unrivaled prestige, and understandably so. No other mechanism for organizing the production and distribution of goods had proved as successful at generating affluence and prosperity. And yet even as growing numbers of countries around the world embraced market mechanisms in the operation of their economies, something else was happening. Market values were coming to play a greater and greater role in social life. Economics was becoming an imperial domain. Today, the logic of buying and selling no longer applies to material goods alone. It increasingly governs the whole of life.

The years leading up to the financial crisis of 2008 were a heady time of market faith and deregulation — an era of market triumphalism. The era began in the early 1980s, when Ronald Reagan and Margaret Thatcher proclaimed their conviction that markets, not government, held the key to prosperity and freedom. And it continued into the 1990s with the market-friendly liberalism of Bill Clinton and Tony Blair, who moderated but consolidated the faith that markets are the primary means for achieving the public good.

Today, that faith is in question. The financial crisis did more than cast doubt on the ability of markets to allocate risk efficiently. It also prompted a widespread sense that markets have become detached from morals, and that we need to somehow reconnect the two. But it's not obvious what this would mean, or how we should go about it.

While it is certainly true that greed played a role in the financial crisis, something bigger was and is at stake. The most fateful change that unfolded during the past three decades was not an increase in greed. It was the reach of markets, and of market values, into spheres of life traditionally governed by nonmarket norms. To contend with this condition, we need to do more than inveigh against greed; we need to have a public debate about where markets belong — and where they don't.

Consider, for example, the proliferation of for-profit schools, hospitals, and prisons, and the outsourcing of war to private military contractors. (In Iraq and Afghanistan, private contractors have actually outnumbered U.S. military troops.) Consider the eclipse of public police forces by private security firms — especially in the U.S. and the U.K., where the number of private guards is almost twice the number of public police officers.

Or consider the pharmaceutical companies' aggressive marketing of prescription drugs directly to consumers, a practice now prevalent in the U.S. but prohibited in most other countries.

Consider too the reach of commercial advertising into public schools, from buses to corridors to cafeterias; the sale of "naming rights" to parks and civic spaces; the blurred boundaries, within journalism, between news and advertising, likely to blur further as newspapers and magazines struggle to survive; the marketing of "designer" eggs and sperm for assisted reproduction; the buying and selling, by companies and countries, of the right to pollute; a system of campaign finance in the U.S. that comes close to permitting the buying and selling of elections.

These uses of markets to allocate health, education, public safety, national security, criminal justice, environmental protection, recreation, procreation, and other social goods were for the most part unheard-of 30 years ago. Today, we take them largely for granted.

Why worry that we are moving toward a society in which everything is up for sale?

For two reasons. One is about inequality, the other about corruption. First, consider inequality. In a society where everything is for sale, life is harder for those of modest means. The more money can buy, the more affluence — or the lack of it — matters. If the only advantage of affluence were the ability to afford yachts, sports cars, and fancy vacations, inequalities of income and wealth would matter less than they do today. But as money comes to buy more and more, the distribution of income and wealth looms larger.

The second reason we should hesitate to put everything up for sale is more difficult to describe. It is not about inequality and fairness but about the corrosive tendency of markets. Putting a price on the good things in life can corrupt them. That's because markets don't only allocate goods; they express and promote certain attitudes toward the goods being exchanged. Paying kids to read books might get them to read more, but might also teach them to regard reading as a chore rather than a source of intrinsic satisfaction. Hiring foreign mercenaries to fight our wars might spare the lives of our citizens, but might also corrupt the meaning of citizenship.

When we decide that certain goods may be bought and sold, we decide, at least implicitly, that it is appropriate to treat them as commodities, as instruments of profit and use. But not all goods are properly valued in this way. The most obvious example is human beings. Slavery was appalling because it treated human beings as a commodity, to be bought and sold at auction. Such treatment fails to value human beings as persons, worthy of dignity and respect; it sees them as instruments of gain and objects of use.

Something similar can be said of other cherished goods and practices. We don't allow children to be bought and sold, no matter how difficult the process of adoption can be or how willing impatient prospective parents might be. Even if the prospective buyers would treat the child responsibly, we worry that a market in children would express and promote the wrong way of valuing them. Children are properly regarded not as consumer goods but as beings worthy of love and care. Or consider the rights and obligations of citizenship. If you are called to jury duty, you can't hire a substitute to take your place. Nor do we allow citizens to sell their votes, even though others might be eager to buy them. Why not? Because we believe that civic duties are not private property but public responsibilities. To outsource them is to demean them, to value them in the wrong way.

These examples illustrate a broader point: some of the good things in life are degraded if turned into commodities.

WATCH THIS VIDEO!
Wealth Inequality in America

This short video examines some infographics on the distribution of wealth in America, highlighting both the inequality and the difference between our perception of inequality and the actual numbers. The reality is often not what we think it is.

tinyurl.com/b3jll79

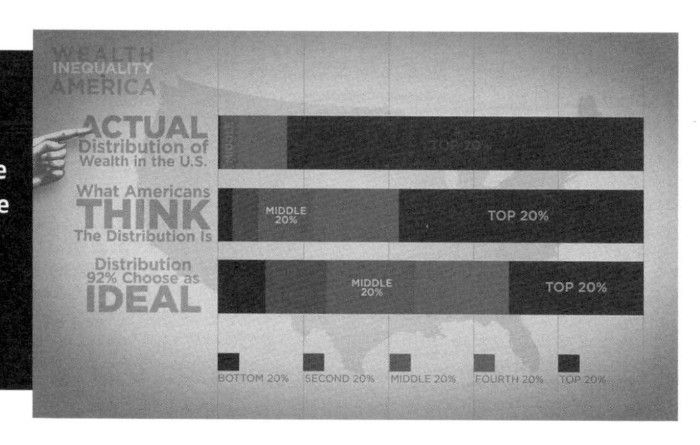

So to decide where the market belongs, and where it should be kept at a distance, we have to decide how to value the goods in question — health, education, family life, nature, art, civic duties, and so on. These are moral and political questions, not merely economic ones. To resolve them, we have to debate, case by case, the moral meaning of these goods, and the proper way of valuing them.

This is a debate we didn't have during the era of market triumphalism. As a result, without quite realizing it — without ever deciding to do so — we drifted from having a market economy to being a market society.

The difference is this: A market economy is a tool — a valuable and effective tool — for organizing productive activity. A market society is a way of life in which market values seep into every aspect of human endeavor. It's a place where social relations are made over in the image of the market.

The great missing debate in contemporary politics is about the role and reach of markets. Do we want a market economy, or a market society? What role should markets play in public life and personal relations? How can we decide which goods should be bought and sold, and which should be governed by nonmarket values? Where should money's writ not run?

Even if you agree that we need to grapple with big questions about the morality of markets, you might doubt that our public discourse is up to the task. It's a legitimate worry. At a time when political argument consists mainly of shouting matches on cable television, partisan vitriol on talk radio, and ideological food fights on the floor of Congress, it's hard to imagine a reasoned public debate about such controversial moral questions as the right way to value procreation, children, education, health, the environment, citizenship, and other goods. I believe such a debate is possible, but only if we are willing to broaden the terms of our public discourse and grapple more explicitly with competing notions of the good life.

In hopes of avoiding sectarian strife, we often insist that citizens leave their moral and spiritual convictions behind when they enter the public square. But the reluctance to admit arguments about the good life into politics has had an unanticipated consequence. It has helped prepare the way for market triumphalism, and for the continuing hold of market reasoning.

In its own way, market reasoning also empties public life of moral argument. Part of the appeal of markets is that they don't pass judgment on the preferences they satisfy. They don't ask whether some ways of valuing goods are higher, or worthier, than others. If someone is willing to pay for sex, or a kidney, and a consenting adult is willing to sell, the only question the economist asks is "How much?" Markets don't wag fingers. They don't discriminate between worthy preferences and unworthy ones. Each party to a deal decides for him- or herself what value to place on the things being exchanged.

This nonjudgmental stance toward values lies at the heart of market reasoning, and explains much of its appeal. But our reluctance to engage in moral and spiritual argument, together with our embrace of markets, has exacted a heavy price: it has drained public discourse of moral and civic energy, and contributed to the technocratic, managerial politics afflicting many societies today.

A debate about the moral limits of markets would enable us to decide, as a society, where markets serve the public good and where they do not belong. Thinking through the appropriate place of markets requires that we reason together, in public, about the right way to value the social goods we prize. It would be folly to expect that a more morally robust public discourse, even at its best, would lead to agreement on every contested question. But it would make for a healthier public life. And it would make us more aware of the price we pay for living in a society where everything is up for sale.

Michael J. Sandel, a political philosopher at Harvard, is the author of *What Money Can't Buy: The Moral Limits of Markets*, from which this article is adapted. This article originally appeared in the April 2012 edition of *The Atlantic*.

BRINGING PEOPLE BACK INTO THE ECONOMY

By Vandana Shiva

Work is energy. Two crises of our times are intimately connected — the climate crisis and the unemployment crisis.

As long as we address these crises separately, we will not solve either. The climate crisis is normally addressed scientifically in diagnosis and economically in terms of solutions. However, economic solutions are offered only within the global market and commodification paradigm. The most recent example of this is the Stern report [a 700-page report by economist Lord Stern of Brentford for the British government on the effect of climate change on the world economy]. In it, people do not figure anywhere. However, substituting the work of people with work done by machines running on fossilized carbon is a major contributor to the pollution of the atmosphere and the climate crisis. Bringing work to people and people to work can be a significant solution of the crisis of human disposability and the crisis of climate disruption.

As the fossil fuel economy has grown, it has substituted energy for humans. On the one hand, this has rendered humans redundant to the economic enterprise of production. It has created the crisis of poverty and unemployment, of dispensability and disposability. On the other hand, it has led to the problem of carbon pollution. Whereas humans are sustained by renewable carbon embodied in plants and biomass, industrial energy consumes fossil fuel, adding more CO_2 to the atmosphere than the planet can recycle.

Industrialization replaces renewable energy of humans and other animals with non-renewable energy. Even though industrial production requires more resources than feeding humans, replacing people with fossil fuel-driven machines is defined as a gain in productivity.

Scientific and technological progress is guided by this narrow and distorted concept of productivity, which externalizes the social costs of livelihood destruction and the ecological costs of ecosystem destruction.

Economic policy seeks to subsidize the spread of industrialization and fossil fuel addiction. Thus, fertilizers are subsidized in industrial agriculture and exports are subsidized in global food systems. Petrochemicals are subsidized; coal and oil are subsidized. Besides the direct financial subsidies are indirect subsidies such as funding the construction of the massive infrastructure for the fossil fuel economy, such as highways. The ultimate subsidy to the fossil fuel economy is militarized support for the extraction of fossil fuels, with the oil wars being an example. Socially, ecologically, and economically high-cost systems of food production, energy production, and transportation are made artificially cheap. Subsidies for globalized, industrialized food make local, organic food appear more expensive; subsidies for private cars and air travel make train travel appear more expensive; subsidies to supermarkets make local shops appear more expensive. These economic distortions lead to social and cultural distortions. Creative and productive human beings are laid to waste, and creative work is perceived as second-class work, as obsolete. Craftspeople are expected to disappear for industrialized production of petro-products; small farmers are expected to disappear to make way for industrial agriculture. And with the disappearance of creative work comes the disappearance of the very knowledge and skills we need to shape economics beyond oil.

SHIFTING THE WAY WE PERCEIVE WORK

We need to shift the way we define and perceive physical work. Replacing people has been defined as liberating people from work. Physical work has been defined as drudgery and as degrading. When the Communist government of West Bengal passed a law to ban hand rickshaws, it justified it on the grounds that it was putting an end to "degrading" work. The rickshaw pullers organized protests and said there was nothing degrading in their work. In fact, it is being without work that is degrading. When Monsanto introduced Roundup, a broad-spectrum herbicide that "kills everything green that comes in contact with it," it proclaimed it was liberation from weeding. Destroyers of work and employment always present destruction as liberation. Yet there is no liberation in being robbed of one's productive capacity. There is no dignity in being treated as disposable.

To make the energy transition beyond oil, we need to bring people back into the economy, bring human energy back into production, respect physical work, and give it dignity. Climate change is giving us adequate warning that substituting people with fossil fuel is ecologically non-sustainable. Social and cultural breakdown should likewise be recognized as a warning about the social non-sustainability of displacing people from work.

There are multiple levels at which the human capacity to do work needs to be put back into the energy equation and into human destiny. First is the internal energy of human beings in all its dimensions — spiritual, cultural, emotional, intellectual, and physical. If it is tapped, this is the largest energy source we have — inexhaustible, replenishable, and ever enlarging. Human energy, combined with the energy of the sun, the plants and animals, the wind, the air, the sea and water, the soil and the earth, is both the basis of work and livelihoods and the source of sustainable and renewable energy.

ENTROPY AND EMERGENCE

In the larger ecological context, mechanistic

growth based on mechanical engineering is leading to impoverishment, both material and spiritual. It is entropic growth — growth that increases waste and pollution. Climate change is, in fact, a result of increasing pollution and increasing entropy.

In The Entropy Law and the Economic Process, Nicholas Georgescu-Roegen, a former professor at Vanderbilt University and the inspiration for all ecological economists, wrote: "Neoclassical economics is mechanistic, like classical mechanics is. It can neither account for the existence of enduring changes in nature nor accept this existence as an independent. Nature on which the economic enterprise and industrial enterprise rests is totally discounted. Neoclassical economists left nature out of their calculus because the "no deposit, no return" analogue befits the businessmen's view of economic life. For if one looks only at money, all he can see is that money just passes from one hand to another: except by a regrettable accident it never gets out of the economic process."

The mechanistic worldview and the industrialization process have promoted the overextraction and overconsumption of resources, and yet it externalizes the energy and resources it uses, as well as the waste and pollution it generates, from the calculus of productivity and profit. This has led to three interrelated effects: the exhaustion of natural resources; the build-up of pollution; and the destruction of people, communities, and cultures.

While the dominant paradigm can ignore the creation of waste, the human activities that it is promoting are subject to the law of entropy. The term "entropy" was first introduced by German physicist Rudolf Clausius more than 100 years ago. Essentially it describes the movement of any system toward disorder.

Georgescu-Roegen illustrates entropy with a simple example of coal being used to run a railway engine. The burning coal creates steam, which runs the engine, and makes the train move. This conversion of coal, into motion on the one hand, and ashes on the other, is subject to the first law of thermodynamics — the conservation of matter and energy. But there is another change taking place, which is governed by the law of entropy, or the second law of thermodynamics. As Georgescu-Roegen writes: "At the beginning of the process before burning, the chemical energy of the coal is free, in the sense that it is available to us for producing some mechanical work. In the process, however, the free energy loses this quality, bit by bit. Ultimately, it always dissipates completely into the whole system where it becomes bound energy; that is energy that we can no longer use for the same purpose."

Entropy is a measure of the bound energy of a system. In a system with a high level of entropy, most or all of its energy is bound; in one with a low level of entropy, the opposite is true. The degradation of energy from free to bound has also been referred to as a turning of order into disorder. In an ordered structure, energy is free, while a structure with bound energy is chaotic and disordered.

Life has the capacity to oppose the qualitative degradation to which inert matter is subject. In fact, life may be characterized as the capacity to create order, to create free energy, to create diversity, and to evade the law of entropy.

Georgescu-Roegen has called the principle that allows life to create new patterns "the principle of emergence of novelty by combination." Living energies allow us to break out of the predictable destructiveness and dissipation inherent to mechanical energy. They create new material possibilities for well being without ecological destruction. We become co-creators or co-producers with nature's creative renewing processes.

Reductionism, which focuses only on plans, cannot see or understand the unexpected creativity of natural processes. The unexpected, orderly patterns created from disorderly elements are known as emergent properties. As eminent development biologist Brian Goodwin points out: "It is now recognized that emergent properties are very widespread in nature, particularly in living systems. Many of the most intriguing characteristics of life, such as the way a complex organism emerges from the interaction of many cells during embryonic development, or the pattern of species extinctions during evolution, are unexpected results of particular patterns of interaction between components in complex systems."

Such emergence is characteristic of all living systems. When society is organized on the basis of the living energy of its citizens, living democracy is an emergent phenomenon, making the impossible possible, creating hope out of hopelessness, unleashing our creative energies in the midst of ecological and social ruin.

Human beings, as living beings, have a choice between two alternatives — the entropic option or an emergent option. The former locks us in a mechanical worldview, based on mechanistic science, mechanical production, and a mechanistic economics whose myth of perpetual growth leads us to death, decay, and disintegration. The latter relies on ecological science, ecological production, and ecological, living economies that provide new levels of human enrichment through biological and cultural diversity. The choice we make will decide whether or not we survive as a species. And the possibilities are not restricted by the present range of choices; in society, too, there are emergent properties, unpredictable forms that emerge through new associations, new networks, and new solidarities.

The high-entropy journey humanity has undertaken under the illusion of growth and progress does not have a future. We will have to change the road we are on, and we will have to change our goals. The goals cannot be set by reductionist science, industrial technologies, and neoliberal economies. The goals cannot be narrowly defined as economic growth or consumerism. The goals have to be the preservation of the earth, her diverse species, and future generations.

The multiple crises of climate insecurity, energy insecurity, and food insecurity create an imperative and an opportunity to transcend the limits of the mechanistic-industrial-capitalist paradigm that has been systematically shrinking our potential even as it peddles progress.

The paths out from this crisis are not being blazed in the boardrooms of the global corporations who dominate our world today and are largely responsible for crimes against nature and humanity. Industrialization of food and agriculture has put the human species on a slippery slope of self-destruction and self-annihilation. The movement for biodiverse, ecological, and local food systems simultaneously addresses the crises of climate, energy, and food. Above all, it brings people back into agriculture and reclaims food as nourishment and the most basic source of energy. New ways of thinking and acting, of being and doing, are evolving from the creative alternatives being employed in small communities, on farms, and in cities.

It is this renewable energy of ecology and sharing, of solidarity and compassion, that we need to generate and multiply to counter the destructive energy of greed that is creating scarcity at every level — scarcity of work, scarcity of happiness, scarcity of security, scarcity of freedom, and even scarcity of the future.

Climate chaos, brutal economic inequality, and social disintegration are jointly pushing human communities to the brink. We can either let the processes of destruction, disintegration, and extermination continue unchallenged, or we can unleash our creative energies to make systemic change and reclaim our future as a species, as part of the earth family. We can either keep sleepwalking to extinction or wake up to the potential of the planet and ourselves.

Dr. Vandana Shiva trained as a Physicist at the University of Punjab, and completed her Ph.D. from the University of Western Ontario, Canada. She later shifted to interdisciplinary research in science, technology and environmental policy at the Indian Institute of Science and the Indian Institute of Management in Bangalore, India. In 1982, she founded an independent institute — the Research Foundation for Science, Technology and Ecology in Dehra Dun — dedicated to high quality and independent research to address the most significant ecological and social issues of our times, working in close partnership with local communities and social movements.

FOSSIL FUEL SUBSIDIES

A fossil fuel subsidy is any government action that lowers the cost of fossil fuel energy production, raises the price received by energy producers, or lowers the price paid by energy consumers.

The most obvious subsidies are direct funding and tax giveaways, but there are many activities that count as subsidies — loans and guarantees at favorable rates, price controls, governments providing resources like land and water to fossil fuel companies at below-market rates, research and development funding, and more.

Fossil fuel subsidies essentially function as a negative carbon price, reducing the cost of developing fossil fuels — so not only are their true costs being shifted onto the poor via climate and health impacts, but the fossil fuel industry is actually being paid for this privilege.

As of October 2017, Oil Change International estimated United States fossil fuel exploration and production subsidies at $20.5 billion annually. Other credible estimates of annual United States fossil fuel subsidies range from $10 billion to $52 billion annually — yet none of these include costs borne by taxpayers related to the climate, local environmental, and health impacts of the fossil fuel industry.

Internationally, governments provide at least $775 billion to $1 trillion annually in subsidies, again, not including other costs of fossil fuels related to climate change, environmental impacts, military conflicts and spending, and health impacts.

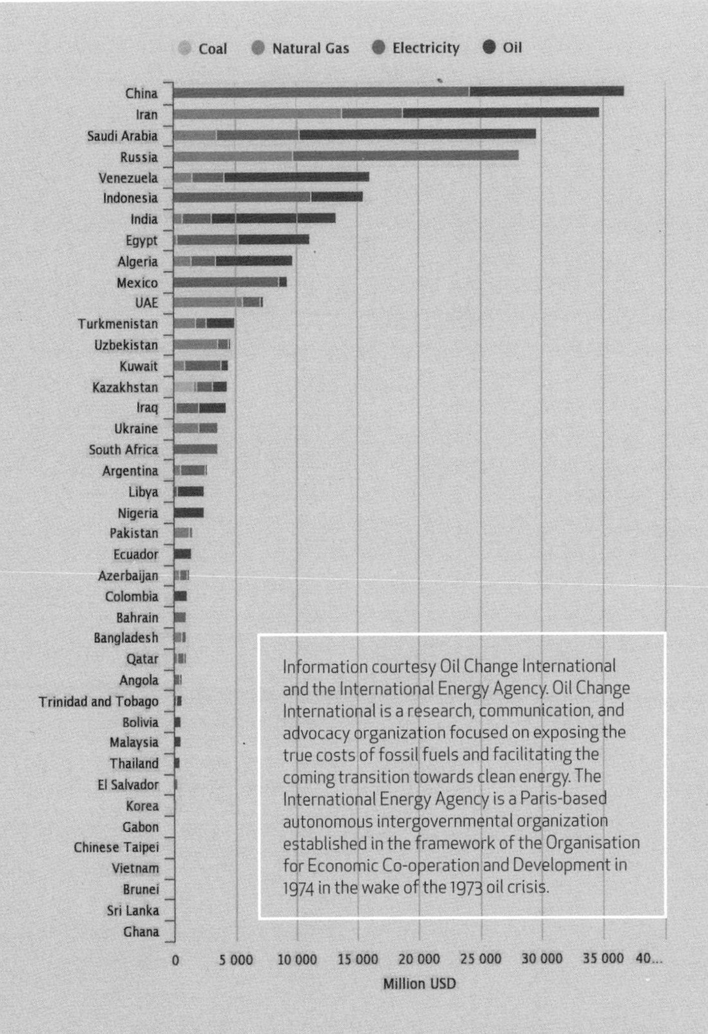

Information courtesy Oil Change International and the International Energy Agency. Oil Change International is a research, communication, and advocacy organization focused on exposing the true costs of fossil fuels and facilitating the coming transition towards clean energy. The International Energy Agency is a Paris-based autonomous intergovernmental organization established in the framework of the Organisation for Economic Co-operation and Development in 1974 in the wake of the 1973 oil crisis.

WHERE OUR PAYCHECKS GO

In these two pie charts, we look at the change in U.S. household spending between 1949 and 2016. Overall, we're spending less on items that can be produced globally, and more on items and services that can't be outsourced (housing, healthcare, etc.). For example, in 1900, food and clothes made up half of a family's budget. In 2000, they comprised a fifth of that budget — mostly because they have been industrialized or can be produced more cheaply elsewhere.

DECEMBER 1949

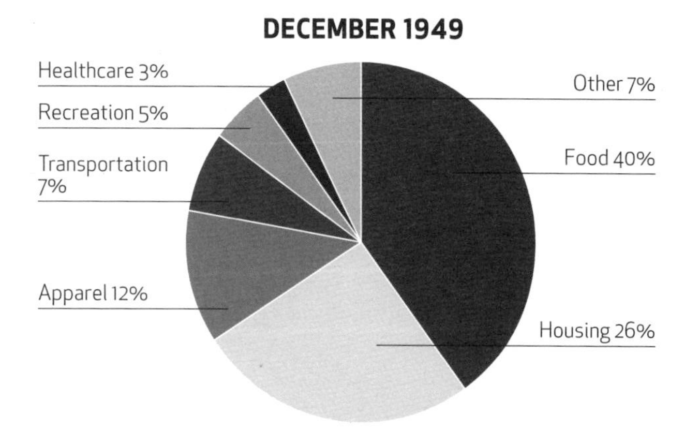

DECEMBER 2016

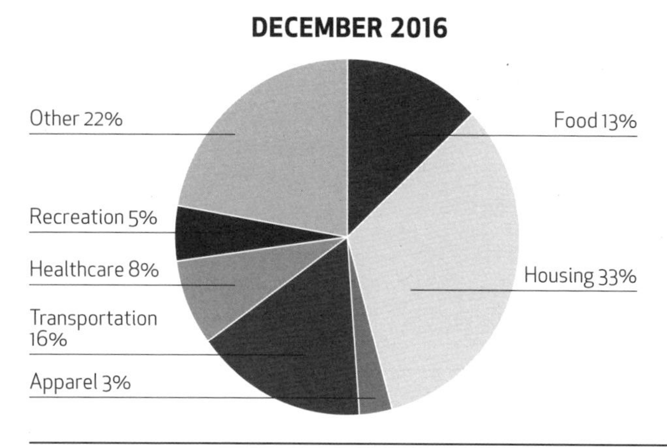

Information from NPR's *Planet Money*, *Sightline Daily*, and the Bureau of Labor Statistics.

BEYOND CONSUMERISM

By New Dream

UNDERSTANDING OBSOLESCENCE

One of the main forces driving high levels of consumption and waste today is obsolescence — the process of an item or technology being replaced, outdated, or falling out of use. Obsolescence can be a spontaneous process by which genuinely innovative technologies win in the marketplace, or it can be planned by manufacturers through methods like regular changes in product styles or deliberately building poor-quality items.

Spontaneous obsolescence is generally a positive process and is a byproduct of genuine innovation — classic examples include the automobile replacing the buggy and the computer replacing the typewriter. In contrast, it is planned obsolescence, combined with other factors like intensive advertising and the rise in disposable income, that is responsible for much of the unnecessary waste we produce. Examples of planned obsolescence include:

Obsolescence of desirability

Have you ever noticed how the "in" color for home appliances is always changing? Recently it's been stainless steel or copper, in the 1980s it was black, in the 1970s it was avocado green — and now green refrigerators are considered "retro."

Home buyers and sellers often replace their well-functioning appliances just to keep up with the style, which will change again in just a few years. To stimulate interest and sales, trade associations carefully research and "forecast" which colors are going to be popular. Or consider the latest microwaves, equipped with "must-have" electronic cook sensors. In these cases, manufacturers and advertisers manipulate consumer demand by promoting attributes that have little to do with an item's real performance or utility. In some cases, utility is even impaired because previously straightforward items are

WATCH THIS VIDEO!
How We Live: Transition Toward a Just Economy

Modern production is based on extraction from the planet, and modern finance is based on extraction from the many for the benefit of the very few. What would a new economy look like and how can we rethink our relationship to resources, work and culture?

The 7-minute video by Kontent Films takes a step back, beautifully defining and breaking down the terms "economy," "ecology" and "ecosystem" to help us look at the role that our current economic system has in our society and the environment, and what can be done to move us towards a more sustainable world. vimeo.com/94603192

complicated with expensive and unrepairable gadgetry.

Obsolescence of durability

We've all sighed over a broken toaster oven or microwave: "they just don't make them like they used to." Do you have a clunky '80s microwave in your basement? It will probably last longer than your new one. Products today are made with cheaper materials and have shorter lifespans; it is widely believed that they often break right around the time the warranty expires. They're often too poorly made to invest in a repair, and repairs can easily cost as much as a replacement, resulting in increasing volumes of waste.

Another example is the non-replaceable batteries common in small electronics. By the time the battery dies a new model will be out, and professional battery replacements are expensive. Apple charges exactly the same price to replace an iPod Shuffle battery as it does for a brand new iPod Shuffle. The economical choice for the consumer is often to buy a new unit and throw out the old one, even though this wastes valuable resources.

Obsolescence by non-compatibility

Until recently, almost every cell phone had a different plug on its charger. Laptop adapter plugs are still widely different, even though the adapters themselves are often identical. Every digital camera seems to need a different proprietary battery and charger. Have you ever tried to find new ink for a printer several years old? Manufacturers could do much more to streamline common items and accessories like batteries, chargers, and adapters.

On a larger scale, obsolescence by non-compatibility takes place when an entire class of products is rendered non-functional, such as the 2009 digital TV switchover that immediately made millions of TVs unable to receive signals without an additional box.

TAKE-HOME MESSAGE: *Although some obsolescence is merely perceived, much of it is intentionally planned — largely in an effort to maximize consumption and profits for companies. Before consumers can take a new approach to their stuff, we need to understand what obsolescence is, how it works, and how it is often created out of thin air.*

REDISTRIBUTION AND SHARING

Think about how much of the stuff we get rid of is still functional, but is just unwanted or out of style. These discarded but usable items represent a huge amount of value in resources, money, and decreased environmental stress. And many of them, like "boxy" televisions and aging computers, are still in demand in economically disadvantaged regions of the United States and around the world.

If you are determined to replace an item that still works, why not pass it on instead of throwing it out? There are a variety of ways to redistribute your unwanted clutter, which could be exactly what someone else is looking for. Or, if you're in the market for a particular item, consider buying used before opting for newly produced stuff.

Share it!

Do you have stuff sitting around in your house that you barely use but don't quite want to get rid of, or that you know still has value? Think about lending it or sharing it! Many home items, such as power tools, are often bought for a specific project and then go more-or-less unused. You can lighten your burden of "stuff" and help others out by sharing.

Check out New Dream's Guide to Sharing to learn more about how you can share things — from clothing and tools to your time and skills — as well as access the products and services you need, without having to buy or own them. Join the emerging sharing economy and embrace access over ownership!

Sell it

If you want to raise a little cash, hold a garage sale. Don't expect to increase your net worth, but if you invite other families and hold a multi-family sale, you can make some money while involving the community. Bargain hunters, collectors, and lower-income families often frequent garage sales. It's a win-win for your wallet, your clutter, and your community.

If you have stuff you don't think anyone wants, think again. Items like retro video games, old computers, records, and 8-track tapes can often be sold on eBay where the listings are visible to millions of people. Online sale sites like eBay and Etsy are great places to sell unique and vintage items, or items with a limited or specialized demand. What might be worthless to most garage sale browsers might interest a collector on eBay.

For higher-quality items, consignment shops and auction houses are often a safe bet for getting rid of stuff, but commissions can be high, so be prepared for lower-than expected returns.

Give it away

If you look a little, there are many ways to give away or donate your unwanted stuff. Freecycle, a popular email-based exchange for offering unwanted items, has thousands of local groups and millions of members. Many communities hold swap meets or item exchanges, like the Really Really Free Market or clothing swaps.

Goodwill and the Salvation Army are popular and reputable places to donate to (and shop at!), and you can even get a tax deduction there. And don't forget small, local thrift shops and annual rummage sales that benefit local schools, churches, and community organizations.

TAKE-HOME MESSAGE: *It's great to own things we need, but too often we end up owning things we don't need. This doesn't mean they have no value. Recognizing the value of "stuff" — not just its economic value, but its community and environmental value — will go a long way toward changing our approach to materialism.*

CONSCIOUS CONSUMERISM

We can all do our part in sharing existing resources and limiting new purchases, but the reality is that we are all still "consumers." When we do need to buy something, we can make an effort to be the most "conscious" consumers we can, taking into account the impacts that our purchases have more broadly on people and the environment. Part of being a conscious consumer is educating ourselves about the hidden costs behind the things we buy. But it also means understanding how our purchases can help us shape more sustainable business practices and a more responsible economy as a whole.

The true value of stuff

In our market economy, almost everything has a price. Prices are useful because they help us gauge the relative value of consumer goods and commodities. But despite the lure of "everyday low prices," in most cases prices do a poor job in reflecting the true cost or value of an item.

Sometimes this price obscurity is due to government interference, like the subsidizing of oil extraction or mining operations. Other times it may be due to the failure of the market to value the broader costs of making or using a product on the environment and society.

In our modern consumer economy, hard-to-quantify values like community, happiness, good health, and a clean environment can suffer when prices are too low, even though these outcomes are arguably more important and valuable than material wealth. How can we continue to enjoy material prosperity while building an economy that truly values everything of value?

Finite planet, finite resources

From oil to precious metals, most of our natural resources are limited and non-renewable. But the broad availability of cheap consumer goods can hide this fact.

Economists and environmentalists are increasingly aware that the economic model of continual economic growth based on increasing material consumption will not work forever, and that we may already be hitting the fixed limits of our planet.

Alternative economic models, and more holistic measurements of progress and well-being, can help us recognize the value in non-material things. Education is another: the more we are aware of the shortcomings of the consumer economy, the more effectively we can work to change them.

The hidden costs of production

When you throw out an old toaster oven, you're throwing out limited, mostly irreplaceable natural resources: steel, plastic (from oil), and expensive metals used in electronic parts. The market price for natural resources does not really take into account the fact that eventually they will be all used up. That day may be decades away, but it must eventually come — underscoring the need for greater respect for our limited resources.

Yet metal is not the only thing that went into that toaster. So did human time and labor (and possibly human suffering, if working conditions were poor), as well as environmental damage due to resource extraction, pollution, and other side-effects of production. In most cases, these unaccounted-for costs, known as "externalities," are not reflected in the price of our consumer goods; the result is that individuals in affluent countries get cheap consumer goods, while the poorer countries where the production often occurs bear the hidden costs.

All externalities can't be eliminated, but we can be more conscious of these hidden costs to both people and the environment, and seek to avoid them in the things we buy. By becoming conscious consumers, we can support the production of more socially and environmentally sound products, including items certified as "fair trade," "organic," "non-GMO," and "sustainably harvested." For tips on buying more responsibly, check out our Conscious Consumer Shopping Guide, with product guides for everyday items from baby goods to seafood.

"Stuff" and happiness

It isn't just the production side of consumerism that depletes resources, physical or otherwise. A major paradox of consumerism is that rather than making us feel more satisfied (as advertisers would like us to believe), the consumption of goods may actually lower our happiness.

If we consider human labor and human happiness to be resources, and consider the research of the very compelling field of happiness studies, then it appears that consumerism wastes not only our natural resources, but our human resources as well. Environmental economist Julian Simon once dismissed fears about resource scarcity, believing instead that human ingenuity was the "ultimate resource." But in an ironic twist, the more we center our lives around consumption, the more damage we do to human resources.

TAKE-HOME MESSAGE: *Part of being a conscious consumer is educating ourselves about the hidden costs behind the things we buy. But we also need to consider what's driving us to buy these things in the first place: will they really enhance our lives and make us happy, or are we buying them simply because we "think" we need them or because advertisers tell us to?*

Founded in 1997 as the Center for a New American Dream, New Dream works with individuals and communities to counter the commercialization of our culture, support community engagement, and conserve natural resources.

TRUE PRICE QUESTIONS

This True Price activity asks us to examine a product, such as a bottle of water, a fast food cheeseburger, or a T-shirt, and ask a series of questions. Try this activity out when considering purchases this week.

1. **Is the item a want or a need?**

   The point of this question isn't to make us feel judged about what we consider a want or need, but to help us unpack what is truly vital to our well-being and happiness. We might also have different criteria for whether certain kinds of objects are a need. For example, some people may consider products like a car, a computer, and a cell phone indispensable. And the way we'd categorize those items might be different from the way we'd categorize an item of clothing.

2. **What are the effects, both positive and negative, on you, other people, animals, and the environment?**

   This question helps us think deeply, broadly, and critically about all the various impacts of a product throughout its entire lifecycle.

3. **What systems support, promote and perpetuate this item?**

   This is a complicated question because our systems are very complex and there are so many underlying systems involved in the production, distribution, use, and disposal of the products we use. We can change our personal choices, but we also need to address the underlying systems involved.

4. **What would be an alternative, or a change to a system, that would do more good and less harm?**

   When we can make choices that do more good and less harm (MOGO choices), that's great. But, many times there is no such choice available. There may be no MOGO cell phone, car, or health care plan, for example. So, it's important that we look at what changes in systems would help do more good and less harm and would also lead to humane and sustainable items becoming ubiquitous.

A TRUE PRICE EXAMPLE

Institute for Humane Education faculty led this activity at a residency for their graduate students. Here are the responses from one group of students, who briefly explored the impacts of soda in a plastic bottle.

1. **Is it a want or a need?**
   It's a want.

2a. What are the positive effects?
caffeine kick; pleasure; jobs; the company does philanthropy; you could repurpose the plastic bottle for building material (e.g., creating a light source).

2b. What are some of the negative effects?
obesity and other negative health effects; plastic is a carcinogen; plastic waste; pollution; the amount of oil used; oil spills that kill animals and destroy habitat; animals consume plastic; habitat destruction, etc.

3. **What systems support, promote and perpetuate this item?**
   economy, cultural, peer pressure, marketing/ads, multinational corporations, globalization

4. **What would be an alternative or a change to a system, that would do more good and less harm?**
   personally: tap water from a reusable glass;

WATCH THIS VIDEO! The Story of Stuff

The Story of Stuff is a 20-minute, fast-paced, fact-filled look at the underside of our production and consumption patterns. The Story of Stuff exposes the connections between a huge number of environmental and social issues, and calls us together to create a more sustainable and just world. It'll teach you something, it'll make you laugh, and it just may change the way you look at all the Stuff in your life forever.

storyofstuff.org/movies/story-of-stuff/

systemically: create a healthier recipe? bring more work back to the U.S.? more corporate responsibility? incentives to phase out unhealthy drinks and the use of disposable plastics?

QUESTIONS AFTER THE ACTIVITY

After doing the True Price activity at residency, students explored the seemingly contradictory facts that there's so much we don't know about the products and services we use; and, we also have a belief that we "know" a lot of facts and information, but that "knowledge" hasn't actually come from a deep investigation of, say, research in peer-reviewed journals. We've claimed these beliefs and this knowledge based on what we've heard or read about what others have heard or read.

True Price, then, forces us to look deeper and more critically at not just the impacts of these products on people, animals, and the planet, but also at our own beliefs and assumptions about what we think we know.

Activity used with permission of Institute for Humane Education (IHE) www.humaneeducation.org. IHE believes that education is the key to creating a just, humane, and sustainable world for all people, animals and the environment, and offer programs and resources designed to train, educate and inspire people to become humane educators and changemakers who live with compassion and integrity and work to solve the most pressing challenges of our time.

WATCH THIS VIDEO!
Going Local: The Solution Multiplier

This video made by Local Futures offers a very short (less than 3 minute) introduction to economic localization and presents it as a solution to many of the issues humans currently face. Local Futures' mission is to protect and renew ecological and social well being by promoting a systemic shift away from economic globalization towards localization. Through its "education for action" programs, Local Futures develops innovative models and tools to catalyze collaboration for strategic change at the community and international level.
vimeo.com/200477467

ECOCHALLENGE: PUTTING IT INTO PRACTICE

Here are some ideas for putting what you learned this week into action. Find more ideas and commit to one Ecochallenge this week at **choices.ecochallenge.org**

- Track your purchases. Maintain a record of all your purchases this week. Where are you spending the most money? What could you buy less of or do without?
- Support local businesses. Buy what you need from local businesses this week instead of buying online. Prioritize your values by intentionally patronizing businesses who support the things you care about: sustainability, social justice, fair trade, or reuse are just a few examples.
- Learn about alternatives to the GDP. Research alternatives (like Gross National Happiness) to measuring economic livelihood and the health of a nation.
- Visit a waste management facility. Visit a local dump/transfer station, material recovery facility, and/or landfill to learn about the waste stream in your region.
- Support a sharing economy. Create or support a sharing economy with family, friends, and neighbors.

SESSION 8

VISIONS OF SUSTAINABILITY

"The sustainability revolution will be organic. It will arise from the visions, insights, experiments and actions of billions of people. The burden of making it happen is not on the shoulders of any one person or group. No one will get the credit, but everyone can contribute."

— Donella L. Meadows

LEARNING OBJECTIVES

- Consider how underlying belief patterns and mental models affect the way we see and act in the world.
- (Re-)envision sustainability at the local, regional and global levels.
- Engage with possible solutions and visions for a more sustainable society/culture.
- Commit to personal and community action toward sustainability.

SESSION DESCRIPTION

In this last session of this discussion course, we examine the underlying assumptions and belief patterns that have created our current systems and consider which mental models can underlie a sustainable and resilient world. Using those new mental models, we envision (and re-envision) a sustainable world and how we can start creating it right now.

REFLECTION

Using "Ecopolis Iowa City" as inspiration, describe what your city or town looks like in a sustainable future. Post your Reflection to your Dashboard on **choices.ecochallenge.org**. If you are not using the Ecochallenge site, write your thoughts in a journal and then reflect with your group.

Circle Question

Paul Gilding states that it is hard to hold the paradox of our times in our heads. How do you deal with the hard issues of our times?

Reminder to the facilitator: The circle question should move quickly. Elicit an answer from each participant without questions or comments from others. The facilitator's guidelines are on page 10.

SUGGESTED DISCUSSION QUESTIONS

1. Based upon "The Story of Change" activity or your own experience, are you most inclined to attempt to elicit change on a personal level, on a community grassroots level, or on a political level?
2. How could encouraging people to envision the future that they want help move people past political debates and into real action? What challenges might arise?
3. Paul Gilding also says, "We have a system problem, so we need a system solution." Referring back to the Iceberg model in the first session, how can we come to systems solutions for the big problems we're currently facing?
4. As you make decisions in your daily life, what consideration do you give to sustainability? How has this changed since taking the course?
5. What did you learn in this course that surprised you?
6. What did you learn about yourself in this course that was unexpected?
7. Where are you feeling inspired or noticing the need to take action now? At a personal level, community level, neighborhood level, civic level or a combination of any of these? What issues draw your attention and passion?
8. How do you plan to begin to make change in your own circles of influence? Who could you work with to create a plan?

SUGGESTED GROUP ACTIVITY

Share your sustainable visions with each other. Are there any similarities/differences? How can you start working toward a shared vision?

FURTHER RESOURCES

Interested in finding out more on the topics presented in this session?
Visit our website for further readings and resources: **ecochallenge.org/discussion-course-resources.**
Follow our blog at **ecochallenge.org/blog/**; we post links to new resources and inspiring stories regularly.

NEOLIBERALISM HAS CONNED US INTO FIGHTING CLIMATE CHANGE AS INDIVIDUALS

By Martin Lukacs

Would you advise someone to flap towels in a burning house? To bring a flyswatter to a gunfight? Yet the counsel we hear on climate change could scarcely be more out of sync with the nature of the crisis.

The email in my inbox last week offered thirty suggestions to green my office space: use reusable pens, redecorate with light colours, stop using the elevator. Back at home, done huffing stairs, I could get on with other options: change my lightbulbs, buy local veggies, purchase eco-appliances, put a solar panel on my roof. And a study released on Thursday claimed it had figured out the single best way to fight climate change: I could swear off ever having a child.

These pervasive exhortations to individual action — in corporate ads, school textbooks, and the campaigns of mainstream environmental groups, especially in the west — seem as natural as the air we breathe. But we could hardly be worse-served. While we busy ourselves greening our personal lives, fossil fuel corporations are rendering these efforts irrelevant. The breakdown of carbon emissions since 1988? A hundred companies alone are responsible for an astonishing 71%. You tinker with those pens or that panel; they go on torching the planet.

The freedom of these corporations to pollute — and the fixation on a feeble lifestyle response — is no accident. It is the result of an ideological war, waged over the last 40 years, against the possibility of collective action. Devastatingly successful, it is not too late to reverse it.

The political project of neoliberalism, brought to ascendence by Thatcher and Reagan, has pursued two principal objectives. The first has been to dismantle any barriers to the exercise of unaccountable private power. The second had been to erect them to the exercise of any democratic public will.

Its trademark policies of privatization, deregulation, tax cuts and free trade deals: these have liberated corporations to accumulate enormous profits and treat the atmosphere like a sewage dump, and hamstrung our ability, through the instrument of the state, to plan for our collective welfare.

Anything resembling a collective check on corporate power has become a target of the elite: lobbying and corporate donations, hollowing out democracies, have obstructed green policies and kept fossil fuel subsidies flowing; and the rights of associations like unions, the most effective means for workers to wield power together, have been undercut whenever possible.

At the very moment when climate change demands an unprecedented collective public response, neoliberal ideology stands in the way. Which is why, if we want to bring down emissions fast, we will need to overcome all of its free-market mantras: take railways and utilities and energy grids back into public control; regulate corporations to phase out fossil fuels; and raise taxes to pay for massive investment in climate-ready infrastructure and renewable energy — so that solar panels can go on everyone's rooftop,

DEFINITIONS

Consumer culture: A form of capitalism in which the economy and culture are focused on the buying and selling of consumer goods and the spending of consumer money. Most economists agree that the United States is a consumer culture.

GDP: GDP stands for Gross Domestic Product and is the measurement of market value of all officially recognized goods and services produced within a country in a given period. GDP per capita is often considered an indicator of a country's standard of living.

Neoliberalism: Neoliberalism is an ideology and policy model which emphasizes the value of free market competition. It views sustained economic growth as the means to achieve human progress and free markets as the most efficient allocation of resources. Neoliberalism emphasizes minimal state intervention in economic and social affairs and the freedom of trade and capital around the globe.

Radical imagination: According to scholar-activists Max Haiven and Alex Khasnabish, the radical imagination is a vital source of social transformation and emerges from the experience of people working together to challenge power. The radical imagination is "radical" not because of the answers it provides or the tactics it suggests, but because of the causes it seeks to understand. The Latin origin of the word radical means "from the root," and a radical imagination is one that sees society's problems as deeply rooted in systemic and structural inequalities and forms of exploitation.

not just on those who can afford it.

Neoliberalism has not merely ensured this agenda is politically unrealistic: it has also tried to make it culturally unthinkable. Its celebration of competitive self-interest and hyper-individualism, its stigmatization of compassion and solidarity, has frayed our collective bonds. It has spread, like an insidious anti-social toxin, what Margaret Thatcher preached: "there is no such thing as society."

Studies show that people who have grown up under this era have indeed become more individualistic and consumerist. Steeped in a culture telling us to think of ourselves as consumers instead of citizens, as self-reliant instead of interdependent, is it any wonder we deal with a systemic issue by turning in droves to ineffectual, individual efforts? We are all Thatcher's children.

Even before the advent of neoliberalism, the capitalist economy had thrived on people believing that being afflicted by the structural problems of an exploitative system — poverty, joblessness, poor health, lack of fulfillment — was in fact a personal deficiency.

Neoliberalism has taken this internalized self-blame and turbocharged it. It tells you that you should not merely feel guilt and shame if you can't secure a good job, are deep in debt, and are too stressed or overworked for time with friends. You are now also responsible for bearing the burden of potential ecological collapse.

Of course we need people to consume less and innovate low-carbon alternatives — build sustainable farms, invent battery storages, spread zero-waste methods. But individual choices will most count when the economic system can provide viable, environmental options for everyone — not just an affluent or intrepid few.

If affordable mass transit isn't available, people will commute with cars. If local organic food is too expensive, they won't opt out of fossil fuel-intensive supermarket chains. If cheap mass produced goods flow endlessly, they will buy and buy and buy. This is the con-job of neoliberalism: to persuade us to address climate change through our pocket-books, rather than through power and politics.

Eco-consumerism may expiate your guilt. But it's only mass movements that have the power to alter the trajectory of the climate crisis. This requires of us first a resolute mental break from the spell cast by neoliberalism: to stop thinking like individuals.

The good news is that the impulse of humans to come together is inextinguishable — and the collective imagination is already making a political come-back. The climate justice movement is blocking pipelines, forcing the divestment of trillions of dollars, and winning support for 100% clean energy economies in cities and states across the world. New ties are being drawn to Black Lives Matter, immigrant and Indigenous rights, and fights for better wages. On the heels of such movements, political parties seem finally ready to defy neoliberal dogma.

None more so than Jeremy Corbyn, whose Labour Manifesto spelled out a redistributive project to address climate change: by publicly retooling the economy, and insisting that corporate oligarchs no longer run amok. The notion that the rich should pay their fair share to fund this transformation was considered laughable by the political and media class. Millions disagreed. Society, long said to be departed, is now back with a vengeance.

So grow some carrots and jump on a bike: it will make you happier and healthier. But it is time to stop obsessing with how personally green we live — and start collectively taking on corporate power.

Martin Lukacs is an independent journalist. He writes regularly on the environment for the *Guardian*.

WATCH THIS VIDEO!
The Story of Change

Over the past several decades, many environmental and social change efforts have come to reflect the centrality of shopping in our culture, suggesting change can be made — or is even best made — through alterations in our individual consumption patterns. These efforts — buy Fair Trade or organic, use a reusable bag, screw in a CFL lightbulb — are a great place to start, but they are a terrible place to stop, ignoring the real source of our power: coming together as engaged citizens. In The Story of Change, Annie Leonard argues that it's not bad shoppers who are putting our future at risk; it's bad policies and business practices. If we really want to change the world, we have to move beyond voting with our dollars and come together to demand rules that work. storyofstuff.org/movies/story-of-change/
After you watch the video, take this quiz to find out what kind of changemaker you are: action.storyofstuff.org/survey/changemaker-quiz/

HOPE IS WHAT WE BECOME IN ACTION

By Fritjof Capra and Frances Moore Lappé

In June 2013, Fritjof Capra and Frances Moore Lappé participated in two conversations, at a Center for Ecoliteracy Circle of Friends gathering and at the Center's Becoming Ecoliterate seminar. The dialogue here is adapted from their wide-ranging discussions.

FRITJOF CAPRA: In your latest book, *EcoMind*, you pose the question, "Is there a way of perceiving the environmental challenge that is at once hardheaded, evidence based, and invigorating?" And then you write, "I believe it is possible that we can turn today's breakdown into a planetary breakthrough on one condition. We can do it if we can break free of a set of dominant but misleading ideas that are taking us down." When did it occur to you that we could have an invigorating approach to solving environmental problems?

FRANCES MOORE LAPPÉ: It was a totally unplanned book, and it has changed my life. It started when I walked out of a conference in Washington, D.C. in 2008. I had just heard the most knowledgeable environmental leaders and the most amazing speeches over several days, but I noticed that, as the hours went by, the crowds were shrinking in these brilliant lectures. I walked out, and I felt deflated, like the proverbial ton of bricks had just hit me.

As I went home to Boston, I said, "Wait a minute. This can't work." I was reacting to the framing of the messages. They seemed still locked in the mechanical, quantitative frame, and thus not really reflecting ecological truths, which for me means focusing on the quality of relationships. It occurred to me that a lot of today's dominant messages — some that are part of the environmental movement and others that seem to just float through our culture — are creating obstacles and standing in the way. So I asked whether we could break through to more of an ecological way of seeing and feeling.

FC: Do you remember the first example that came to your mind?

FML: One message has to do with the fundamental notion, which you hear everywhere, that "We've hit the limits of the finite Earth." Gradually I realized that this is a mechanical metaphor — it's quantitative, not ecological.

This message confirms the dominant belief system characterized by the premise that there's not enough of anything: not enough goods, not enough goodness — meaning that there are not enough material things, nor enough good qualities of human character.

I love to quote the dear, now deceased, Hermann Scheer, the great German environmental leader, who reminded people that the sun provides us 15,000 times the daily dose of energy compared to what we're currently using in fossil fuel. Hit the limits of the Earth? No. Of human violation of nature's rules? Yes!

FC: That really relates to your early work about food. You said then that it's not the quantity of food that's not enough, but it's the distribution and unbalance of power and so on.

FML: The premise of scarcity creates a culture driven by fear. That puts us in a perpetual state of feeling we're in competition over crumbs — creating a spiral that intensifies, as everyone feels that they have to get theirs before it all runs out. The message of "hitting the limits" is especially scary for people who are just at the edge of survival themselves, which is the case for most people on Earth.

I'm very sensitive to messages that make people feel more fearful. That's one reason why I love the Center for Ecoliteracy and the work you do. You know that beauty opens people up and reduces fear and that people learn to trust themselves through working with the Earth itself and exploratory learning.

I also don't like saying that growth is the problem, because for most people, growth is really positive. You love it when your grandchildren grow, your love grows, your flowers grow. We should not bless what we're doing now with the term "growth." We should call it what it is, an economy of waste and destruction.

So the reframe I'm asking all to consider, which you're living at the Center for Ecoliteracy, is a shift from assuming that the problem is that we've hit the limits to recognizing this: the global crisis is that our human-made systems are perversely misaligned, both with human nature and the wider nature. The challenge is not, "How do we pull back?" but, "How do we remake our human-made systems to align positively with what we know creates sustainable and resilient communities?"

FC: In the book, you say that there are three S's: scarcity, separateness, and stasis. Can you talk about them?

FML: My fundamental realization when I wrote *Diet for a Small Planet* at age twenty-six — though I didn't have the language then — was that we create the world according to the mental maps we hold. We hear the cliché "Seeing is believing," but we should realize that "Believing is seeing." I'll quote Albert Einstein: "It is theory which decides what we can observe."

So today we see through a lens of scarcity. We see lack everywhere, including with food. We see it with love. We see it with energy. We see it with, you name it, parking places — all things, but also we see a scarcity of the qualities we need, including basic goodness.

Stasis is the idea that things are relatively fixed, and even human nature is fixed: "We are what we are. We don't have the capacity to change."

And finally there is the premise that we are all separate, from one another and from all earthly creatures.

Those are the three "S's" of the scarcity mind that blocks us from solutions right in front of our noses.

FC: How does the EcoMind overcome these pitfalls?

FML: EcoMind focuses on the three C's, the opposite of the S's. Instead of separateness, there's connectedness. Instead of stasis, reality is continuous change, and instead of scarcity is co-creation. If the nature of life is that we're all connected and that change is continuous, then we are all co-creators.

As I was saying in the car driving over, it dawned on me that from this perspective, "If we're all connected, then we're all implicated." So we can stop pointing fingers. And the good news is, with this worldview, we see that we all have power, and that's changed my whole concept of how I can change myself.

It reminds me of the motto of the organization my daughter and I founded, the Small Planet Institute. These are the words you'll see on our website, capturing what we learned traveling the world together and meeting people facing the greatest obstacles: "Hope is not what we find in evidence; it's what we become in action." Really, it should say, "Hope is what we become in action together in community."

FC: That brings to mind something you said in a lecture, maybe 30 years or so ago, which I still remember: "If I have relationships to many people rather than competitively to only a few, that enriches me, and because I am enriched, it also enriches all my relationships."

Over the last five years or so, I've thought a lot about networks, because I wrote a textbook about the systems view of life, which is all about networks. And then I came to think about what is power in the social network.

I arrived at the idea that there are two kinds of power. There's power as domination over others, and for that, the ideal structure is the hierarchy, as we know from the military, the Catholic Church, and other hierarchies. But power in a network empowers others through connecting them.

At the same time, while we are writing our books and having these inspiring conversations, there are massive forces like Monsanto and the oil companies and the pharmaceutical industry and all these corporate powers who own the media and the politicians and get their tax breaks and their subsidies and everything, and totally distort the playing field.

How do we deal with them? How do we turn this reality into an invigorating approach? When I get depressed, that's what I get depressed about.

FML: Me, too. I think it starts with the ecological worldview in which we grasp that we humans, too, are products of the contexts that we create together.

History and lab experiments and personal experience show us that human beings do not do well under three conditions: when power is concentrated, when there is no transparency, and when blaming is the cultural norm.

So, one of the most important messages of EcoMind to me is to think of ourselves as a social ecology in which we can identify the characteristics that bring out the worse or the best in us. For the best, I would start with three conditions: the continual dispersion of power, transparency in human relationships, and society's cultivating mutual accountability instead of blame, blame, blame.

I think that "growing up as a species" means that we must step up and say, "True democracy is possible. Democracy is not just elections and a market economy, because we can have both and still have power that's so concentrated that it will bring out the very worst in human beings, including greed and callousness."

Right now we are experiencing the scarcity of a vision of democracy that works. That's one scarcity that I believe truly exists. And yet we know there are societies that do much better than ours. I was just in Germany, where they don't allow political advertising. Can you imagine? Their campaign seasons are just a fraction of ours in length, and most of the election costs are covered publicly or with small donations rather than corporate funded. So Germany is able to pass laws encouraging citizens to invest in green energy and to become the world's leader in solar energy by 2020, even though Germany is a small, cloudy country.

FC: You talk about "living democracy." What do you mean by that?

FML: I mean both meanings of "living": that it's a daily practice, and that it's a living organism, ever evolving. I love to quote the first African American federal judge, who said, "Democracy is not being. It is becoming. It is easily lost, but never finally won. Its essence is eternal struggle." I used to always drop that last line, thinking it would scare people, but now I'm thinking, "Okay, we know it's a struggle. So let's make it a good struggle."

A living democracy to me starts with what we teach our children at the earliest age about their relationships to nature and understanding what makes our social ecology work: How do we accept differences in our peers? How do we learn to create inclusive groups instead of bullying and "othering"? We know now that human beings are soft-wired to see others unlike themselves as threatening. But we also now know the kind of teaching and coaching that takes us beyond that reaction.

Many of the best schools today are enabling children to be real decision makers and doers. Once you have children with that experience of knowing they have a voice, you cannot put that genie back in the bottle. Are they then going to just turn over their fates to the president or the political party? No, of course not. They're going to ask, why can't we solve our problems? What can I do? They are going to be engaged.

Fritjof Capra, Ph.D., is a scientist, educator, activist, and author of many international bestsellers that connect conceptual changes in science with broader changes in worldview and values in society. Frances Moore Lappé is the author or co-author of 19 books about world hunger, living democracy, and the environment, beginning with the three-million copy *Diet for a Small Planet* in 1971. Her fall 2017 book is *Daring Democracy: Igniting Power, Meaning, and Connection for the America We Want* coauthored with Adam Eichen.

WHY SOCIAL MOVEMENTS NEED THE RADICAL IMAGINATION

By Alex Khasnabish and Max Haiven

The radical imagination often emerges most brilliantly from those who encounter the greatest or most acute oppression and exploitation, and is often stunted and diluted in those who enjoy the greatest privileges. This is an edited excerpt from The Radical Imagination: Social Movement Research in the Age of Austerity, *published by Zed Books June 2014.*

At its most superficial, the radical imagination is the ability to imagine the world, life, and social institutions not as they are but as they might otherwise be. It is the courage and the intelligence to recognize that the world can and should be changed. The radical imagination is not just about dreaming of different futures. It's about bringing those possibilities back from the future to work on the present, to inspire action and new forms of solidarity today.

Likewise, the radical imagination is about drawing on the past, telling different stories about how the world came to be the way it is, remembering the power and importance of yesterday's struggles, and honouring the way they live on in the present.

The radical imagination also represents our capacity to imagine and make common cause with the experiences of other people. It undergirds our ability to build solidarity across boundaries and borders, real or imagined. In this sense, it is the basis of solidarity and the struggle against oppression, which are key to building of robust, resilient, and powerful movements. Without the radical imagination, we are left only with the residual dreams of the powerful and, for the vast majority, they are experienced not as dreams but as nightmares of insecurity, precarity, violence, and hopelessness. Without the radical imagination, we are lost.

We approach the radical imagination not as a thing that individuals possess in greater or lesser quantities but as a collective process, something that groups do and do together through shared experiences, languages, stories, ideas, art, and theory. Collaborating with those around us, we create multiple, overlapping, contradictory, and coexistent imaginary landscapes, horizons of common possibility and shared understanding. These shared landscapes are shaped by and also shape the imaginations and the actions of those individuals who participate in them.

The concept of the "radical" inherits its most powerful meaning from the Latin word for "rooted," in the sense that radical ideas, ideologies, or perspectives are informed by the understanding that social, political, economic, and cultural problems are outcomes of deeply rooted and systemic antagonisms, contradictions, power imbalances, and forms of oppression and exploitation.

As a result, radicalism does not so much describe a certain set of tactics, strategies, or beliefs. Rather, it speaks to a general understanding that, even if the system as a whole can be changed through gradual institutional reforms, those reforms must be based on and aimed at a transformation of the fundamental qualities and tenets of the system itself. The idea of radicalism cannot be monopolized by any one point on the political spectrum: fundamentalists, far-right militias, neoconservative pundits, and others also display elements of radicalism as much as (sometimes more than) the anarchist organizers, anti-racist activists, feminist campaigners, or independent journalists, academics, and writers who make up the cast of characters in this book.

Based on this approach, we understand social movements are convocations of the radical imagination: they are convened (collectively called into being) by individuals who share some understanding and imagination of the world in a radical sense. That is, they see the problems confronting us as deeply rooted in social institutions and systems of power and, importantly, they believe these institutions and systems can and should be changed. While social movements may be many things and take many forms, we suggest that at least one dimension that binds them together is the (sometimes intentional, sometimes incidental) cultivation of common imaginary landscapes, something which is an active process, not a steady state.

So we can say that social movements are animated by the radical imagination. This is not to say that all members share identical imaginary landscapes; the driving dynamic of social movements are the tensions and conflicts and dialogues between imaginative actors. The radical imagination is no static thing to be studied under the microscope or measured through quantitative analysis. It must be observed as it "sparks" from the friction between individuals, groups, ideas, strategies, and tactics. Indeed, the radical imagination emerges from the conflicts and tensions germane to the experience of a highly unequal world. And for that reason, the radical imagination often emerges most brilliantly from those who encounter the greatest or most acute oppression and exploitation, and is often stunted and diluted in those who enjoy the greatest privileges.

A DOUBLE CRISIS OF SOCIAL MOVEMENTS

We understand that social movements and the radical imagination today are caught in a contradiction, one we identify as a "double crisis" of social reproduction. Social reproduction here refers to the dense network of relationships and forms of labour that reproduce social life, and conversely the assemblage of forces necessary to reproduce those relationships and forms of labour. Capitalism, neo-colonialism, patriarchy and white-supremacy are all systems of power that are reproduced by the actions of and relationships between people, but also reproduce people and relationships. We, as individuals,

WATCH THIS VIDEO!
Vincent Harding: Creating America

In this video, Vincent Harding, chair of the Veterans of Hope Project and author of Martin Luther King: The Inconvenient Hero, draws a word-picture of the future all advocates are fighting for at the Children's Defense Fund's 2012 National Conference. Vincent Harding was a historian, author and civil rights activist. He was a friend and speechwriter for Dr. Martin Luther King Jr., and co-wrote King's famous antiwar address, "Beyond Vietnam."

tinyurl.com/creatingamerica

reproduce ourselves within our communities, and we also reproduce our communities, warts and all.

On the one hand, social movements inherently envision and seek to bring about a radical change in the way society is reproduced. Whether they seek to alter government policy, institutional and organizational systems or cultural norms, movements do not want society to be reproduced in its current form. This is especially, but not exclusively, the case for radical social movements that see the problems they face as deeply rooted in the social order, and recognize that a radical change to that order at its very roots is necessary if these problems are to be solved.

On the other hand, whether intentionally or not, social movements also become spheres of alternative social reproduction for their participants: spaces of identity formation, friendship, meaning, care, and possibility, though, as we shall see, they are never unproblematic utopias (far from it). They often seek to create, within their organizational forms or norms, a paradigmatic alternative to the society they seek to change, a tendency that has become much more conscious and common since the 1960s with the rise of "new social movements" and especially since the "anarchist turn" in the 1990s.

We pay attention to this tension because, to a very real extent, the crisis of social reproduction in global capitalist society is intensifying on at least three fronts. First, the ramping-up of neoliberalism in the form of an unapologetic and vicious austerity regime has seen the further subjugation of governments to the will of capital and the evisceration of what remained of the welfare state. Second, the "War on Terror" continues to justify the amplification of repression, surveillance, war, and policing around the world, as well as fortifying a culture of fear backed by racist fantasies and neocolonial ambitions. Third, the deepening ecological crisis, notably the increasing toxicity of the environment and the climate chaos unleashed by global warming, threatens to set loose yet unimagined terrors on the world's populations, terrors that will likely be suffered and endured alone as governments and communities continue to be dismantled and capitalist impunity is enshrined.

The sum of these factors is a wholesale global crisis of social reproduction, where social life itself is made to pay the cost of the reproduction of a renegade, cancerous capitalist system. This crisis manifests as the intensification of fundamentalisms, prejudices, and hatreds, as well as a retreat further into competitive individualism and consumerism.

In these times, when the majority of us live increasingly isolated lives, social movements are not merely important as vehicles for patently necessary social change. They become islands of refuge in an uncaring world. On the one hand, in their organizational forms and group norms, they often strive to "prefigure" the world we might like to see, one that values individuality and communality, radical democracy and solidarity, equality and acceptance, passion and reason, hope and love. They often serve as spaces of friendship, community, romance, and empowerment. This is true even of those more severe and formal organizations and groups that intentionally disavow their social dimensions.

Yet at the same time, we and others have observed that movements and activists all too often fall prey to the crises of reproduction within their own organizations and movements. Sometimes this manifests as open conflicts over strategy and tactics. Other times (indeed, we'd suggest, usually) it manifests — at least on the surface — as personality conflicts or social tensions. Frequently, both of these are the result of the way the movement or group in question continues to reproduce the oppressive behaviours or patterns it has inherited from the society of which it is a part, notably tensions regarding masculinist behaviour, sexual politics and the continued devaluation of people of colour and other marginalized peoples.

In this book, we wanted to imagine and experiment with what "prefigurative" research might look like, a form of research borrowed from a post-revolutionary future of which we can only catch glimpses. We wanted to imagine a form of common research, beyond enclosure. In this, we hoped to do justice to the radical imagination by helping create the conditions of its emergence and flourishing.

Alex Khasnabish teaches about movements, social change, and engaged research at Mount Saint Vincent University and is the author of *Zapatistas: Rebellion from the Grassroots to the Global* and *Zapatismo Beyond Borders*. Max Haiven teaches political economy and cultural studies at the Nova Scotia College of Art and Design in Halifax, and is the author of *Crises of Imagination, Crises of Power: Capitalism, Creativity and the Commons* and (with Alex Khasnabish) *The Radical Imagination* (2014). Together, they direct the Halifax-based Radical Imagination Project on Canada's East Coast.

ECOPOLIS IOWA CITY: ENVISIONING A REGENERATIVE CITY IN THE HEARTLAND

By Jeff Biggers

This is an abbreviated version of the multimedia "Ecopolis" theatre show performed in the spring of 2016 by author Jeff Biggers and the Awful Purdies musical group in the historic Old Capitol in Iowa City. "Ecopolis" has also been adapted and performed in Chicago, in various cities in Iowa including Cedar Rapids, Dubuque, Cedar Falls, and in Carbondale, Illinois.

NEBI

I don't get to see my grandchildren very often, but we never miss the Ralston family reunion in Iowa City. The kids always want to know how it happened. How did Iowa City become an ecopolis, the first regenerative city in the heartland?

There's only one way to answer that question, of course. When we return home to Iowa City now, we arrive at the train station, where kinetic panels power the electrical grid, and while the kids always want to take the kayaks into town along the river, or race their bikes downtown along the green wave without a traffic light or car, I feel there's only one way to understand our city — and that is by walking.

Iowa City began as a vision on foot; one of the first cities west of the Mississippi that was named, surveyed, and laid out before a single limestone was lifted from the river to build this historic capitol.

The capital of Iowa, Iowa City was envisioned before it came into existence — envisioned as a laboratory of democracy. My great-great-grandfather, Robert Ralston, was one of the three commissioners who picked this spot; he stood right on this bluff above the river, gazed out at the amphitheater of limestone, the Big Grove of 20 square miles of hardwood forests, and had the audacity to envision a city of risk takers, innovators, and visionaries.

As Robert Ralston always told the story, Iowa City was not unoccupied — it was on the edge of the so-called Black Hawk Purchases. Purchase, of course, is a misnomer; with Black Hawk in prison, the surrender of Iowa by the Sauk and Meskwaki came easy. That is why I first take my grandkids to Black Hawk Park and show them the solar road memorial to the Sauk and Meskwaki.

The past is always a presence, as Mexican poet Octavio Paz once wrote, and the spirits of the past — of the people, the landscape, and the river — still speak to us, if we listen.

Grandpa, grandpa, my kids shout, tugging at my shirt: Look, I created a sail on my canoe, just like the Meskwaki did on the Iowa River.

The Ralston family reunion, of course, takes place on Ralston Creek. It's a troublesome creek — but we were a troublesome family. The city staff just wanted us to go away, so they could do their jobs. The Chauncey was always a problem — Chauncey Swan that is. He was a towering presence, another administrator who wanted to grow our river town into a Midwestern city.

At the creek that bears our name, we play a game: What's that? A freckled madtom. And that? A spotted bass. And that? An American eel. And that? A redear sunfish — and oh, the paddle fish — the shark of the Iowa River, squeals my little grandkid. Not all sharks are in the city hall.

What a wonder: the native fish have returned to the creek and river, and along Iowa Ave, I take them to the mineral springs site that once brought visitors to our town. Ralston Creek had healing waters. But didn't they know how to protect them, my grandkids ask? Yes, but they needed lights in those days, gas lights manufactured at the gas plant on Burlington Avenue, and the coal tar bled into Ralston Creek, along with cyanine, lead, and arsenic, until it became a Superfund site in 2002.

This kind of oversight, of not understanding the river valley, led to the "great crisis."

You see, the town leaders said it would never happen again. We could mitigate the flooding. Didn't even need flood insurance. That we could mitigate climate change — adaptation, we called it. But what if you are adapting to a failed system?

The city council had voted to use USD$60 million dollars of concrete to raise the main road one foot above the 100-year flood plain. But that didn't matter much with a 500-year flood.

And the rain came. And it came hard. When it rains in Iowa, thanks to industrial agriculture, three out of every four inches runs, runs hard across the erosion, with no native prairie or forests to stop it and the natural drainage system gone. The water runs through the gateway into the river, into our city. First, it was 1.5 inches in a day. Then, 2.5 inches in a day. Then up to five inches in a day. For days. And the waters rose.

Nebi. Nebi. The Meskwaki warned us about nebi — water. You must understand the water. You must understand our watershed — that trees and native prairie are your only gateway to a future.

Over a hundred years before, in the 1890s, the President of the University of Iowa had always warned the town. President Thomas MacBride declared: Iowa's woodland should be religiously preserved and in a thousand places extended. Every rocky bank, every steep hillside, every overhanging bluff, every sandhill, every clay-covered ridge, every rain-washed gully should be kept sacredly covered with trees; every gorge, sinkhole, should be shaded, every spring be protected, every streamlet and every stream and lake bordered and overshadowed...The question is whether we do the right thing now or wait until the expense shall have increased a hundredfold. Macbride was ignored.

Soon we will be gone, the Meskwaki told Robert Ralston, and your people will plant corn where we bury the dead. And you will regret it.

In 1827, a flood wiped out the riverfront; boats topped log cabins in the 1872 flood; 300 tons of coal spilled from a barge on the 1885 flood, and after the floods of the 1940s we came together to build that little dam and all those drainage systems. The engineers told us that they could control nature. Until the next flood. In the great flood of 1993, the water reached 26.81 feet, then 30 feet in 2008, and then 50,000 cubic feet per second of water raised the river 45 feet high, and raw sewage came knocking on our doors.

Iowa City was wiped out.

A crisis is never a crisis until it's validated by disaster — and that is exactly what happened when the 500-year flood hit. It was 2016 or 2017 — I forget now, the year doesn't matter. No, it was 2016, because a new group of people came to power with some exciting ideas to create a regenerative future.

At first, we waited for city hall to act. I mean, I recycled my beer bottles. My wife drove a Prius, and we bought organic (most of the time, well, sometimes, well, at least the first week of the month). But we knew we were part of the problem — that 60 percent of the grid, burning fossil fuels, came from coal. We didn't pay attention to the waterways or the retreating land. We were trying to do less bad.

Mildred Augustine Benson diving into the Iowa River at Iowa City in the mid-1920s. (University of Iowa Libraries)

My grandchildren don't believe me when I tell them about my generation in the year 2016.

They mock me. Grandpa, Iowans knowingly dumped five billion gallons of hog manure as fertilizer, even though you knew it ran off into your waterways? You burned toxic fossil fuels, even though you knew it had huge health care and environmental costs, and produced the highest CO2 emissions, and even though you knew Germany, Scotland, and Denmark already had 100 percent renewable energy regions? You imported 90 percent of your food in the heartland? You couldn't even eat the fish in your river because of mercury and other problems?

Grandma said you ate asparagus imported from Chile? And tomatoes picked by the hands of a 7-year-old migrant worker in Mexico?

Yes, yes yes...but we changed. Thanks to the "great crisis," the 500-year flood. And thanks to Ayman, a father and University of Iowa student, originally from Sudan.

I'll never forget Ayman and the crowd huddled at the Tim Dwight Solar Stadium — I think we used to call it Kinnick Stadium. We were standing in line for rations — you see the flood had knocked out the roads of commerce, and therefore the food stores.

But Ayman didn't need rations. He brought a box of food from his farm. And so did another man, David Burt, who brought loads from his community garden, and then farmer Shanti Sellz brought sacks of potatoes. And Miriam Alarcon arrived from the food coop, and said, *ellos tienen que comer.* I will make tamales.

Gars me greet, David said, the best laid plans gone aft agley.

Yalla' naaquel, Ayman said. *Yalla' naaquel*. Come let us eat. It's time Iowa City sits down and has a *shai magreb*.

Ayman commented, if you can get 60,000 people to fill a football stadium to watch grown men chase a pig skin, now is the time to sit and eat and talk about our future.

And David, Ayman, Miriam, Shanti, and everyone else set a table. And the table grew. And people brought food. A food truck arrived from the Mennonites in Kalona. And the table grew across Burlington Avenue, across the river, across our segregated neighborhoods. And Kurt Freise, the pioneering slow food author and chef, offered recipes. And Iowa City came together at the same table, black and white and Indigenous and newcomer, for a table that grew three-miles long.

Let us talk about our future, Ayman said, as a regenerative city. *Khalena nict quellem. An mostakbelna.*

And then I heard a voice: Dianne Dillon-Ridgley, the great environmental justice activist in our town, stood up, rang a bell, silenced the table, and said, it's time for Iowa City to rethink our ways in an age of climate change, to rethink ways that regenerate our energy, our food, our land, our ways of getting around — beyond sustainability, we must heal our damage to this land. We need to go back to our roots as a laboratory of democracy on the river.

RESTORATION

Perhaps before we could say what kind of regenerative city we wanted, we had to ask: What kind of city do we want? What kind of university? What is our relationship with our hinterlands and nature? Did we recognize Iowa City as a melting pot, or as a smorgasbord where all of our cultures are recognized?

How could we put the roots of culture back into our neighborhoods? Culture. From the Latin root, colere. *Cultivare*. Cultivate. Food. Nature. Diversity. Restoration. Regeneration.

By restoring our relationship with nature — not simply in a series of more parks and ball fields, but a deeper commitment to healing and restoring our surroundings — we also found our sense of place, our sense of community. Adelaide planted three million trees — that's stunning — not only as a carbon sink, but as a roadmap on how we orient our lives. So, we took the challenge: we planted 400,000 trees.

Less than five minutes from Iowa City, Versaland farmer Grant Schultz and his crew planted 30,000 trees in a couple of years and restored a once eroded corn and bean farm. It's now a living farm, evolving, regenerative, and productive with fruit, vegetables, and livestock — a carbon sink.

Grant never talked about sustainability — nothing is sustainable, of course. He asked how we moved beyond doing less bad and actually do something that enhances rather than harms our environment. To begin the healing process. That climate action was not just pulling the plug, but it was first and foremost about putting carbon back into the soil.

At that same long table, always with food, we asked ourselves: how do we heal and restore our waterways and neighborhoods, the new strata of segregation? How do we protect ourselves from unacceptable levels of nitrates and industrial run-off in our water? How do we make sure those who can least afford the changes in electricity rates, the cost of food, and the vector-borne illness from climate change, are in the forefront of our plans?

The eco-district along the river — as a collaboration between the campus, hospital, and city — began the process of answering the question of who we are today in Iowa City in different ways.

No true eco-district could emerge without inclusionary zoning: low-income units mixed with higher income and older communities with new communities. Immigrants. Urban immigrants. Students. And most importantly, senior citizens, the ranks who bring so much experience and wisdom and chutzpah. The Iowa City 100 Grannies planted a solar tree in every neighborhood.

In 2016, in the year of the great crisis, a new opportunity opened up again in an area called Mosquito Flats, which had been flooded and destroyed in 2008. The city owned scores of properties. So, people simply asked: Why not follow the river, and plant native trees for soil and green absorption, and why not get some food in the process?

Mosquito Flats became the Paw Paw Patch. At its planting celebration, the mayor of Iowa City stood on the riverfront, chanting, Asimina triloba, Asimina triloba. I said, Jim, are you OK? And he said, since Iowa City was the first UNESCO City of Literature, he thought using Latin, instead of "paw paw" tree, gave it a literary touch.

Just like Robert Ralston — we had to re-envision ourselves.

The Vauban eco-district in Freiburg ultimately concluded they needed to reduce the use of cars — to the point of creating a walkable environment that didn't need them. Within three years of living in Vauban, 80 percent of the residents gave up their cars.

Reviving the historic tram, the walkable eco-district in Riverfront Crossings did the same.

In its mission to make regenerative city studies a part of the required freshman curriculum, all on-campus university students were required to learn by living, like students at.Berea College in eastern Kentucky, in 100 percent renewable-energy dormitories, powered by solar, wind, geothermal, and recycled materials. Special credit was given to those who tended to the garden and compost.

In the tradition of university president and nationally recognized ecologist Thomas MacBride, the university president, mayor, city manager, and city councilors turned over their homes as showcases of permaculture, with edible lots, energy efficiency renovations, and renewable energy. The town and campus leaders got their hands dirty in a community garden.

We didn't just envision the future; we cultivated it, ate it, and took comfort in it.

I tell my grandkids that the regenerative city didn't happen overnight. It took ages just to talk it out, across the long table. Other cities, like Adelaide, even hired a "thinker in residence." But every day, new breakthroughs reminded us that we needed to think anew and recognize watershed events as turning points. To not defer the pressing realities and mounting costs of climate change but embrace them as opportunities.

How many floods did it take? How many billions did we lose? How many lives?

Economics lose meaning when we calculate the price of our own demise, of the declining hopes of our own futures and that of the next generations.

The best way for my grandkids to learn this, like my generation of crisis, was to talk to our new neighbors from Sudan, who understood resiliency and adaptation, or those from Mexico who left drought conditions, and even those from Decorah, who had created an amazing river town in northern Iowa. To bring the mayor of Dubuque here and ask why he went to the Paris climate summit in 2015 — and how he brought its mandates home.

And then I asked my kids the same question we asked ourselves during the great crisis: How can you be a catalyst for this regenerative city? What is my role — and the role of artists, innovators, engineers, and entrepreneurs? What is growing in my garden? And can I walk there? Where does your electricity come from?

It could begin with a simple act, like that of a concerned school parent like Geoff Lauer, who worked to get Iowa City schools to halt the use of toxic pesticides on school grounds and start using goats.

There are so many examples, but I keep seeing this image in Iowa City: the endless line of volunteers filling six million sand bags in 2008 in an effort to hold back a great flood on the river — a record beyond New Orleans. A record of resilience. But resilience, in this situation, was a state of loss, surrender, and ultimately, ruin. After the great crisis in 2016, we asked those same people who were heroes in filling six million sand bags in a vain attempt to hold back a flood, to do the same for climate action now, in a real and possible way. To create the regenerative city.

So, back to our family reunion on Ralston Creek. The grandkids laugh. What's that?

An American eel. And that? The madtom. There's a redear sunfish and a northern hog sucker. What's that? The paddle fish. The lovely sharks of Iowa River.

Jeff Biggers is the author of several books of memoir, history, investigative reporting and theatre. As a playwright and performer of monologues, he appears frequently at theatres, festivals, conferences and schools. His most recent book, *Trials of a Scold: The Incredible True Story of Writer Anne Royall*, came out in the fall of 2017.

IT WAS A BLIGHTED CITY BLOCK. BUT THIS WOMAN IS TURNING IT INTO A SOLAR-POWERED ECOVILLAGE

By Zenobia Jeffries

Shamayim Harris ran three times for city council in her hometown of Highland Park, Michigan. Each time the voters rejected her. "They didn't want me," she says, with a smile. But that didn't stop her from fulfilling her plans to give Highland Park residents new opportunities, starting with her own block on Avalon Street.

The city of Highland Park is in the middle of the much larger city of Detroit, and could easily be mistaken for another of its neglected neighborhoods. Highland Park has been without a library for 14 years. Its high school was permanently closed by the state last year, leaving just one school, a K–8 program, within its borders. In 2011, utility company DTE Energy removed all the street lights; local and national headlines read some variation of "Highland Park goes dark: City removes lights to pay bills." The city has struggled financially for over a decade, and was one of several financially challenged local units of government in Michigan where Gov. Rick Snyder took control of operational and fiscal duties away from local elected officials and gave it to appointed "emergency managers."

These were the conditions Harris, widely known as "Mama Shu," considered when tossing her hat in the political ring. Her desire, she says, wasn't simply to be in office or hold any political titles. It was simply to "make things better" for the residents of Highland Park. "I'm looking at the conditions and wondering what can I do, intimately understanding what's going on?" she says.

Her tone is reflective. But Shu, a business owner and ordained minister, is not resentful. The vision she had for the city over a decade ago is finally coming to fruition with Avalon Village, an ecologically sustainable project being built in four phases, beginning with a study center for local children. "We want what any community wants," says Shu. "All these other cities have all these wonderful things.

Why can't we?"

With that spirit, and with the help of contributors from around the world, in May she raised over $240,000 days (?) on Kickstarter. Prior to that campaign, the project received a $100,000 donation from the Big Sun Foundation, a nonprofit founded by members of the Grammy award-winning band Edward Sharpe and the Magnetic Zeros.

That seed money went to Moon Ministries, a nonprofit organization. Then Shu used it to purchase more than 10 properties on her block, including vacant lots and salvageable abandoned homes, and to start renovating Homework House, which she describes as a place where children will be able to get meals and help with schoolwork.

A totally redesigned 2,400-square-foot two-family home, Homework House will have a computer center and a lab for specialized help in science, technology, engineering, and mathematics, as well as a recording studio and a commercial kitchen. In the yards outside, children will have three recreational courts to play basketball, tennis, and volleyball.

Moon Ministries is handling all the funds associated with the project for now, but Shu says she's submitted the paperwork to make Avalon Village itself a 501(c)3 nonprofit. Once that's approved, the resulting group will handle the costs of running the village over time.

The greening of Avalon Street began in 2014, with the installation of a solar street light in front of Shu's home. The rest of the block will soon have more solar lights. Homework House will have geothermal heating and cooling, as well as a metal roof designed to save on cooling costs. The project received an $18,000 in-kind donation from Luma Resources, a company that manufactures shingle-style solar panels for rooftops.

Meanwhile, local contracting firm Ako Building Corporation volunteered to help with construction and design.

The support for Avalon Village continues to roll in with big names like Ellen Degeneres, who on her show in September surprised Shu with a $100,000 prefab energy-efficient home from Cocoon 9. Shu points to the area where it'll go as if it's already there, adding that the space will be used for Avalon Village's offices.

But before the big names and money started to come in, Shu depended on her friends and family and her weekly check from the charter school where she worked as an office administrator. It was this combination of funds that helped her to purchase her home for $3,000 in 2009.

"I didn't have $3,000," she says, "but I put it together."

A former neighbor who asked that her last name not be used, Ashaki says her mother still lives on Avalon Street. She explains that her sister used to live in the lower unit of what is now Homework House. "It got really bad over the years," she said. "It's good what she's doing."

Ashaki and another neighbor, named Tyrone, who's lived in the same house on Avalon for 50 years, remember the days when Highland Park was a vibrant community. "It was called the City of Trees," says Tyrone. "You don't see many trees now." But he says that Shu is bringing life back to the block. "They keep the grass cut," he says. "It's looking good."

A DIFFICULT JOURNEY

Mama Shu's two-story brick home sits on the corner of Avalon Street and Woodward Avenue. It's been a welcome center of sorts to Highland Park and Detroit residents for the seven years that she's lived there — one of seven occupied homes amid blighted houses and vacant lots. The street's bright colors, green grass, and activity today are all things she says she used to envision when driving past on her way to work. The houses appeared dilapidated, and mattresses, tires, toilets, bricks, and other discarded items filled the vacant lots. Her now warm and inviting home was boarded up and occupied by squatters.

"They kept it clean, though," she says, laughing. The wood floors were still in good condition, but all the plumbing had been torn out. After she moved in, in 2009, callers kept coming by, expecting to find someone else there. She recalls performing a cleansing ceremony — with incense, oils, and sage — on the third night.

That time was the end of a long transition for Shu and her family. To see her infectious smile today and hear her laughter, one wouldn't suspect the trauma she's endured: In 2007, at only "two years, one month, and six days" old, her younger son, Jakobi Ra, was killed by a neighbor speeding down the street.

Shu and her then-husband were at work, and her boys — Jakobi and his older brother, Chinyelu, who was 10 at the time — were outside playing under their neighbors' supervision. She tears up when talking about what happened. "They were walking across the street when my neighbor ... turned the corner and blew the stop sign and ... the impact just snatched Jakobi out of Chin's hand."

Shu recalls thinking that she wouldn't make it. "My girlfriends and I would say things like, 'I'd die if something happened to one of my children.'" But when she woke up the next day, after her son had passed, she said, "Damn, I didn't die." And today, she says, Jakobi is still with her. The Jakobi Ra Park, named in 2011 after Shu's son, was the first venue of what eventually would become Avalon Village. And at the September ribbon-cutting ceremony for the project — held on the same day her son was killed nine years ago — a headstone was unveiled in his memory.

It's his spirit, she says, and the energy and help of her family, friends, and all the project's volunteers that help her to keep going.

Zenobia Jeffries wrote this article for *YES! Magazine*. Zenobia is the racial justice associate editor at *YES!*

ENVISIONING A SUSTAINABLE WORLD

By Donella H. Meadows

This article is excerpted from a speech Donella wrote for the Third Biennial Meeting of the International Society for Ecological Economics, October 24-28, 1994, in San Jose, Costa Rica.

To bring our world toward sustainability — or any other goal — we need to take different kinds of steps, which require different kinds of knowledge, talent, skill, and work.

We need, for example, to make things happen — pass laws, make budgets, find resources, hire people, establish and manage organizations, invent technologies, build, restore, protect, tax, subsidize, regulate, punish, reward, **DO THINGS. Implementation** is the active, visible phase of achieving a goal, and therefore it is the most discussed phase.

Probably 90% of all public discourse involves arguing about implementation. Most policy debates start and end with this phase, unfortunately.

I say "unfortunately," because any talk of implementation is necessarily based on **models**, which explain how we got to whatever state we are in, and what we should do to get to a better state. Models may be in computers, on paper, or in our heads. They may be sophisticated, but usually they are very simple — for example: "freeing the market from regulation will make things better," or "new technology is all we need to solve our problem." We debate and challenge our models far too little, especially the models in our heads. Most of them are too narrow, too linear, too lacking in understanding of feedback, time-lags, exponentiality, variability, diversity, and other aspects of real-system complexity.

Obviously, if our models are faulty, all the skillful and well-funded implementation in the world will not get us to sustainability or any other goal.

There are at least two more ingredients of the policy process that precede and are even more important than modeling. One of them is information. We need to know where we are and where we have been. Information not only validates or disproves our models, it helps us form and develop them and turn them into action. If information about our history and present situation is biased, delayed, incomplete, noisy, disorganized, or missing, our models will be wrong, and our implementation will be untimely and misdirected. Improving information means, among other activities, monitoring, organizing data, choosing wise indicators, education, communication (especially through the public media), and — an issue vital to ecological economics — the removal of bias from price signals.

If 90% of policy discussion focuses on implementation, virtually all the remaining 10% focuses on modeling and information. That leaves 0% for the last step of policy formation, which should be first — the establishment of clear, feasible, socially shared goals. What do we want? Where would we like all these models, this information, this implementation to take us? What is our vision of the world we are trying to create for ourselves, our children, and our grandchildren?

Environmentalists have failed perhaps more than any other set of advocates to project vision. Most people associate environmentalism with restriction, prohibition, regulation, and sacrifice. Though it is rarely articulated directly, the most widely shared picture of a sustainable world is one of tight and probably centralized control, low material standard of living, and no fun. I don't know whether that impression is so common because puritanism is the actual, unexpressed, maybe subconscious model in the minds of environmental advocates, or whether the public, deeply impacted by advertising, can't imagine a good life that is not based on wild and wasteful consumption. Whatever the reason, hardly anyone envisions a sustainable world as one that would be wonderful to live in.

The best goal most of us who work toward sustainability offer is the avoidance of catastrophe. We promise survival and not much more. That is a failure of vision.

Even if information, models, and implementation could be perfect in every way, how far can they guide us, if we know what direction we want to move away from but not what direction we want to go toward? There may be motivation in escaping doom, but there is even more in creating a better world. And it is pitifully inadequate to describe the exciting possibilities of sustainability in terms of mere survival — at least that's what my vision of sustainability tells me.

But I didn't always have such a vision. I had to learn, or perhaps I should say relearn, to create and express vision. In our industrial culture, particularly in the cultures of science and economics, envisioning is actively discouraged. We have to rediscover and practice it again. Perhaps if I tell you the story of my own experience with vision, you will understand what I mean.

A WORLD WITHOUT HUNGER

About ten years ago I ran a series of workshops intended to figure out how to end hunger. The participants were some of the world's best nutritionists, agronomists, economists, demographers, ecologists, and field workers in development — people who were devoting their lives in one way or another to ending hunger.

Peter Senge of MIT, a colleague who helped design and carry out the workshops, suggested that we open each one by asking the assembled experts, "What would the world be like if there were no hunger?" Surely each of these people had a motivating vision of the goal he or she was working for. It would be interesting to hear and collect these visions and to see if they varied by discipline, by nationality, or by personal experience.

I thought this exercise would take about an hour and would help the participants get to know each other better. So I opened the first workshop by asking, "What is your vision of a world without hunger?" Coached by Peter, I made the request strongly visionary. I asked people to describe **not the world they thought they could achieve, or the world they were willing to settle for, but the world they truly wanted.**

What I got was an angry reaction. The participants refused. They said that was a stupid and dangerous question. Here are some of their comments:

- Visions are fantasies, they don't change anything. Talking about them is a waste of time. We don't need to talk about what the end of hunger will be like, we need to talk about how to get there.
- We all **know** what it's like **not** to be hungry. What's important to talk about is how terrible it is to be hungry,
- I never really thought about it. I'm not sure what the world would be like without hunger, and I don't see why I need to know.
- Stop being unrealistic. There will always be hunger. We can decrease it, but we can never eliminate it.
- You have to be careful with visions. They can be dangerous. Hitler had a vision. I don't trust visionaries and I don't want to be one.

After we got those objections out of our systems, some deeper ones came up. One person said, with emotion, that he couldn't stand the pain of thinking about the world he really wanted, when he was so aware of the world's present state. The gap between what he longed for and what he knew or expected was too great for him to bear. And finally another person said what may have come closer to the truth than any of our other rationalizations: "I have a vision, but it would make me feel childish and vulnerable to say it out loud. I don't know you all well enough to do this."

That remark struck me so hard that I have been thinking about it ever since. Why is it that we can share our cynicism, complaints, and frustrations without hesitation with perfect strangers, but we can't share our dreams? How did we arrive at a culture that constantly, almost automatically, ridicules visionaries? Whose idea of reality forces us to "be realistic?" When were we taught, and by whom, to suppress our visions?

Whatever the answers to those questions, the consequences of a culture of cynicism are tragic. If we can't speak of our real desires, we can only marshal information, models, and implementation toward what we think we can get, not toward what we really want. We only half-try. We don't reach farther than the lengths of our arms. If, in working for modest goals, we fall short of them, for whatever reason, we reign in our expectations still further and try for even less. In a culture of cynicism, if we exceed our goals, we take it as an unrepeatable accident, but if we fail, we take it as an omen. That sets up a positive feedback loop spiraling downward. The less we try, the less we achieve. The less we achieve, the less we try.

Without vision, says the Bible, the people perish.

Children, before they are squashed by cynicism, are natural visionaries. They can tell you clearly and firmly what the world should be like. There should be no war, no pollution, no cruelty, no starving children. There should be music, fun, beauty, and lots and lots of nature. People should be trustworthy and grownups should not work so hard. It's fine to have nice things, but it's even more important to have love. As they grow up, children learn that these visions are "childish" and stop saying them out loud. But inside all of us, if we haven't been too badly bruised by the world, there are glorious visions.

We discovered that in the hunger workshop. Having vented all the reasons why we shouldn't share our visions, we shared our visions. Not just what we expected, but what we really wanted. It was the first time I had been in a prolonged, shared, visionary space. As we constructed together a picture of the world we wanted to create, our mood lifted, our faces softened, our bodies woke up, we gained energy and clarity and solidarity.

The vision we pulled out of each other that day has gone on powering me for years. The end of hunger need not just mean that the hungry fifth of the world's people become like the rest of us, with all our stresses and strains. It need not mean massive, constant, expensive transfers of food from the rich to the poor. It would not, in my vision, mean chemical- intensive agriculture taking over the world, or populations exploding, or centralized control of anything.

The world seems to expect the end of hunger to be like that — if it thinks of ending hunger at all — and so it's no wonder that we don't work very hard to achieve it.

In my vision of the end of hunger, every child is born into the world wanted, treasured, and lovingly cared for. Because of that, many fewer children are born and not one of them is wasted. Every person can become all that she or he is capable of becoming, in a world that is beautiful, where cultures are diverse and tolerant, where information flows freely, untainted by cynicism. In my vision food is raised and prepared as consciously and lovingly as are children, with profound respect for nature's contribution as well as that of people. In a world without hunger I can take care of my own nearby community and be taken care of by it, knowing that other people in other communities are also doing their caring close at hand. There would be plenty of problems to solve — I want problems to solve — but I could travel anywhere in the world without encountering deprivation, terror, or ugliness.

What I would find, everywhere, would be natural integrity, human productivity, working communities, and the full range of human emotions, but dominated not by fear and therefore greed, but by security, serenity, and joy.

I could go on. I can see this vision clearly and in detail. I can see the farms; I can see the kitchens. But you get the point. Maybe you are already filling in your own details, or maybe you are uncomfortable in the presence of such visionary language. Whatever your reaction, notice where it comes from, notice what has been laid upon you by your culture, and notice that there is a place inside you, close to the surface or deeply buried, that desperately wants a world something like the one I've just sketched out.
I have noticed, going around the world, that in different disciplines, languages, nations, and cultures, our information may differ, our models disagree, our preferred modes of implementation are widely diverse, but our visions, when we are willing to admit them, are astonishingly alike.

SOME GENERALIZATIONS ABOUT VISION

So I have been honing my capacity to envision. I rarely start a garden, a book, a conference, or an organization, without formally envisioning how I want it to come out — what I really want, not what I am willing to settle for. I go to a quiet place, shut down my rational mind, and develop a vision. I present the vision to others, who correct and refine it and help it to evolve. I write out vision statements. When I lose my way, I go back to those statements.

Sometimes I still feel silly doing all this. I was raised in a skeptical culture, after all, and worse, I was trained as a scientist, with all "silly irrationality" drummed out of me. But I keep practicing vision, because my life works better when I do.

I am a practical person. I think of myself as relentlessly realistic. I want to create change in the world, not visions in my head. I am constantly amazed, but increasingly convinced, that envisioning is a tool for producing results. Olympic athletes use it to make the difference between the superior performance their trained bodies can achieve and the outstanding performance their inspired vision can achieve. Corporate executives take formal classes in vision. All great leaders have been visionaries. Even the scientific, systems-analyst side of me has to admit that we can hardly achieve a desirable, sustainable world, if we can't even picture what it will be like.

ENVISIONING A SUSTAINABLE WORLD

So I invite you to join with me in building that vision. What kind of sustainable world do you WANT to live in? Do your best to imagine not just the absence of problems but the presence of blessings. Our rational minds tell us that a sustainable world has to be one in which renewable resources are used no faster than they regenerate; in which pollution is emitted no faster than it can be recycled or rendered harmless; in which population is at least stable, maybe decreasing; in which prices internalize all real costs; in which there is no hunger or poverty; in which there is true, enduring democracy. But what else? What else do YOU want, for yourself, your children, your grandchildren?

The best way to find your answer to that question is to go to a quiet place, close your eyes, take a few deep breaths, and put yourself in the middle of that sustainable world. Don't push, don't worry, and don't try to figure it out. Just close your eyes and see what you see. Or, as often happens for me, hear what you hear, smell what you smell, feel what you feel.

Many of my visions are bright, detailed, and visual, but some of the most profound ones have come not through "seeing," but through sensing in other ways.

In short, relax, trust yourself and see what happens. If nothing happens, don't worry, try again sometime, or let your visionary talent surface in your sleeping dreams.

But keep asking yourself: What would my home be like in a sustainable world? What would it feel like to wake up there in the morning? Who else would live there; how would it feel to be with them? (Remember this is what you WANT, not what you're willing to settle for.) Where would energy come from, and water, and food? What kinds of wastes would be generated and where would they go? When you look out the window or step out the door, what would it look like, if it looked the way you really want? Who else lives near you (human and non-human)? How do you all interrelate? Go around your neighborhood and community and see it as clearly as you can. How is it arranged, so that the children and the old people and everyone in between will be surrounded by security and happiness and beauty?

What kind of work do you do in this sustainable world? What is your particular and special role? With whom do you do it? How do you work together and how are you compensated? How do you get to work? (Do you have to "get" to work? Is "work" a distinguishable activity in your ideal world? Is it separate from the rest of life?)

Travel farther in your vision, to surrounding communities. Look not only at the physical systems that sustain them — water, energy, food, materials — but look at how they relate, what they exchange with each other, how they know of each other. How do they make joint decisions? How do they resolve conflicts? (How do you WANT them to resolve conflicts?) How do they treat different kinds of people, young and old, male and female, intelligent and talented to different degrees and in different ways? ?) How do they fit within nature? How do they treat, how do they think about plants and animals, soils and waters, stones and stars?

Look at your nation (if your visionary world has nations — if it doesn't, what does it have?). How does it meet its physical needs sustainably? How does it make decisions, resolve conflicts within and without its borders? What do your people know of other people, and how do they think about them? How much and what kinds of people and goods and information travel between your place and other places? Is your nation and your world diverse or homogeneous (the way you WANT it, not the way you expect)?

How does it feel to live in this world? What kind of consciousness or worldview, or tolerance of diverse worldviews do people use to keep things sustainable? What changes in this world, and what stays the same? What is the pace of everyday life? How fast, if at all, do people travel and by what means? What fascinates them? What kinds of problems do they work on? What do they regard as progress? What makes them laugh?

Whatever you can see, or can't see, keep looking. NOT being able to see something in a vision may be as meaningful as seeing it. Once when I did a visioning session with some German engineering students, they had no trouble seeing sustainable farms, sustainable forestry, even "sustainable chemistry." (That, seen by a chemist, was interesting. It involved minimizing rather than maximizing the amount of chemical needed to do any job, deriving chemicals from nature, making them the way nature does — at low temperatures in small batches with no harmful emissions — and recycling them as nature does.) But none of these engineers could envision a sustainable transportation system, though some of them actually worked in designing solar vehicles. Finally they concluded that transportation is a cost, not a benefit, that it's noisy, disrupting, energy- and time-consuming, and inherently unsatisfying, and that it would be best if everyone were already where they wanted to be, with whom they wanted to be. In a sustainable society, they concluded, travel would be almost unnecessary. (But they wanted to have, for fun, sailboats and horses and hang gliders!)

CONCLUSIONS, CAVEAT, AND MANIFESTO

Of course having a vision isn't enough. Of course it's only the first step toward any goal. The grandest vision will get nowhere without proper information and models and implementation (and resources, labor, capital, time, and money). There are great difficulties in all these steps of social change and much work to do. I'm by no means indicating that we all become nothing but visionaries. I think what I'm advocating is simply that we make the world safe for vision.

That means, at the least, that we take a mutual vow not to go around squashing vision — our own, or anyone else's, and especially not that of young people. That we don't try to keep our loved ones or ourselves from disappointment or from looking silly by urging them to "be realistic."

Beyond that we could occasionally take the social risk of displaying not our skepticism but our deepest desires. We could declare ourselves in favor of a sustainable, just, secure, efficient, sufficient world (and you can add any other "value word" you like to that list), even at the expense of being called idealistic. We could describe that world, as far as we can see it, and ask others to develop the description further. We could give as much credit to the times when we exceed our expectations as to the times when we fall short. We could let disappointments be learning experiences, rather than fuel for pessimism.

Above all, we could strengthen ourselves to endure the pain of the enormous gap between the world we know and the world we profoundly long for. I believe that it's only by admitting, permitting, and carrying that pain that we can gradually move our world away from its present suffering and unsustainability and toward our deepest values and dearest visions.

Dr. Donella H. Meadows was a Pew Scholar in Conservation and Environment and a MacArthur Fellow. After receiving a Ph.D in biophysics from Harvard, she joined a team at MIT applying the relatively new tools of system dynamics to global problems. She became principal author of *The Limits to Growth* (1972), which sold more than 9 million copies in 26 languages. She went on to author or co-author eight other books.

ECOCHALLENGE: PUTTING IT INTO PRACTICE

Since this is the last Session of your course book, we'd like to challenge you to commit to some bigger actions in your future. Here are some ideas to get you started on systemic change. Find more ideas and commit to one Ecochallenge this week at **choices.ecochallenge.org**

- Organize a course. Organize one of Ecochallenge.org's discussion courses, such as A Different Way, with family, friends, coworkers, or classmates.
- Do an online energy audit. Complete an online energy audit of your home, office, or dorm room and identify your next steps for saving energy.
- Write letters or emails. Write a letter once a week to local leaders and representatives advocating for sustainable and just policies.
- Advocate for greener vehicles. Assess the vehicles used by your company or college and advocate for a purchasing policy focused on fuel-efficient vehicles.
- Ditch the lawn. Replace your lawn with a drought-tolerant landscape and save the water, money, and time you used to spend cutting the grass.
- Start a project. Organize a local restoration project such as tree planting, planting native species, removing non-native species from local green spaces, or organizing a river or wild habitat clean-up.

CALL TO ACTION

"The character of a whole society is the cumulative result of countless small actions, day in and day out, of millions of persons."

— DUANE ELGIN

CELEBRATION AND CALL TO ACTION

This final session of *Choices for Sustainable Living* is an optional celebration — an opportunity for both reflection on your experience and a discussion of possible next steps. After spending several weeks together exploring new ideas, sharing information and observations, this session provides an opportunity to share what you each will take away from this experience.

Ecochallenge.org discussion groups have closed their Discussion Courses in a variety of different ways. You may choose to have a potluck meal together or attend a sustainability event.

This meeting is also the perfect opportunity for groups to plan to work together on a collective action project. The following list provides examples of inspiring actions taken by discussion groups that have completed this Ecochallenge.org course:

- Commit to conducting an energy or a waste audit for your homes, workplaces, or places of worship.
- Schedule a monthly hike or other group gathering.
- Look up volunteer opportunities for your group.
- Organize a local restoration project such as tree planting, planting native species, removing non-native species from local Green Spaces, or organizing a river or wild habitat clean-up.
- Attend a local or regional planning meeting to weigh in on sustainability concerns.
- Write letters to leaders advocating for the changes you wish to see.
- Tour local recycling or waste facilities to find out where your "garbage" goes. Next, find out where to recycle those recyclables that cannot be placed into curbside containers and organize a weekly or monthly neighborhood or workplace pick-up or drop-off.
- Organize a neighborhood yard sale.
- Support a local farmers' market, community garden, or Community Supported Agriculture (CSA) group and take a tour. If a CSA exists in your community, sign up individually or as a group and share the produce.

continued

- Organize a speaker or film highlighting simplicity and sustainability in your neighborhood or organization.

Once your group reaches a consensus about what project you'll undertake, create a specific follow-up plan and delegate responsibilities.

Please mail your completed evaluation forms to Ecochallenge.org, or complete the online form at **ecochallenge.org/discussion-course-evaluations**.

If you are interested in offering or participating in other Ecochallenge.org programs, please visit our website for a complete list of current program offerings. You may also call us at (503) 227-2807.

We hope you were enriched by your experience of this Discussion Course. Please contact us if you are interested in finding out what you can do to help bring these courses to others in your community, school or workplace.

If you enjoyed this experience and would like to support Ecochallenge.org's work, please see our donation page on page 155. We rely on support from individuals like you to keep our work going and to engage new generations and leaders.

"Action is eloquence."

— William Shakespeare

Your support makes our work possible!

Connecting the dots.

Thank you for participating in this Ecochallenge.org discussion course! With the support of thousands of Ecochallenge.org donors over the past 25 years, we have helped more than 200,000 people from around the world take small steps that lead to big changes for our planet. You make Ecochallenge.org stronger!

We hope that you found your experience to be meaningful and inspiring. If you would like to help others discover their role in fostering a healthy planet, please consider making a donation to support our work and inspire others.

To make a donation, please visit ecochallenge.org/donate or mail this form to Ecochallenge.org, 107 SE Washington St., Portland, OR 97214.

☐ **I'd like to make a donation to Ecochallenge.org.**

Name(s)____

Address____

City________________________ State______ Zip code__________

Telephone: Day (______)____________ Email address____________________

Tax deductible gift of:
- ☐ Regular $35
- ☐ Household/Contributor .. $50
- ☐ Earth Steward $100
- ☐ Sustainer $250
- ☐ Patron $500
- ☐ Founder's Circle........ $1,000

Please see our website or contact us for more information on donor benefits.

☐ **I'm already a member. Here's an additional gift. $__________**

Pay by credit card: ☐ Visa ☐ MasterCard

Card number______________________________ Expiration date__________

Signature____

☐ **I would like information on other Ecochallenge.org Discussion Courses:**____________________

☐ **I would like information on Ecochallenge.org online events.**

Thank you for your support!

PERMISSIONS

SESSION 1

"Our View of Sustainability" by Felipe Ferreira for Ecochallenge.org

"The Culture Tree" by Zaretta Hammond. From Hammond, Culturally Responsive Teaching and The Brain: Promoting Authentic Engagement and Rigor Among Culturally and Linguistically Diverse Students pp. 22-24. Copyright © 2015 by Corwin. Reprinted by permission of SAGE Publications, Inc.

"You are Brilliant and the Earth is Hiring" by Paul Hawken, YES! Magazine, May 27, 2009. Used with permission of YES! Magazine, www.yesmagazine.org

"Our Home on Earth" excerpted and updated from "Voices from White Earth: Gaa-waabaabiganikaag," by Winona LaDuke, from the Thirteenth Annual E.F. Schumacher Lecture, given at Yale University, October 1993. Used with permission.

Calvin and Hobbes cartoon © Watterson. Reprinted with permission of Universal Press Syndicate. All rights reserved.

"Systems Thinking: A Necessary Perspective in our Changing World." From EarthEd: Rethinking Education on a Changing Planet by The Worldwatch Institute. Copyright © 2017 Worldwatch Institute. Reproduced by permission of Island Press, Washington, D.C.

"How Wolves Change Rivers." This video was created by Sustainable Human, a project co-founded by Chris and Dawn Agnos, that is helping the world shift from a perspective of separation to one of interconnection.

"A Systems Thinking Model: The Iceberg" by Northwest Earth Institute. © Copyright Northwest Earth Institute.

SESSION 2

"You Can't Just Do One Thing: A Conversation with Richard Heinberg" by Michael K. Stone was originally published by the Center for Ecoliteracy. © Copyright 2004-2015 Center for Ecoliteracy. Reprinted with permission. All rights reserved. For more information, visit www.ecoliteracy.org.

"Ecological Principles" by Michael K. Stone was originally published by the Center for Ecoliteracy. © Copyright 2004-2015 Center for Ecoliteracy. Reprinted with permission. All rights reserved. For more information, visit www.ecoliteracy.org.

"The Anthropocene Epoch: Scientists Declare Dawn of Human-Influenced Age" by Damian Carrington. Published by Guardian Media Group, August 29, 2016. Used with permission.

"The Four System Conditions of a Sustainable Society" published by The Natural Step. Used with permission."The Refugee Crisis Is a Sign of a Planet in Trouble" by David Korten, YES! Magazine, March 8, 2017. Used with permission of YES! Magazine, www.yesmagazine.org

Climate Change cartoon. Copyright © Chris Madden. Used with permission.

"The Earth Is Full" TED Talk (edited transcript) by Paul Gilding. Used with permission of Mr. Paul Gilding, www.paulgilding.com

"Too Many People, Too Much Consumption" by Paul and Anne H. Ehrlich, Yale360, August 4, 2008. Used with permission of Yale360, www.e360.yale.edu, for Conservation Biology.

"The Ecological Footprint Explained" by Moovly. Made to adapt. www.moovly.com

SESSION 3

"What's Eating America" by Michael Pollan, appeared in Smithsonian, June 15, 2006. Reprinted with permission by the author.

"The Dirty Dozen" and "Clean Fifteen" produced by the Environmental Working Group, 2017. Copyright © Environmental Working Group, www.ewg.org. Reprinted with permission.

"Cutting Meat Consumption Can Make A Huge Dent in Climate Change." Original headline: "Eat less meat to avoid dangerous global warming, scientists say" by Fiona Harvey. Published by Guardian Media Group, March 21, 2016. Used with permission.

"Stalking the Vegetannual," from Animal, Vegetable, Miracle by Barbara Kingsolver and Steven Hopp & Camille Kingsolver. Copyright © 2007 by Barbara Kingsolver, Stephen L. Hopp, and Camille Kinsolver. Reprinted with permission of HarperCollins Publishers.

"Perspectives: Food Access" Courtesy Nourish Initiative: www.nourishlife.org. Copyright WorldLink, all rights reserved.

"From Food Security to Food Sovereignty" by Antonio Roman-Alcalá. Published by Civil Eats, May 29, 2013. Used with permission.

"Beyond "Free" or "Fair" Trade: Mexican Farmers Go Local" by Mike Wold, YES! Magazine, January 23, 2012. Used with permission of YES! Magazine, www.yesmagazine.org

"Growing Power - A Model for Urban Agriculture" by ShareAmerica on October 13, 2010. This video comes from shareamerica.gov and is in the public domain.

"We Can Feed the World with the Food We Waste" by Joanne Will. Featured in Quench Magazine, April 22, 2017. Used with permission.

SESSION 4

"Water Is Life," excerpted from Uprisings for the Earth: Reconnecting Culture with Nature by Osprey Orielle Lake. Used with permission by White Cloud Press.

"How Your Diet Contributes to Water Pollution" by Paul Greenberg, appeared in Eating Well Magazine, July 2017. Reprinted with permission.

"Water and Climate Change" published by Union of Concerned Scientists. Used with permission by Union of Concerned Scientists, www.ucsusa.org.

"What is a Watershed" video by Caring for Our Watersheds. Used with permission. Caringforourwatersheds.com

"The Oceans Are Drowning In Plastic - And No One's Paying Attention" by Dominique Mosbergen, appeared in Huffington Post, April 2017. Reprinted with permission.

"The Story of Bottled Water." Courtesy of The Story of Stuff Project

"Ocean Acidification." Original headline: "Global Warming's Evil Twin: Ocean Acidification," published by The Climate Reality Project, June 21, 2016. Reprinted with permission.

"The Race To Save Florida's Devastated Coral Reef From Global Warming" by Chris Mooney. Appeared in the Washington Post June 25, 2017. © The Washington Post. Reprinted with permission.

SESSION 5

"This is What Democracy Looks Like" by Fred Kent, appeared in Project for Public Spaces. Reprinted with permission by the author.

"Six Foundations for Building Community Resilience," Copyright © 2015 by Post Carbon Institute. Published November 2015. Full text at http://sixfoundations.org. Edited and used with permission.

"The Urban Common Spaces That Show Us We Belong to Something Larger" by Sarah van Gelder, YES! Magazine, April 26, 2017. Used with permission of YES! Magazine, www.yesmagazine.org

"Connecting the Lots" by Diana Budds. Photography by Justin Fantl. Originally published in Kinfolk Magazine. Used with permission.

Comic. Copyright © Chris Madden. Used with permission.

"What It Looks Like When Communities Make Racial Justice a Priority" by Zenobia Jeffries and Araz Hachadourian, YES! Magazine, January 16, 2017. Used with permission of YES! Magazine, www.yesmagazine.org

"How to Turn Neighborhoods Into Hubs of Resilience" by Taj James and Rosa González, YES! Magazine, April 14, 2017. Used with permission of YES! Magazine, www.yesmagazine.org

"Real Money, Real Power: Participatory Budgeting" was created by the Participatory Budgeting Project. Find out more at https://www.participatorybudgeting.org/

"How to Build Community." Artist/Copyright: Karen Kerney, SCW © 1997. Used with permission. www.syracuseculturalworkers.com/ Syracuse Cultural Workers "Tools for Change" catalog is 40 color pages of feminist, progressive, multicultural resources to help change the world and sustain activism. The Peace Calendar, Women Artists Datebook, over 100 posters on social, cultural and political themes, holiday cards for Solstice, Christmas, Chanukah, plus buttons, stickers, T-shirts, notecards, postcards, and books. Great fundraising products. Box 6367, Syracuse, NY 13217 800.949.5139; Fax 800.396.1449. 24-hour ordering – Visa/MC email: scw@syracuseculturalworkers.com

SESSION 6

"Reimagining Our Streets as Places: From Transit Routes to Community Roots" by Dr. Annah MacKenzie, was first published on the Project for Public Spaces website, on March 3, 2015. Reprinted with permission by the author.

"The Environmental Cost of Free 2-day Shipping" by the University of California. Video, first published on Vox.com on November 17, 2017; with an accompanied article by Andy Murdock. Used with permission. URL: https://www.youtube.com/watch?v=5HOijUtExiM

"America's 'Worst Walking City' Gets Back on its Feet" by Jay Walljasper, originally published by Resilience, March 24, 2016. Reprinted with permission by the author.

"Millennials in transit" by Derek Prall, originally published by American City and Counsel, September 26, 2017. Reprinted with permission

"City Planners Respond to Demands for Better Neighborhood Mobility and Bicycling Infrastructure," originally published as "Nashville Teens Mapped Their Daily Routes—And Got a New Bike Lane as a Result" by Araz Hachadourian, YES! Magazine, January 3, 2017. Used with permission of YES! Magazine, www.yesmagazine.org

"Possibilities for Cars" Reprinted with permission from www.drawdown.org © 2017 Project Drawdown

"Retrofitting Suburbia: Communities Innovate Their Way Out of Sprawl" by Erin Sagen, YES! Magazine, April 25, 2016. Used with permission of YES! Magazine, www.yesmagazine.org

SESSION 7

"Detroit Speech" by Robert F. Kennedy used with permission by the Robert F. Kennedy Memorial Center for Justice and Human Rights, www.rfkcenter.org

"Beyond the GDP" compiled by Betty Shelley and Lacy Cagle for Northwest Earth Institute.

"What Isn't For Sale?" by Michael J Sandel, The Atlantic, April 2012. Used with permission by Tribune Media Services, www.tribunemediaservices.com

"Bringing People Back into the Economy" by Vandana Shiva was originally published by the Center for Ecoliteracy. © Copyright 2004-2015 Center for Ecoliteracy. Reprinted with permission. All rights reserved. For more information, visit www.ecoliteracy.org.

"Understanding Obsolescence", "Redistribution and Sharing", "Conscious Consumerism". Reprinted with permission from New Dream, www.newdream.org

"How We Live: Transition Toward a Just Economy" video by Kontent Films. Used with permission.

"True Price Questions," True Price Activity used with permission of Institute for Humane Education (IHE) www.humaneeducation.org. IHE believes that education is the key to creating a just, humane, and sustainable world for all people, animals and the environment, and offer programs and resources designed to train, educate and inspire people to become humane educators and changemakers who live with compassion and integrity and work to solve the most pressing challenges of our time.

"The Story of Stuff," Courtesy of The Story of Stuff Project.

"Going Local: the Solution-Multiplier," By Local Futures Staff, originally published by Local Futures. February 1, 2017. Used with permission.

SESSION 8

"Neoliberalism Has Conned Us into Fighting Climate Change as Individuals," by Martin Lukacs. Published by Guardian Media Group, July 17, 2017. Used with permission.

"The Story of Change." Courtesy of The Story of Stuff Project.

"Hope Is What We Become in Action" by Fritjof Capra was originally published by the Center for Ecoliteracy. © Copyright 2004-2015 Center for Ecoliteracy. Reprinted with permission. All rights reserved. For more information, visit www.ecoliteracy.org.

"Why Social Movements Need the Radical Imagination," by Alex Khasnabish and Max Haven, published July 22, 2014. Originally published in the independent online Open Democracy magazine, www.opendemocracy.net. Used with permission of Open Democracy. Adapted excerpt from The Radical Imagination: Social Movement Research in the Age of Austerity, published by Zed Books, June 2014.

Vincent Harding, chair of the Veterans of Hope Project and author of Martin Luther King: The Inconvenient Hero, at the Children's Defence Fund's 2012 National Conference.

"Ecopolis Iowa City: Envisioning a Regenerative City in the Heartland," by Jeff Biggers, published January 2017. Originally published in The Solutions Journal. Used with permission. Adapted from "Ecopolis" theater show by Jeff Biggers and the Awful Purdies musical group, Spring 2016.

"It Was a Blighted City Block. But This Woman Is Turning It Into a Solar-Powered Ecovillage" by Zenobia Jeffries, YES! Magazine, December 7, 2016. Used with permission of YES! Magazine, www.yesmagazine.org

"Envisioning a Sustainable World" by Donella H. Meadows, 1996. Edited and used with permission by the Academy for Systems Change.